ISAAC NEWTON'S
Papers & Letters
On Natural Philosophy

SIR ISAAC NEWTON

DRAWN AND SCRAPED MDCCLX BY IAMES MACARDEL, FROM AN ORIGINAL PORTRAIT
PAINTED BY ENOCH SEEMAN NOW IN THE POSSESSION OF THOMAS HOLLIS F.R.AND A.S.S.

LES ITALIENS CES PEVPLES INGÉNIEVX ONT CRAINT DE PENSER LES FRANÇAIS
N'ONT OSÉ PENSER QV'À DEMIE ET LES ANGLAIS QVI ONT VOLÉ IVSQV'AV CIEL *PARCE*
QV'ON NE LEVR A POINT COVPÉ LES AILES SONT DEVENVS LES PRÉCEPTEVRS DES
NATIONS NOVS LEVR DEVONS TOVT DEPVIS LES LOIX PRIMITIVES DE LA GRAVITA-
TION DEPVIS LE CALCVL DE L'INFINI ET LA CONNAISSANCE PRÉCISE DE LA LV-
MIÈRE SI VAINEMENT COMBATTVES IVSQV'À LA NOVVELLE CHARVE ET À L'IN-
SERTION DE LA PETITE VÉROLE COMBATTVES ENCORE
ODE SVR LA MORT DE MADAME DE BAREITH AVEC VNE LETTRE PAR MGNS DE VOLTAIRE

ISAAC NEWTON'S
Papers & Letters
On Natural Philosophy

and related documents

Edited, with a general introduction, by

I. BERNARD COHEN

assisted by Robert E. Schofield

Containing Newton's contributions to the Philosophical Transactions of the Royal Society, his letter to Boyle about the æther, "De Natura Acidorum," Newton's letters to Bentley and the "Boyle Lectures" related to them, the first published biography of Newton, Halley's publications about Newton's "Principia," &c.

With explanatory prefaces by Marie Boas, Charles Coulston Gillispie, Thomas S. Kuhn, & Perry Miller.

HARVARD UNIVERSITY PRESS
Cambridge, Massachusetts   ·   1958

© Copyright 1958 by the President and Fellows of Harvard College

Library of Congress Catalog Card Number 58-5607
Printed in the United States of America

Preface

Students of intellectual history and the history of science need no reminder that the majestic figure of Isaac Newton dominates the 18th century. The "Age of Newton" must be studied in the works of Newton himself, as well as in the writings of his commentators and the scientific books and articles that either continued the investigations undertaken by Newton or ventured into new domains of knowledge which he had not explored. The intention of the present volume is to bring together for the first time Newton's scattered papers and letters on natural philosophy (excluding mathematics, pure theology, and biblical chronology) as they were actually available *in print* during most of the 18th century, that is, prior to Horsley's edition of Newton's works in 1779–1785. Newton's two major books on physical science, the *Principia* and the *Opticks,* are today readily accessible, and in print; this volume complements them by placing in the hands of students all of Newton's related publications issued during his lifetime or soon after his death. The *Principia,* the *Opticks,* and the papers collected in this volume thus represent the complete corpus of Newton's writings on physical science that actually influenced the scientists and thinking men of

the "Age of Newton"; the *Optical Lectures,* however interesting, were
of less importance in conditioning the advance of science or mod-
erating the general climate of opinion on the frame of the universe
or the mechanism of nature.

Since the aim of this volume is to present to the modern scholar
the very works studied during Newton's life and the decades following his death, each document is reproduced in facsimile from
the original publication; a facsimile is provided of a standard
translation into English of those documents which are in Latin.
Since many of Newton's communications are letters, as was cus-
tomary in the 17th and 18th centuries, there have also been included
facsimiles of the printed letters and documents written by others
that were the occasion of each of Newton's communications. In
every case, the page numbers of the originals have been kept, so
that the scholar will have available to him in facsimile the actual
pages of many rare works which are not to be found in all libraries,
and certainly not on the shelves of students who wish to study the
development of physical thought in the age of Newton.

In addition to Newton's own letters and papers, and documents
immediately relating to them, several Newtonian productions of
rarity have been included. Fontenelle's *éloge* is the first published
biography of Newton and was widely read in England and abroad.
Halley's review of the *Principia* and the account of the theory of the
tides which he wrote for James II are as useful today as they were
then, serving to orient the nonspecialist to some major aspects of
Newton's monumental achievement. Finally, all students of Newton
will be grateful for a "Newtonian index" to Birch's *History of the
Royal Society.*

The editor wishes to acknowledge the kindness of the scholars
who have aided this coöperative venture by contributing prefaces
to the several sections of the volume: Marie Boas, University of
California (Los Angeles); Charles Coulston Gillispie, Princeton
University; Thomas S. Kuhn, University of California (Berkeley);
and Perry Miller, Harvard University. Dr. Robert E. Schofield, of
the University of Kansas, has helped in every stage of preparing
the book and has written several contributions to it.

The editor respectfully acknowledges the stimulation to the production of this volume given by Professor A. Koyré of the Ecole

Pratique des Hautes Etudes of the University of Paris (Sorbonne), who urged upon him the necessity of producing it. The editor gratefully records the sincere interest in the history of science of Mr. Bern Dibner, the guiding spirit in the formation of the Burndy Library of the history of science in Norwalk, Connecticut, who has sponsored many important publications in the history of science as well as this one. Valuable information was provided by Professor H. W. Turnbull, editor of the projected edition of Newton's correspondence, Mr. A. N. L. Munby, Librarian of King's College, Cambridge, and Curator of the Keynes Collection of Newton Manuscripts, and Professor E. N. da C. Andrade of London, master interpreter of science in our day, whose many publications on Newton and his times have provided illumination with an elegance and charm all too rare in the current literature of the history of science.

The editor hopes that this volume may be conceived as a transatlantic tribute to the Royal Society of London, whose role was of such major importance in the development of Newton's thought. All scholars who have had the privilege of using the great library of the Royal Society are aware of the feeling of awe that arises from confronting the manuscripts that record the major progress of science in a continuous succession of almost three centuries; the remembrance of that experience is always tempered by a warm feeling of gratitude for the extreme kindness and helpfulness of the present and past librarians, Messrs. I. Kaye and H. W. Robinson, and especially of the Assistant Secretary, Dr. D. C. Martin. In saluting the Royal Society, and its two Newtonian scholars, Professors Andrade and Turnbull, a word may be said about the forthcoming Royal Society edition of Newton's correspondence, being prepared under Professor Turnbull's editorship. This task, of immense complexity and beset by extremely difficult questions at every turn, will prove to be one of the most important collections of source material for the study of 17th-century science. Based upon a careful study of the manuscripts, it will provide a complete and accurate text of each document. Hence the student who wishes to know exactly what Newton wrote, or exactly what Newton's correspondents wrote, must always turn to the Royal Society edition of Newton's correspondence. But for the student who wishes to find out what the men of the late 17th and the 18th century actually read, on which they based whatever they in turn said or wrote, there can be no substitute for the original printed versions which are gathered together in the present volume.

The publication of this volume was made possible through a grant from the Burndy Library, Norwalk, Connecticut. All readers will share our gratitude to the Burndy Library and to its scholarly director, Bern Dibner, for continued generous support of research in the history of science. Unfortunately, owing to circumstances beyond our control, there has been a delay of almost three years between the initial completion of the volume and its present publication.

I. Bernard Cohen

Contents

III. Newton on chemistry, atomism, the æther, and heat

IV. Newton's Four Letters to Bentley, and the Boyle Lectures Related to Them

V. Halley and the *Principia*

VI. The first biography of Newton

I.

General Introduction

General Introduction

I. Bernard Cohen

Scholars are unanimous in describing the 18th century as the "age of Newton," but the exact sense of this phrase requires some clarification. Pope's couplet, about nature and her laws being "hid in night" until God created Newton "and all was light," has probably misled the many historians who have quoted it and it betrays a wonderful ignorance of the nature of science. We do not understand nature by the revelation of single laws, but rather by an apparently endless sequence of discoveries and of theories invented to explain them. If any stage of this sequence seems to represent so great an advance that it marks a new era, it may appear as a revelation but the revelation is never complete. The greatest work in science is as much characterized by the creation of new questions for the next generations as by the formulation of partial answers to questions raised in the past. Newton may be esteemed as the dominating figure of the 18th century—and even, to some degree, the 19th—because the questions he raised were so fundamental that the best brains in science were hardly up to answering them.

Those who have written about the "age of Newton" have tended

3

to concentrate their attention on the *Principia,* admittedly his masterpiece and one of the greatest productions of the human mind, and on the problems Newton solved rather than the fruitful questions his work raised. In Newton's lifetime as during the 18th century—and ever since—the *Principia* was a formidable book to read and, prior to the appearance of the second edition in 1713, it was also a difficult book to obtain, owing to the small size of the original edition, which has been estimated at somewhere between 300 and 400 copies. The *Principia* was a difficult book to read, making enormous demands on the reader because of the mathematical complexities and abstract approach to the subject matter—terrestrial and celestial dynamics, and the general physics of fluids.

The major result of Newton's heroic endeavor was the law of universal gravitation, which enabled him to account for planetary motion in accordance with Kepler's laws, the motion of the moon and the phenomena of the tides, the falling of bodies to the earth, and the precession of the equinoxes as a result of the earth's figure. But simple as the form of the law of universal gravitation was—stating that any two bodies in the universe would attract each other with a force directly proportional to the product of their masses and inversely proportional to the square of the distance between them—the application of this law created a problem of fundamental importance which Newton could never answer to his complete satisfaction, and which has been of concern to men of science ever since; even in our own day it has not been resolved.

This problem can be stated simply in the following question: how can one body act upon another that it does not touch? "Contact forces" seem readily understandable, whereas "action-at-a-distance" is puzzling. A horse that pulls a wagon, for example, acts upon it through the physical medium of the traces, just as a man who pushes a cart exerts his force at the point of contact between his hands and the cart. But, according to Newton's concept of universal gravitation, the sun must exert a considerable force upon the earth at a distance of some hundred million miles, and upon Jupiter and Saturn at even greater distances. How can this be possible?

Newton's critics were quick to sieze upon this obvious flaw in the great system, and they accused him of reintroducing into physics those "occult" qualities which were supposed to have been banished. Friend and foe of Newtonian dynamics explored the question of action-at-a-distance, and so did Newton himself. The problem of how a body might "act where it is not" was not discussed by Newton in the first edition of the *Principia* but in the second edition of 1713, in the General Scholium added to Book Three. Here Newton stated that he "framed no hypotheses" and that it was enough to account mathematically for the motion of moon and planets and for the tides, even though the cause or mechanism of gravitational action remained unknown. But he did give the reader a hint

concerning a certain most subtle spirit which pervades and lies hid in all gross bodies; by the force and action of which spirit the particles of bodies attract one another at near distances, and cohere, if contiguous; and electric bodies operate to greater distances, as well repelling as attracting the neighboring corpuscles; and light is emitted, reflected, refracted, inflected [that is, diffracted], and heats bodies; and all sensation is excited, and the members of animal bodies move at the command of the will, namely, by the vibrations of this spirit, mutually propagated along the solid filaments of the nerves, from the outward organs of sense to the brain, and from the brain into the muscles.[1]

The character of this "electric and elastic spirit" was explored more fully by Newton in other publications or communications. It is the subject of various queries in the successive editions of the *Opticks* and is there applied to the problem of universal gravitation, curiously omitted from the list of phenomena in the General Scholium to Book Three of the *Principia,* even though that scholium as a whole was largely devoted to gravitation. This elastic "æther" and its various properties also appear in a letter to the Hon. Robert Boyle, dated Feb. 28, 1678/9, which was published in Boyle's works in 1744,[2] reprinted in 1772, and was published separately with a commentary by Bryan Robinson in 1745. In this letter,

[1] *Sir Isaac Newton's Mathematical Principles of Natural Philosophy,* a revision of Andrew Motte's English version of 1729 (University of California Press, Berkeley, 1934), General Scholium at the end of Book Three.

[2] See John F. Fulton, "A bibliography of the Honourable Robert Boyle, Fellow of the Royal Society," *Oxford Bibliog. Soc. Proc. and Papers 3,* 1–172, 339–365 (1932); also I. B. Cohen, *Franklin and Newton, an inquiry into speculative Newtonian ex-*

Newton attempted to show that the æther was responsible for the cohesion of bodies, played a part in the actions of acids and other chemical reactions, operated to produce and maintain the gaseous state, caused various optical phenomena, and could be considered "the cause of gravity." This letter was widely studied in the middle of the 18th century, and its influence on chemists and physicists was marked.[3] It was quoted or cited by many students of electricity and affected the form that was taken by theories of electrical action. The hypothesis of the æther also turns up in Newton's optical papers, published in the *Philosophical Transactions* during his young manhood,[4] and was the subject of a famous long paper read at the Royal Society in 1675/6, and published by Birch in his *History of the Royal Society* in 1757.[5] Finally, the æther is seen to be of importance in the letters Newton wrote to Richard Bentley in 1692/3, which were published in 1756.[6]

The ability of the æther, or "ætherial medium," to produce so many different types of natural phenomena must have been particularly satisfying to Newton in demonstrating a kind of unity of nature. In a letter to Oldenburg, 25 Jan. 1675, Newton wrote:

Where I say, that *the frame of nature may be nothing but æther condensed by a fermental principle,* instead of these words write, that it may be nothing but various contextures of some certain ætherial spirits or vapours condensed, as it were, by precipitation, much after the manner, that vapours are condensed into water, or exhalations into grosser substances, though not so easily condensable; and after condensation wrought into various forms, at first by the immediate hand of the Creator, and ever since by the power of nature, who, by virtue of the command, *Increase and multiply,* became a complete imitator of the copies set her by the Protoplast. Thus perhaps may all things be originated from æther, *&c.*

Yet Newton's hypothesis of the æther was not entirely satisfactory, even to all his admirers. In the new scholium for the second edition of the *Principia,* Newton observed that we are not "furnished with

perimental science and Franklin's work in electricity as an example thereof (American Philosophical Society, Philadelphia, 1956).

[3] This letter is reprinted below in Section Three.

[4] These papers or letters are reprinted below in Section Two.

[5] Reprinted below in Section Two.

[6] Reprinted below in Section Four.

that sufficiency of experiments which is required to an accurate determination and demonstration of the laws by which this electric and elastic spirit operates." Although he always presented his thoughts on the æther with some degree of tentativeness, he did so over so long a period of time that the conclusion is inescapable that a belief in an ætherial medium, penetrating all bodies and filling empty space, was a central pillar of his system of nature.

As postulated by Newton, the æther was composed of particles that mutually repelled one another or that were endowed with a centrifugal force. The æther was imponderable, odorless, tasteless, and colorless, but had certain implied properties of rigidity so as to support undulations, such as those which were a concomitant part of optical phenomena and also those allied with the transmission of sensations to the brain. Differing in density throughout space according to the location of bodies in that space, the ætherial medium was capable of causing gross bodies to move toward one another according to the law of universal gravitation. Thus Newton could, by invoking the æther, satisfy the criterion set forth in a letter to Bentley:

It is inconceivable, that inanimate brute matter should, without the mediation of something else, which is not material, operate upon, and affect other matter without mutual contact, as it must be, if gravitation in the sense of Epicurus, be essential and inherent in it. And this is one reason why I desired you would not ascribe innate gravity to me. That gravity should be innate, inherent, and essential to matter, so that one body may act upon another at a distance thro' a vacuum, without the mediation of any thing else, by and through which their action and force may be conveyed from one to another, is to me so great an absurdity, that I believe no man who has in philosophical matters a competent faculty of thinking, can ever fall into it.

Newton's speculations were studied very carefully during the next two centuries, and they produced important consequences. The writings about a universal fluid gave sanction to the creation of other imponderable fluids, such as the electrical "fluid" and the "fluid" of caloric. The development of the concepts of these "fluids" did not slavishly follow Newton's principle of "density." The scientists who tried to explain electrical phenomena by variations in density of some "subtle fluid" were not able to produce results of importance, while those who sought to identify the "electric fluid" or the "fluid of heat" with Newton's universal æther appear never to have advanced beyond the stage of hypothesis and speculation.

Newton's suggestion that many of the phenomena which were categorized by "action-at-a-distance" might be explained on the supposition of a single universal fluid undoubtedly inspired Faraday in his attempt to uncover by experiment the relations between the various ways in which the several forces of nature are manifested. Newton, concentrating attention on what happened in the space between bodies rather than on the bodies themselves, prepared the way for the fruitful concept of "field," in particular for Faraday's version of it as a set of "strains" in the ætherial medium around charged or magnetized bodies—the famous theory of "lines of force." In turn, Faraday's research led to Clerk Maxwell's theory of "displacement currents" in the æther, and Clerk Maxwell's electromagnetic theory may be considered legitimately the high point of "classical" physics, the physics of the 19th century. Faraday loved to quote the passage from Newton's letter to Bentley, cited above, and Clerk Maxwell also repeated it with enthusiastic approval. To be sure, since the acceptance of Einstein's restricted theory of relativity (published in 1905), the concept of the æther, along with all Newtonian "absolute" space and time, has vanished from the discourse of physics—apparently having served a useful function for at least two centuries but needed no longer. It is not amiss, however, to note that P. A. M. Dirac, one of the most distinguished physicists of our era, has just raised the question whether the æther is completely dispensable.

Even in the early 19th century, some physicists discerned inherent difficulties in applying the concept of the æther in the fashion proposed by Newton. John Playfair put the whole problem in succinct form:

It is very true that an elastic fluid, of which the density followed the inverse ratio of the distance from a given point, would urge the bodies immersed in it, and impervious to it, toward that point with forces inversely as the squares of the distances from it; but what could maintain an elastic fluid in this condition, or with its density varying according to this law, is a thing as inexplicable as the gravity which it was meant to explain. The nature of an elastic fluid must be, in the absence of all inequality of pressure, to become everywhere of the same density. If the causes that produce so marked and so general a deviation from this rule be not assigned, we can only be said to have substituted one difficulty for another.[7]

Another difficulty came from the fact that the æther as postulated by Newton acted as it did because the particles of which it was supposed to be made were mutually repulsive. While this very fact delights the student of Newton in affording an example of that atomism which was fundamental to the Newtonian view of nature, it raises the thorny question why a wholly inexplicable short-range repulsive force between tiny particles of æther may be considered more satisfying than an equally inexplicable long-range attraction between gross bodies.

The profound puzzle of Newton's views on the æther disturbs Pope's view that after the revelation according to the *Principia* "all was light." Newton's discussion of how nature might produce the forces whose laws he had illuminated is, therefore, essential to our understanding of the whole Newtonian natural philosophy. The development of physics in the 18th and 19th centuries cannot be studied without a clear view of Newton's own statements on what we may call the mechanism of nature's actions. To this end, the present volume reprints, with commentaries, the original documents that were the vehicles for transmitting Newton's speculations —and it does so in the exact form in which scientists and philosophers and men of learning studied them during most of the 18th century, and afterwards.

There are only three books by Newton that deal with physical subjects. The best-known of these are his *Principia* and *Opticks,* both published during the author's life and revised by him in later editions. The *Optical Lectures,* published posthumously in 1728, were based on a translation made from Newton's Latin manuscript; a Latin edition was published in 1729. The *Principia* is available to the modern reader in the edition published in 1934 by the Univer-

[7] John Playfair, "Dissertation third: exhibiting a general view of the progress of mathematical and physical science since the revival of letters in Europe," pages 433–572 of *Dissertations on the history of metaphysical and ethical, and mathematical and physical science,* by Dugald Stuart, the Right Hon. Sir James Mackintosh, John Playfair, and Sir John Leslie (Adam and Charles Black, Edinburgh, 1835), Section IV, "Astronomy."

sity of California Press, containing the 18th-century translation of Andrew Motte as revised by Florian Cajori. This handsomely printed volume is based on a version that was never completed by the editor and it appeared only after Cajori's death; perhaps this may serve to explain why it has neither a table of contents nor an index, so that the reader encounters extreme difficulty in finding his way about in it.[8] The *Opticks* was reprinted in 1931 by Messrs. Bell of London, and was reissued in 1952 by Dover Publications of New York City with the welcome addition of an analytical table of contents.[9] The *Optical Lectures* has not been reprinted since the 18th century in either the Latin or the English version, although a Russian translation by S. I. Vavilov, late president of the Russian Academy of Sciences, was published in Moscow in 1946.

The intention of the present volume is to bring together in complete form all of Newton's publications on physical subjects—save for the above-mentioned three books—that were available in the 18th century. To our knowledge, this is the first time that even all the Newtonian material in the *Philosophical Transactions* of the Royal Society of London has been gathered together. All of Newton's letters that were published in the *Philosophical Transactions* were printed by the Rev. Samuel Horsley in his five-volume edition of Newton's works (1779–1785), even though it is often stated that they are not to be found in Horsley's edition! Horsley, however, based his texts on manuscript versions of the letters, so that there are notable differences between them and the first printings. The student of Newton's *thought* may, therefore, profit by consulting Horsley's edition, supplemented by the great new edition of Newton's correspondence to be published by the Royal Society of London. But the student of the history of physical thought in the *17th and 18th centuries* must use the texts as they were actually printed and read in the *Philosophical Transactions* and as they are reproduced in the present

---

[8] What is needed at the present time is a critical and variorum edition in which there will be displayed all the changes made by Newton in the successive versions he produced during his lifetime. Such an edition is presently being undertaken by Professor Alexandre Koyré and the writer.

[9] Regrettably, in the first printing of 1952, the printer omitted part of the valuable Analytical Table of Contents that had been prepared by Professor Duane H. D. Roller. This fault has been corrected in the second printing.

volume. Horsley did not include the letters about Newton's discoveries that were published in the *Philosophical Transactions,* and to which Newton replied; since a reply is meaningless without the document that occasioned it, the present reprinting includes all the contemporaneous printed material relevant to the controversy—by Newton and also by those who took issue with him. Horsley reprinted Newton's four letters to Bentley, but he did not include the two sermons—or Boyle Lecture—relating to them. We have included the latter because they help the reader to understand Newton's letters and also because they represent the first popularization of Newton's system, and inaugurate the doctrine that Newtonian celestial mechanics may prove the existence of the God who created the universe.

In addition to the Bentley material and the Newtonian letters and papers from the *Philosophical Transactions,* we have included a letter by Hooke and the long paper by Newton (explicating his hypothesis of the æther) from Birch's *History of the Royal Society.* Both were made public by having been read at meetings of the Royal Society, but neither one was published in the *Transactions.* Since all too few readers in the 20th century are familiar with Latin, the 19th-century translations of the Latin documents have been included. But the short "Theory of the Moon" is not represented in the present collection, since it consists primarily of a problem in applied celestial mechanics. It may be found in various eighteenth-century works, e.g., the English version of David Gregory's *The Elements of Astronomy* (2 vols., London, 1715), and its Latin predecessor, and in John Harris's *Lexicon Technicum.* Also omitted is Newton's table of refractions of stars, published by Halley in an article of his own in *Phil. Trans.* No. 368.

Finally, the volume also contains Fontenelle's *éloge* of Newton, the first biography of Newton to be printed, which was based in large measure on materials furnished to him by John Conduitt, Newton's nephew and amanuensis. This work was immediately translated into English from the French and was widely reprinted; it gives us some indication of the popular reaction to what Newton did, and also serves as one of the primary documents in the struggle between Newtonianism and Cartesianism. There is a certain anomaly about Newton's position as *associé étranger* of the Académie

Royale des Sciences (Paris), since his *Principia* was so largely devoted to an attack on the Cartesian philosophy, which was then
the reigning system in France. Not only did Newton show in the
Principia that the "hypothesis of vortices" is inconsistent with observed phenomena, but his *Opticks* also confuted the Cartesian system. We know that Newton's antagonism to Descartes was extreme, that he not only made a pointed attack on Cartesian physics
again and again in the *Principia,* but in his own copy of Descartes'
geometry "marked in many places with his own hand, *Error, Error,
non est Geom.*"[10] So strong was this feeling on the part of Newton
that we are led to suspect that the title of his masterpiece, *Philosophiæ Naturalis Principia Mathematica,* was intended to show its superiority over Descartes's *Principia Philosophiæ,* of which a copy of
the edition of 1656 in quarto was in his library. And it is tempting
to suspect further that when Newton altered the HYPOTHESES
at the beginning of Book Three of the *Principia* (in the first edition
of 1687) to "Hypotheses," "Phænomena," and "Regulæ Philo-
sophandi," the latter were intended to supplant Descartes' "Regulæ
ad Directionem Ingenii."

Newton is generally said to be one of the first group of eight
associés étrangers elected to the Académie Royale des Sciences, and
the official list of members includes his title as *premier titulaire.* The
manuscript Régistres show, however, that he was the last of the
eight to be chosen, and that the choice was made only on the
fourth discussion of the question. Under the new charter of 1699,
there was place for eight *associés étrangers,* of whom the first three
were G. G. Leibniz, E. W. v. Tschirnhaus, and Domenico Guglielmini, who were already members when named to the new title on
28 January 1699. According to the manuscript Régistres, on Saturday 14 February 1699, "On a resolu a la pluralité des voix de
proposer au Roy M^{rs}. Hartsoëker, et Bernoulli, l'ainé et le cadet,
pour Associez Etrangers," the Bernoullis being the brothers Jacques
and Jean (Ier). Then, according to the Régistres, on Saturday 21
February, "M^r. Roëmer qui a été autrefois membre de l'Académie
et qui est retourné en Dannemarc depuis longtemps, et M^r. Newton

---

[10] Sir David Brewster, *Memoirs of the Life, Writings, and Discoveries of Sir Isaac Newton* (Thomas Constable and Co., Edinburgh, 1875), vol. 1, p. 22n.

ont été nommés pour les deux places qui restoient d'Associés Etrangers."

The juxtaposition of the papers and letters of Newton in this volume clarifies at once one of the major Newtonian problems. It is clear that throughout his life Newton regarded the concept of the æther as a hypothesis. However much he may have cherished this particular hypothesis, hypothesis it always remained. Whatever Newton meant by the word hypothesis—and his writings disclose a variety of usages[11]—he was certainly aware that the æther had never attained that same high level of demonstrable certainty and accuracy that seemed to characterize his experiments and his theory of light and colors, and his principles of terrestrial and celestial physics. In the General Scholium written for the conclusion of the third book of the *Principia* in the second edition of 1713, Newton said specifically that there was not "that sufficiency of experiments which is required to an accurate determination and demonstration of the laws by which this electric and elastic spirit operates." But in the preceding paragraph of that General Scholium, the penultimate paragraph with which the final approved version of the *Principia* concludes, Newton had said unequivocally that he framed or feigned no hypotheses—*Hypotheses non fingo*. Why, then, did he give a vague hint of just such a hypothesis as he said had no place in his philosophy? Clearly, the results displayed in the *Principia* seemed to him independent of any hypotheses like that of the æther, and, so long as the æther remained merely a hypothesis, it could have no place in the system of the *Principia*. But why mention it at all?

This baffling question is at once resolved by reading Newton's papers and letters printed below. In 1713, when Newton published the concluding General Scholium in the second edition of the *Principia,* his own hypothesis had already become known to a fairly large group. It appears in the early optical papers, in the famous letter to Boyle, and at great length in the long statement that had been read at meetings of the Royal Society years earlier and that still reposed in the archives of the Society, where presumably it

---

[11] The major ways in which Newton used the word "hypothesis" are classified in *Franklin and Newton* (see note 2, above), Appendix One.

could be read by anyone who was interested. He had, furthermore, discussed his hypothesis with friends such as David Gregory. When, therefore, in all sincerity he wrote that he would not feign hypotheses as a substitute for sound demonstrable theory, he must have been aware that there were many people who knew full well that—even so—he had at various times explored just such a hypothesis, however tentatively he may have considered the æther. The final paragraph must then have served as a reminder to the cognoscenti that Newton had not forgotten that he had framed a rather elegant hypothesis of the æther, one that might account for gravitation and a host of other phenomena.

In the second (1717, 1718) and third (1721) English editions of the *Opticks,* the Queries at the end of Book III were enlarged from the original sixteen in the first edition (1704) to thirty-one. Query 17 takes up the problem of vibrations in the medium in which light travels, vibrations which put the rays of light into "fits" of easy reflection and easy transmission; Query 18 deals with further properties of this medium in relation to radiant heat; Queries 19 and 20 suggest that variations or differences in the "density" of the "ætherial medium" may account for refraction and inflection. In Query 21 Newton addressed himself to gravitation, the possibility that variations in the "density" of the "medium" may produce gravitation since the "medium" is much rarer within dense bodies such as the sun, planets, comets, stars, than in empty celestial space. Query 22 is devoted to the demonstration that this "æther" can offer a negligible resistance to the motion of planets and comets. Finally, in Query 23 vision is said to result chiefly from vibrations of this medium propagated through the optic nerve, and in Query 24 the vibrations of the medium are related to animal sensation being conveyed to the brain.

In 1706, two years after the first English edition and seven years before the second Latin edition of the *Principia* with the famous concluding General Scholium, a Latin version of the *Opticks* was published, prepared by Samuel Clarke at Newton's request. In this edition the number of Queries was increased from the original sixteen to twenty-three. But the new Queries in this Latin version do not correspond to Queries 17–23 in the second and third English editions of the *Opticks;* they do not deal with the æther at all.

These new Queries of 1706 rather correspond to Queries 25–31 in the later English editions of the *Opticks*.

When Newton brought out the second English edition of the *Opticks* in 1717, he printed for the first time the Queries there numbered 17–24, which presented his general views on the nature, properties, and effects of a supposed æther; and these were followed by revised English versions of the Queries he had added in the Latin version of 1706, now renumbered 25–31. In respect to these new Queries about the æther, Newton said (in this English edition of the *Opticks*, 1717), that "to shew that I do not take gravity for an essential property of bodies, I have added one question concerning its cause, chusing to propose it by way of a question, because I am not yet satisfied about it for want of experiments."

Evidently, in 1717 Newton was willing to discuss the æther since he had already given a hint about this hypothesis in the 1713 edition of the *Principia* and there was no longer any secret about it. He did so in the *Opticks* and not the *Principia*, where the possibility of the æther as a cause of gravity was scrupulously avoided. This, too, is not surprising. The *Opticks* already contained a considerable amount of speculative material; it was not inappropriate to add more. Furthermore, the placement of the fuller discussion of the æther outside the *Principia* maintained the point of view that the principles of gravitation could be adequately discussed without solving the problem of the cause of gravitation and without recourse to any ancillary hypotheses, even Newton's.

The publication of the present volume brings to the fore certain major questions of Newtonian scholarship at the present time. Our interest in Newton takes two forms, which are complementary to each other. The first of these is to understand Newton's complex personality and the nature of the creative process as illustrated by his activity; the second, to trace the influence of what he said on the development of physical thought and general culture. To comprehend Newton requires a knowledge of everything that he wrote, and is difficult today because there is not yet available a complete edition of his works. The Royal Society's edition of the correspondence of Newton will illuminate many facets of Newton's personality, and will unquestionably be a rich source of information on the scientific life of Newton's day. Valuable as this collection will be—and its value cannot be overstated—the student who wishes to understand Newton the man will have to consult the whole corpus of the manuscript writings of Newton, much of which deals with problems of theology, alchemy, and administration. That these are extremely important for an understanding of the mind and character of Newton goes without saying, though they may not contribute anything specifically to our estimate of his actual scientific achievement. We cannot separate Newton's creative activity according to the canons of departments of learning in our modern universities, because Newton's thoughts were closely intertwined in his own mind. His reflections on alchemy were undoubtedly colored by his theological studies and his writings on physical subjects always bear the mark of his theological concern. The atomism he developed had also a theological cast and serves to link his studies of optics, chemistry, and the physics of gross bodies. We cannot say of Newton, Let us take the chemistry and let the alchemy go, or, Let us take the physics and forget the theology. The "absolute space," so essential to his conception of dynamics, was for him identified with the "sensorium" of God, and even the atomism of his optics and chemistry was connected with his view of the form of the Creation.

Newton's *Observations upon the Prophecies of Daniel, and the Apocalypse of St. John* was published in 1733 and has remained his major theological study. Although a few of Newton's theological manuscripts were published recently under the editorship of H. McLachlan,[12] we do not know the basis of his selection, and it is difficult to know whether the works he reprinted are in any sense truly representative.

But not all of Newton's manuscripts and uncollected writings are theological or alchemical. In King's biography of Locke, for example, there is to be found a statement of the principles of mechanics prepared by Newton for Locke; it deserves study and should be reprinted with an adequate commentary. It is not included in the present volume because it was not printed until the 19th century and so was not read by the physicists of the 18th century.

[12] *Sir Isaac Newton: Theological manuscripts.* Selected and edited, with an introduction, by H. McLachlan (University Press, Liverpool, 1950).

A critical edition of the *Principia* is very much needed. As I mentioned earlier, there is no available edition of the *Principia* that contains a decent index, or even a full analytical table of contents, nor has there been prepared a modern edition that is fully annotated. What is needed is a true critical edition, in which there would be plainly displayed the variations from one edition to the next. Curiously enough, there was prepared in the 19th century, by J. C. Adams, a list of the variations between the second and the third editions of the *Principia*,[13] but I do not know of any similar work on the differences between the first and second editions, which are in many ways more fundamental. Thus, all too many writers about Newtonianism have ignored the fact that the famous General Scholium to Book Three was not a part of the original edition at all, but was written for the second edition, and in answer to criticisms.

The late Lord Keynes collected a large number of unpublished Newton manuscripts, which are now in the library of King's College, Cambridge,[14] and which he discussed in a brilliant essay on Newton which was published in the Royal Society's volume, *Newton Tercentenary Celebrations 15–19 July 1946*.[15] It is greatly to be hoped that these unpublished Newton manuscripts may soon see the light of printed day, and that they may be supplemented by other volumes containing Newton manuscripts in other collections.

As matters now stand, there seems to be no immediate prospect of an edition of all of Newton's manuscripts and other writings, nor of a critical annotated edition of his published works on mathematics and physical science. But the major sources of Newton's contributions to physical thought that were available to scientists and nonscientists in the "age of Newton" are now in print: the *Principia* and the *Opticks*, and the letters and papers included in the present volume.

[13] Published by Brewster (see note 10, above).

[14] A. N. L. Munby, "The distribution of the first edition of Newton's *Principia*. The Keynes Collection of the works of Sir Isaac Newton at King's College, Cambridge," *Notes and Records Royal Soc. of London 10*, 28–39, 40–50 (1952).

[15] Published by Cambridge University Press, 1947. This volume also contains an important essay by Professor E. N. da C. Andrade, which should be supplemented by his "Newton and the science of his age," *Proc. Royal Soc. A 181*, 227–243 (1943).

Those who have learned physics from modern textbooks may be surprised at the violence of the controversy that followed the announcement of Newton's discovery of dispersion and the composition of white light. Scientific publications were apt to be more polemical in the 17th century than nowadays, but we must also keep in mind that great discoveries jar the cherished beliefs of scientists and are apt to produce a shock reaction at all times. The argument over Newton's theory of light and colors continued into the 18th century; it may be seen in the papers of J. T. Desaguliers in the *Philosophical Transactions* of 1716 (No. 348, pp. 433–451) and of 1722 (No. 374, p. 206) and, later on in the century, in Goethe's *Farbenlehre*.

Newtonian science in the 18th century was apt to have two aspects, one mathematical and the other experimental. The *Principia*, as its full title indicates, was devoted (or, perhaps, limited) to the "mathematical principles of natural philosophy" but the *Opticks* was a primer of experimental physics and contained, largely in the section of "Queries," Newton's speculations on all aspects of physical science. The distinction between experimental Newtonian natural philosophy and mathematical Newtonian experimental philosophy, I believe, becomes clear from a study of what the scientists of the 18th century did, and the Newtonian works they read—or were able to read.

Newton said that the science of colors was mathematical and as certain as any other part of optics (for example, geometric optics), but he later felt the need to clarify his statement. The clarification was omitted from the publication in the *Philosophical Transactions* but was printed in Horsley's edition (vol. 4, p. 342):

In the last place, I should take notice of a casual expression, which intimates a greater certainty in these things, than I ever promised, *viz. the certainty of Mathematical Demonstrations.* I said, indeed, that the science of colours was mathematical, and as certain as any other part of Optics; but who knows not that Optics, and many other mathematical sciences, depend as well on physical sciences, as on mathematical demonstrations? And the absolute certainty of a science cannot exceed the certainty of its principles. Now the evidence, by which I asserted the propositions of colours, is in the next words expressed to be from experiments, and so but physical: whence the Propositions themselves can be esteemed no more than physical principles of a science. And if those principles be such, that on them a mathematician may determine all the phænomena of colours, that can be caused by refractions, and that by disputing or demonstrating after what manner, and how much, those refractions do separate or mingle the rays, in which several colours are originally inherent; I suppose the science of colours will be granted mathematical, and as certain as any part of Optics. And that this may be done, I have good reason to believe, because ever since I became first acquainted with these principles, I have, with constant success in the events, made use of them for this purpose.

The Newtonian documents that follow are chiefly illustrative of experimental and speculative Newtonianism. They provide the exciting experience—alas! no longer possible, owing to the terse and formal style of our scientific journals—of reading how one of the world's greatest scientists actually made one of his major discoveries. We are rapidly transported backward in time through almost three centuries to the time of Newton, as we follow the reactions of the scientists of his day to that discovery and as we read Newton's answers to each objection: sometimes patient and kind, but at other times curt and even rude. We may "listen" to the long paper as it was read to the Royal Society and perhaps understand why Newton did not want to have it published. Above all, we may glimpse some of Newton's innermost thoughts about the mechanism of nature, the creation of the universe, and the need for proving by the "phænomena" about us that there was a creating God and that the universe was His handiwork. Like the scientists, philosophers, and ordinary thinking men of the 18th century, we cannot help being moved at the enormity of the fundamental questions to which Newton addressed himself and, like them, we will appreciate the ingenuity of his speculations and the often lofty and poetic rapture that was the result of his profound insight.

BIBLIOGRAPHICAL NOTES
Robert E. Schofield

The Newton material appearing in this volume is reproduced in facsimile from the texts as they originally appeared, preserving the pagination, spelling, and general format. In a few instances, at the beginning or end of an article, material at the top or bottom of a page has been blanked out, being the work of another person and unrelated to the text reproduced.

There are three general bibliographies of Newton material: a short one by H. Zeitlinger in the Newton bicentenary volume, *Isaac Newton* (London: G. Bell and Sons, Ltd., 1927), edited for the Mathematical Association by W. J. Greenstreet; George J. Gray's *A Bibliography of the Works of Sir Isaac Newton* (first edition, Cambridge: MacMillan and Bowes, 1888; second edition, Cambridge: Bowes and Bowes, 1907); and *A Descriptive Catalogue of the Grace K. Babson Collection of the Works of Sir Isaac Newton* (New York: Herbert Reichner, 1950). None of these is complete and in all of them the listing of Newton's papers in the *Philosophical Transactions* is more or less inadequate. We believe that the table of contents of this volume contains a complete list of all of Newton's papers in the *Philosophical Transactions* and the related letters, except the writings on mathematics and those on biblical chronology.[1]

The optical papers from the *Philosophical Transactions* are reproduced from the copies owned by the Burndy Library. All other papers from the *Philosophical Transactions*—namely, II, 17: "An Instrument for observing the Moon's Distance from the fixed Stars at Sea"; III, 4: "Scala Gradum Caloris"; and V, 2 and 3: Halley's review of the *Principia* and the "True theory of the tides," are reproduced from the numbers of the *Philosophical Transactions* in the Harvard College Library. The citations to the *Philosophical Transactions* (in the table of contents) are by number rather than volume, as this seemed the only reasonably satisfactory way of identifying the original sources without confusion. Although present custom dictates reference by volume, the erratic publication of the early issues of the *Transactions* is inimical to the consistent assigning of volume numbers, while the issue numbers offer a consistent continuous pattern.

The English translations from the Latin originals are reproduced from the *Philosophical Transactions, Abridged* (London, 1809).

Two of the documents (II, 9: Hooke's critique of Newton's theory of light and colors, and II, 16: Newton's second paper on color and light) were read at meetings of the Royal Society, but never printed in the *Philosophical Transactions*. The Hooke critique is discussed, in a somewhat misleading way, in document II, 9: "Mr. Isaac Newtons Answer to some Considerations upon his Doctrine of Light and Colors." The "second paper on color and light" was originally withheld from

[1] *A Supplement to the Catalogue of the Grace K. Babson Collection of the Works of Sir Isaac Newton* was published by Babson Institute in 1955.

publication at Newton's request. Much of the information contained therein appeared publicly for the first time in Newton's *Opticks* (1704), but we may assume that some of it was in the air from the time of its presentation at the meetings of the Royal Society in 1675–76. The reproduction of these papers, taken from the Burndy Library copy of the only edition of Birch's *History of the Royal Society of London* (London, 1756–57 [see facsimile of title page on page 478, below]), provides a more complete opportunity to follow the course of Newton's thinking, leading to the *Opticks*, than is generally available.

Newton's letter to Boyle (III, 2) first appeared in the introduction to Birch, *The Works of the Honourable Robert Boyle* (London: A. Millar, 1744). Our reproduction is taken from the Harvard College Library copy [see facsimile of the title page on page 249 below] (not in Babson, Gray, or Greenstreet).

"De Natura Acidorum" first appeared in both a Latin and an English version in the introduction to the second volume, first edition, of John Harris's *Lexicon Technicum*. The first volume of this edition appeared in 1704, the second volume not until 1710. The *Lexicon Technicum* was a general "dictionary" of arts and sciences, justly famous in its day, and has been called the prototype of the numerous "dictionaries" of the sciences that were published in the 18th century. It went through at least five editions (the fifth printed for T. Walthoe, etc., in 1736, with a supplement by a Society of Gentlemen, London, 1744); all editions subsequent to the first edition of the second volume in 1710 contain "De Natura Acidorum." Our reproduction [the title page of volume II is reproduced on page 255 below] is from the copy of the 1710 (volume II) first edition, in the Harvard College Library (not in Gray or Babson; mentioned briefly by Greenstreet).

The *Four Letters from Sir Isaac Newton to Doctor Bentley* . . . first appeared in a pamphlet printed in 1756. Our reproduction is from the Harvard College Library copy [title page, page 279 below] (Babson 226, Gray 345, not in Greenstreet).

The sermons of Richard Bentley are reproduced from a collection, in one volume, of the eight sermons preached by Bentley in 1692 as the Boyle Lectures. According to Rev. Alexander Dyce, editor of *The Works of Richard Bentley, D. D.*, (London: Francis MacPherson, 1838, vol. 3, pp. v and vi) each sermon was originally published independently, the first six in 1692, the seventh and eighth in 1693, each with its own title page, imprimatur (that of the seventh and eighth is signed Ra. Barker), and separate pagination. In 1693, a general title page was prefixed to them reading: *The Folly and Unreasonableness of Atheism Dem-*

onstrated from the Advantage and Pleasure of a Religious Life, the Faculties of Human Souls, the Structure of Animate Bodies, & the Origin and Frame of the World . . . London, printed by J. H. for H. Mortlock . . . 1693 (Babson 40; not in Gray or Greenstreet).

The Elogium of Sir Isaac Newton (London: J. Tonson, 1728) is reproduced from the copy in the Yale Medical School Library, loaned by Dr. John F. Fulton. Mr. A. N. L. Munby, Fellow and Librarian of King's College, Cambridge, describes the Tonson *Elogium* as probably the "official" translation. In addition to the 1728 Tonson printing of the *Elogium* (Babson 270, Gray 388), there were published several other English translations (for example, Babson 271 and Gray 389, 390). One of the most interesting of these is *An account of the life and writings of S^r. Isaac Newton. Trans. from the Eloge of M. Fontenelle.* . . . The Second Edition. 8⁹. London, T. Warner, 1728 (not in Babson; perhaps this is Gray 390); the Harvard College Library contains a copy of the T. Warner "second edition," dated 1727. There is some question whether the date 1727 is a typographical error or whether possibly this is a printing made during the months of January to March, a period during which dates could be given as 1727, 1727/28, or 1728, depending upon feelings toward the old or the new style of dating since the official acceptance of "new style" dating did not occur in England until 1751/52. There is also a question about the designation "Second Edition." The Harvard 1727 Warner second edition is the earliest translation that we have found, but we have encountered no reference to a Warner first edition. Unfortunately the Harvard 1727 copy is imperfect, lacking a first leaf which is presumably the half title. Mr. Munby has kindly sent us a copy of the following advertisement which appears on the verso of the half title of a Warner, 1728, Second Edition, in the Trinity College, Cambridge, Library:

> The first Edition of this Translation was printed in Quarto, in order to be bound up with Sir Isaac Newton's Chronology: But for the Benefit of those who cannot afford to purchase a Book of so high a Price, it was thought necessary to publish this edition . . .

This possibly may be a reference to the edition by John Conduitt of *Newton's Chronology of Ancient Kingdoms Amended* . . . printed in quarto for J. Tonson in 1728, but the Harvard College Library copy of this work does not include the translation of Fontenelle's *éloge,* nor do the descriptions of Babson 214 or Gray 309 indicate its presence. It is possible that the J. Tonson 1728 quarto which we reproduce here is the first edition mentioned by Warner and that it was published separately instead of being included with the *Chronology*.

NOTE ON THE PRINTING OF BENTLEY'S SERMONS

WILLIAM B. TODD

Each of Bentley's last two discourses against atheism is here reproduced from a previously undifferentiated first edition represented at the Yale University Library (Mpd50.B69.1692). Both of these copies, together with the six earlier sermons, were separately issued, much thumbed by the original owner, bound in a single volume, and eventually rebound in modern library buckram.

At Harvard, the copies of these two sermons (*EC65.B4465.B693f) represent a later edition, not hitherto recognized. These were issued under a general title as part of a collected set and shortly thereafter included with other tracts in an early 18th-century binding. As the collected set was first advertised in the Term Catalogue for Easter, 1693 (Arber II.449), it doubtless comprised, upon issue, the original edition of the final sermon, bearing an imprimatur dated 30 May 1693. The Harvard set, however, though still exhibiting a general title dated 1693, appears to be of a later issue, since it incorporates, among the eight sermons, three reprints dated 1694. One of these is properly called a "Second" and the two others a "Third Edition."

Of these reprints the Second Edition, part 1 of the last three sermons (No. VI), is especially significant, for it indicates that the two other parts are of a date somewhat later than that assigned by the printer. Like the corresponding piece in the Yale series, this sermon, in title, imprimatur, and scriptural text heading page 1, is composed of type retained for the most part in the other two tracts. The settings both old and new provide the various points listed in the accompanying table, all of which demonstrate not only successive presswork in each series but, for the latter, a printing of the two "1693" sermons some time in 1694.

	Line	Reading	First Edition Part	First Edition Variant	Second Edition Part	Second Edition Variant
Title	7	SERMON	1	S intact	1	S correctly imposed
			2–3	S broken	2–3	S reversed
	11	Being	1–3	B broken	1–3	B intact
Edition			1–3	—	1	Second Edition
					2–3	—
Imprint		*LONDON*	1–3	swash italic	1–3	straight italic
			1	for *Henry Mortlock* ...1692.	1	by *J. H.* for *Henry Mortlock*...1694.
			2–3	for *H. Mortlock* ...1693.	2	by *J. H.* for *Henry Mortlock* ...1693.
					3	for *H Mortlock* ...1693.
Imprimatur	3	Dⁿᵒ Dⁿᵒ	1–3	1st D broken	1–3	D intact
	3	Archiep.	1–3	A intact	1	A intact
					2–3	A broken
	5	[place]	1	*LAMBETH*	1–3	*LAMBETH*
			2–3	*LAMBHITH*		
Text		[italic heading]	1–3	9 lines, first ends *unto the*	1–3	7 lines, first ends *the living*
					1	1st setting, double *s* ligatured, lines 5, 7.
					2–3	2d setting, double *s* separate.

II.

Newton's Papers on the Improvement of the Telescope and on Physical Optics

Newton's
Optical Papers

THOMAS S. KUHN

The original publication of the optical papers of Isaac Newton marked the beginning of an era in the development of the physical sciences. These papers, reprinted below, were the first public pronouncements by the man who has been to all subsequent generations the archetype of preëminent scientific creativity, and their appearance in early volumes of the *Philosophical Transactions of the Royal Society of London* constituted the first major contribution to science made through a technical journal, the medium that rapidly became the standard mode of communication among scientists.

Until the last third of the seventeenth century most original contributions to the sciences appeared in books, usually in large books: Copernicus' *De Revolutionibus* (1543), Kepler's *Astronomia Nova* (1609), Galileo's *Dialogo* (1632), Descartes's *Dioptrique* (1637), or Boyle's *Experiments and Considerations Touching Colours* (1664). In such books the author's original contributions were usually lost within a systematic exposition of a larger subject matter, so that constructive interchange of scientific experiment and hypothesis was hampered by premature systematization or, as in the case of Boyle, by the mere bulk of the experimental compilation.[1] Each scientist tended to erect his own system upon his own experiments; those experiments that could not support an entire system were frequently lost to the embryonic profession.

The first important breaches of this traditional mode of presentation occurred in the decade of 1660. The chartering of the Royal Society in 1662 and of the Académie Royale des Sciences in 1666, the first publication of the *Journal des Sçavans* and of the *Philosophical Transactions* in 1665, gave institutional expression and sanction to the new conception of science as a coöperative enterprise with utilitarian goals. The immediate objective of the individual scientist became the experimental contribution to an ultimate reconstruction of a system of nature rather than the construction of the system itself, and the journal article—an immediate report on technical experimentation or a preliminary interpretation of experiments—began to replace the book as the unit communiqué of the scientist.

Newton was the first to advance through this new medium an experimentally based proposal for the radical reform of a scientific theory, and his proposal was the first to arouse international discussion and debate within the columns of a scientific journal. Through the discussion, in which all the participants modified their positions, a consensus of scientific opinion was obtained. Within this novel pattern of public announcement, discussion, and ultimate achievement of professional consensus science has advanced ever since.

Newton's optical papers have a further importance to the student of the development of scientific thought. These brief and occasionally hasty communications to the editor of the *Philosophical Transactions* yield an insight into the personality and mental processes of their author that is obscured by the more usual approach

---

[1] For example, Experiments IV and V in Part III of Boyle's *Colours* are almost identical with the first and last of the three experiments that Newton employed in his first published presentation of the new theory of light and color. In Experiment IV Boyle generates a spectrum and in V he uses a lens to invert the order of the colors. But in Boyle's Baconian compilation these are but two among hundreds of experimental items. There is no evidence that they had the slightest effect on Boyle's contemporaries or successors. See *The Works of the Honourable Robert Boyle,* ed. Thomas Birch (London, 1744), vol. 2, p. 42.

to Newton through his *Principia* (1687) and *Opticks* (1704). In these later monumental creations, from which has emerged our picture of Newton the Olympian father of modern science, the creative role of the author is deliberately hidden by the superfluity of documentation and illustration and by the formality and impersonality of the organization.[2] It is primarily in his early papers, as in his letters, his notes, and his largely unpublished manuscripts, that Newton the creative scientist is to be discovered. And the shock of the discovery may be considerable, for this Newton does not always fit our ideal image.

Newton's first paper, the "New Theory about Light and Colors," is almost autobiographical in its development, and so it facilitates, more than any of Newton's other published scientific works, the search for the sources of the novel optical concepts that he drew from the "celebrated phaenomena of colours."[3] The prismatic colors to which Newton referred had been well known for centuries: white objects viewed through a triangular glass prism are seen with rainbow fringes at their edges; a beam of sunlight refracted by a prism produces all the colors of the rainbow at the screen upon which it falls. Seneca recorded the observations, which must be as old as shattered glass; Witelo, in the 13th century, employed a water-filled globe to generate rainbow colors; by the 17th century prisms, because of their striking colors, were an important item in the negotiations of the Jesuits in China.[4] Before Newton began his experiments at least four natural philosophers, Descartes, Marcus Marci, Boyle, and Grimaldi, had discussed in optical treatises the colored iris produced by a prism, and Hooke had based much of his theory of light upon the colors generated by a single refraction of sunlight at an air-water interface.[5] The "phaenomena" were

[2] The "Queries" that Newton appended to the *Opticks* are the one portion of his later published scientific works in which he allowed the fecundity of his creative imagination to appear. These speculative postscripts to his last technical work do provide a more intimate view of their author. Of course even the *Opticks* proper is a less impersonal work than the *Principia*, but, despite the frequent informality of literary style, the contents and organization are those of a treatise.

[3] The phrase is Newton's. See the beginning of the first optical paper, below.

[4] Joseph Priestley, *The History and Present State of Discoveries Relating to Vision, Light, and Colours* (London, 1722), pp. 7, 21, 169.

[5] Descartes's discussion of the prism occurs in Discours VIII of *Les météores* (1637). For Boyle's experiments see note 1, above. Marci's experiments are de-

indeed "celebrated." Newton, when he repeated them for his own
edification, can have had no reason to anticipate a result that he
would later describe as "the oddest, if not the most considerable
detection, which hath hitherto been made in the operations of
nature."[6]

But Newton's version of the experiment differed in an essential
respect from that employed by most of his predecessors; furthermore, as we shall see, Newton's optical education and experience
were not those of the earlier experimentalists who had employed
the prism. Previously, when white light had been passed through
a prism, the image of the refracted beam had normally been observed on a screen placed close to the prism.[7] With such an arrangement of the apparatus, the diverging beams of "pure" colors
had little opportunity to separate before striking the screen, and
the shape of the image cast on the screen was therefore identical
with that produced by the unrefracted beam. But in passing
through the prism the beam had acquired a red-orange fringe
along one edge and a blue-violet fringe along the other.

The colored fringes on an otherwise unaltered beam of white
light seemed to bear out an ancient theory of the nature of the
rainbow's colors, a theory which held that a succession of modifications of sunlight by the droplets of a rain cloud produced the
colors of the bow. In the century and a half preceding Newton's
work such a theory was repeatedly and variously reformulated and
applied to the colored iris generated by the prism. In all theories
the colors were viewed as a minor perturbation restricted primarily
to the edges of the homogeneous beam of sunlight. They were due

scribed in his *Thaumantias liber de arcu coelesti* . . . (Prague, 1648) and are discussed
by L. Rosenfeld in *Isis 17*, 325–330 (1932). Grimaldi's *Physico-mathesis de lumine* . . .
(Bologna, 1665) includes many discussions of prism experiments. Hooke's theory
and experiments appear in his *Micrographia* (1665), reprinted by R. T. Gunther as
vol. XIII of *Early Science in Oxford* (Oxford, 1938), pp. 47–67. There is no reason
to suppose that Newton in 1672 knew of the work of either Marci or Grimaldi,
but it is an index of the state of optical experimentation in the 17th century that
Grimaldi, Marci, and Boyle had, among them, performed all three of the experiments that Newton employed in his first optical paper.

[6] Letter from Newton to Oldenburg, the secretary of the Royal Society, dated
Cambridge, 18 January, 1671/2. Thomas Birch, *The History of the Royal Society of
London* (London, 1757), vol. 3, p. 5.

[7] See particularly Descartes's diagrams and discussion, cited in note 5, above.

to a mixture of light and shade at the region of contact between the refracted beam and the dark (Descartes); or they were a consequence of the varying "condensation" and "rarefaction" produced at the edges of the beam by the variation in the angle at which rays from the finite sun were incident upon the prism (Grimaldi); or they were generated by some other mechanical modification (Hooke and the later Cartesians).

There was no consensus as to the nature of the particular modification that tinted white light, but there was agreement that there was only one such modification and that its positive or negative application (for example, condensation or rarefaction) to white light could produce only two *primary* colors. These two colors, usually red and blue, represented the extreme applications of the modification, so that their mixture in appropriate proportions would generate any other color by producing the corresponding intermediate degree of modification. More recent experiments have, of course, shown that two primary colors will not suffice, but color-mixing experiments performed with crude equipment are extremely deceptive, a fact that may also account for Newton's initially surprising assertion that spectral yellow and blue combine to produce a green.[8]

All of the modification theories of prismatic colors fail ultimately because of their inability to account quantitatively for the elongation of the spectrum observed when, as in Newton's version of the experiment, the screen is placed a long distance from the prism. But even with the equipment so arranged, it is not immediately apparent that the elongation of the spectrum is incompatible with the modification theories. For since the sun has a finite breadth, rays from different portions of its disk are incident upon the prism at different angles, and even in the absence of dispersion this dif-

---

[8] In modern terminology, blue and yellow *light* are complementary; that is, they mix to give white. The green produced when blue and yellow *pigments* are mixed is the result of subtractive color mixing, a process different from the mixing of spectral colors. But in fact a long-wavelength spectral blue and a short-wavelength spectral red can be combined to produce a light-green tint. By combining in different proportions a blue near the green region of the spectrum with a red near the yellow it is actually possible to produce a number of shades of blue, green, red, yellow, and intermediate colors. The two-color theories were not so foreign to experience as has been imagined.

ference in angle of incidence will normally produce an elongation of the refracted beam qualitatively similar to that observed by Newton. Those of Newton's predecessors who, like Grimaldi, had noted the elongation of the spectrum had employed this device to account for it, and this was the explanation given by the Jesuit Ignatius Pardies, in his first letter objecting to Newton's theory.[9] To destroy the modification theory it was necessary to notice a *quantitative* discrepancy between the elongation predicted by that theory and the elongation actually observed, and this required an experimenter with a knowledge of the mathematical law governing refraction (not announced until 1637) and with considerable experience in applying the law to optical problems. In 1666 these qualifications were uniquely Newton's. Descartes, who shared Newton's mathematical interests, had performed the experiment with the screen close to the prism, and had noted no elongation. Boyle and Hooke, whose apparatus probably generated an elongated spectrum, shared with Grimaldi a prevalent indifference to the power of mathematics in physics.

It was, then, the large elongation produced in the Newtonian version of the experiment plus the recognition that the size of the spectrum was not that predicted by Snel's new law of refraction that transformed a routine repetition of a common experiment into the "oddest . . . detection, which hath hitherto been made in the operations of nature." The oddity was not the spectrum itself, but the discrepancy between the observed length of the spectrum and the length predicted by existing theory. And this discrepancy, emphasized and investigated with far more mathematical detail in Newton's earlier oral presentations of the experiment, forced Newton to search for a new theory.[10]

[9] Ignace Gaston Pardies, S.J. (1636–1673), was born at Pau in Southern France. At the time of his dispute with Newton he was the professor of rhetoric at the Collège Louis-le-grand in Paris.

[10] Newton first presented his new theory in a series of lectures delivered at Cambridge during 1669. The lectures were not printed until 1728, after his death, when they appeared in an English translation from the Latin manuscript. A Latin edition, containing lectures for the years 1669, 1670, and 1671, appeared in 1729. Certain of the features emphasized in the present discussion emerge with even greater clarity from the lectures than from the first optical paper. The two may profitably be read together.

Newton found the clue to the new theory in the geometrical idealization that he reported as the shape of the spectrum rather than in the elongation that had caused the search. His beam of sunlight was a cylinder ¼ inch in diameter, formed by allowing sunlight to enter his chamber through a circular hole in his "window shuts." After refraction the beam fell upon the opposite wall of the room, distant 22 feet from the prism, where, according to Newton, it produced an elongated spectrum, 13¼ inches in length, bounded by parallel sides 2⅜ inches apart, and capped by semicircular ends. The shape suggested its own interpretation. For the semicircular "caps" could be viewed as the residua of the shape imposed by the circular hole in the shutter, and the spectrum could then be analyzed into an infinite series of differently colored overlapping circles whose centers lay on a straight line perpendicular to the axis of the prism. In his early lectures, as in the later *Opticks,* Newton frequently sketched the spectrum in this way, one end formed by a pure blue circular image of the original hole, the other formed by a pure red image, and the intermediate region composed of a number of variously colored circles displaced along the axis of the spectrum. By this device the existing laws of refraction, which for Newton's arrangement of the prism predicted a circular image, could be preserved. But the law now had to be applied, not to the incident beam as a whole, but to every one of the colored beams contained in the original beam. Sunlight was a mixture of all the colors of the rainbow; each of the incident colored beams obeyed the laws of optics; but each was refracted through a different angle in its passage through the prism. This was the essence of Newton's new theory, derived primarily from the reported shape of the spectrum.[11]

[11] The preceding reconstruction of Newton's research follows the essentially autobiographical narrative provided by Newton himself in the first of the optical papers. It may require important modification as a result of a recent study of Newton's manuscripts by A. R. Hall, "Sir Isaac Newton's Note-Book, 1661–1665," *Cambridge Historical Journal 9,* 239–250 (1948). Hall believes that Newton discovered the variation of refractive index with color by observing a two-colored thread through a prism, and he suggests that the experiment in which a beam of sunlight is passed through a prism was not performed until a later date. For a variety of reasons (to be discussed elsewhere) I find this portion of Hall's reconstruction implausible. The textual and historical evidence available, though not

The reported shape leaves a puzzle illustrative of the nature of
Newton's genius. Though the spectrum described cries aloud for
the interpretation that Newton provided, it is very doubtful that
he saw any such shape. Only the central 2-inch strip of his 2⅝-
inch-wide spectrum was illuminated uniformly by light from
the disk of the sun. The balance of the width of the spectrum con-
sisted of a penumbral region in which the various colors gradually
shaded off into the black. Since the eye can distinguish red much
farther into the penumbral region than it can distinguish blue,
Newton probably saw a figure appreciably narrower and more
pointed at the blue end than at the red.[12] This is the shape that
Newton's bitterest and least intelligent critic, Franciscus Linus, described, and this is the only one of Linus's criticisms to which Newton never responded.[13] Newton combined a precise and detailed

decisive, persuades me that Newton had already passed a beam of sunlight
through a prism when he performed the experiments that Hall has discovered in
the "Note-Book."

If so, Newton's account of the development of the new theory remains autobiographical in the sense that the prism experiment did provide the initial impetus as well as an important clue for the new theory, as discussed above. But, as
Hall does conclusively show, the implication of Newton's account is wrong in that
Newton did not proceed so directly or so immediately from the first prism experiment to the final version of the theory as the first paper would imply. When he
made the entries in his college notebook, Newton had not arrived at the final
form of the new theory. So far as I can tell from the fragments reproduced by
Hall, Newton then believed that different colors were refracted through different
angles, but he still held that the individual colors were generated within the prism
by modifications of the initially homogeneous white light. This intermediate stage
of Newton's thought provides a fascinating field for further study.

[12] It is impossible to be precise about the actual shape of the spectrum viewed
by Newton. The sensitivity of the human eye to short-wavelength blue varies from
one individual to another, and the relative intensity of the blue in the spectrum
is also a function of atmospheric conditions.

[13] Linus's description occurs midway through the first paragraph of his second
letter of criticism. Although the position of Linus's prism was different from that
of Newton's, the "sharp cone or pyramis" described by Linus is due to the same
penumbral effects that must have caused the sides of Newton's spectrum to de-
viate from parallelism.

Franciscus Linus (Francis Hall or Line), S.J., was born in London in 1595. During his controversy with Newton he was a teacher of mathematics and Hebrew
at the English college of Liège. He spent much of his later life attempting to
reconcile the results of 17th-century experimentation with Aristotelian physics.
Linus was the author of the "funiculus" hypothesis by which he claimed to explain the results of Boyle's barometer experiments without recourse to the vacuum

description of his experimental apparatus with an imaginative idealization of his experimental results.

Newton's leap from the full and unintelligible complexity of the observable phenomenon to the geometrical idealization underlying it is symptomatic of the intellectual extrapolations that mark his contributions to science. And he was apparently aware of and concerned with the extrapolation, though he made it explicit in none of his communications to the Royal Society. In the optical lectures, which he delivered in Cambridge prior to the composition of his first published paper, Newton included a description of two experiments that he had designed to investigate the shape of the spectrum produced without a penumbral region. In one of these he used a lens, placed one focal length in front of the screen, to refocus the colored circular sun images of which the spectrum was composed. In a second he utilized the planet Venus, effectively a point source, instead of the sun in order to generate his spectrum. He had justified his extrapolation to himself, but, except for implicit references to the problem in his correspondence with Moray and in the *Opticks*, he did not tell his readers how to follow him.

Newton's announcement in 1672 of the discoveries made six to eight years earlier induced a great controversy within the columns of the *Philosophical Transactions*.[14] The prismatic colors that he discussed were well known, at least qualitatively, and there was

or atmospheric pressure, and experiments designed to refute him led to the discovery of Boyle's Law. Linus died in 1675, midway through the dispute with Newton, but his cause was taken up by two of his students, Gascoigne and Lucas.

Anthony Lucas (1633–1693), another British Jesuit, appears to have been a meticulous experimenter. His inability to obtain the large dispersion reported by Newton must have been due to his use of a different sort of glass. Lucas's experimental "proofs" of the inadequacy of Newton's theory are a fascinating index of the difficulties in designing unequivocal dispersion experiments. In most experiments the effects are so small that they can be fitted to any theory, so incisive documentation of a particular theory requires careful selection from the multiplicity of available phenomena. At first glance Newton's failure to answer any of Lucas's experimental criticism seems strange, particularly since Newton did respond at such length to the one remark by Lucas that did not reflect at all upon the validity of Newton's conclusions. But see the discussion, below, of Newton's attitude toward controversy.

[14] A. R. Hall, "Sir Isaac Newton's Note-Book," has pointed out that Newton probably intended to write "1665" rather than "1666" for the date of the prism experiment which opens his first paper. He also argues that Newton's work with the prism may have begun as early as 1664.

widespread conviction among 17th-century opticians that they could be adequately treated by existing optical theories. No wonder there was resentment of a newcomer who claimed that precise analysis of a well-known effect necessitated discarding established theories. Opponents could easily find grounds for rejecting the proposals. They could, for example, deny the existence of the experimental effect. The sun is an unreliable and a moving source of light; the prism generates a number of emergent beams, only one of which satisfies Newton's description; quantitative results vary with the sort of glass employed in the prism. Alternatively, they could accept Newton's experimental results, but deny the necessity or even the validity of his interpretation.

The nature and psychological sources of the controversy were typical, but the reaction was less severe than that usually produced by so radical a proposal. Newton's predecessors had all employed some form of modification theory, but, having reached no consensus on the nature of the modification, they lacked a stable base for a counterattack. And Newton's experimental documentation of his theory is a classic in its simplicity and its incisiveness. The modification theorists might finally have explained the elongation of the spectrum, but how could they have evaded the implications of the *experimentum crucis?* An innovator in the sciences has never stood on surer ground.

As a result the controversy that followed the original announcement is of particular interest today for the light it sheds upon Newton's character.[15] In particular the controversial literature illuminates the genesis of Newton's relation with the Royal Society's curator, Robert Hooke, with whom he later engaged in a priority battle over the inverse-square law of gravitation.[16] Hooke's claim to the authorship of the inverse-square law almost caused Newton to omit the Third Book of the *Principia,* and it was apparently

[15] There are, however, many points of technical interest in the debate. These are discussed more fully in L. Rosenfeld, "La théorie des couleurs de Newton et ses adversaires," *Isis 9,* 44–65 (1927). A stimulating elementary account of some of the same material has been provided by M. Roberts and E. R. Thomas, *Newton and the Origin of Colours* (London: G. Bell & Sons, 1934).

[16] For bibliography and a definitive account of the gravitation controversy, see A. Koyré, "An Unpublished Letter of Robert Hooke to Isaac Newton," *Isis 43,* 312–337 (1952).

Hooke's continuing opposition to Newton's optical theories that caused Newton to delay publication of the *Opticks* until long after his own active research in the field had ended. Hooke died in 1703, and the *Opticks,* much of which had existed in manuscript for years, first appeared in the following year.

Newton's first paper was read to the assembled members of the Royal Society on February 8, 1671/2. On February 15 Hooke delivered, at the request of the Society's members, a report on and evaluation of Newton's work. Coming from a senior member of the profession, a man already established as the most original optical experimentalist of the day, the report was most judicious, though it contained important errors and displayed Hooke's typically Baconian indifference to quantitative mathematical formulations. Hooke praised and confirmed Newton's experimental results, and he conceded that the theory which Newton had derived from them was entirely adequate to explain the effects. His only major criticism (excepting the remarks on telescopes, for which see below) is that Newton's interpretation was not a *necessary* consequence of the experiments. Hooke felt that Newton had performed too few experiments to justify the theory, that another theory (his own) could equally well explain Newton's experiments, and that other experiments (particularly his own on the colors of thin films) could not be explained by Newton's theory.

Hooke's Baconian criticism is an index of the prevalent methodological emphasis upon experimentation, an emphasis that made the "experimental history" a typical scientific product of the day. Most members of the Royal Society would have concurred. But Hooke was quite wrong in thinking that his own version of the modification theory could explain Newton's results; at least he never gave a satisfactory explanation of the production of colors.[17] On the other hand, Hooke was right that Newton's theory could

[17] The difficulty in adapting a pressure-wave theory of light like Hooke's to the various color phenomena explored by Newton is well illustrated by the experience of Huygens, who brought these theories to their most perfect 17th-century form in his *Traité de la lumière* (1690). Huygens wrote Leibniz that he had "said nothing respecting colours in my *Traité de la lumière,* finding this subject very difficult, and particularly from the great number of different ways in which colours are produced." Sir David Brewster, *Memoirs of the Life, Writings, and Discoveries of Sir Isaac Newton* (Edinburgh, 1855), vol. 1, p. 95 n.

not explain some of the experiments upon which Hooke had based his own theory. In particular, Newton's theory, as of 1672, would not explain either diffraction or the colors of thin sheets of mica, both of which Hooke had described in his *Micrographia* (1665). Nor would Newton's theory explain the colors produced by confining air between sheets of glass, an observation that Hooke reported to the Society on April 4 and June 19 in his further examination of Newton's doctrine.[18] The latter communication, incidentally, included a clear description of the phenomenon usually known as "Newton's rings," and it seems probable that Newton borrowed it from Hooke and employed it to develop a revised theory adequate to handle Hooke's experiments. For Newton, in his long letters of December and January 1675/6, did succeed in solving Hooke's problems to his own satisfaction and to that of most of his contemporaries. But to do so he had to modify his original theory by the introduction of an explicit æthereal medium which could transmit impulses as pressure waves, and this was an immense step toward Hooke's theory. Hooke, of course, did not accept even this later modification. He always felt that Newton's use of *both* corpuscles and æther impulses violated Occam's injunction against the needless multiplication of conceptual entities.[19]

In the final analysis Hooke was wrong. As Newton clearly showed in his belated reply, Hooke's pulse theory of light was incapable of accounting for linear propagation; nor could Hooke's modification theory of color account either for the *experimentum crucis* or for any of the novel color-mixing experiments that Newton apparently designed specifically to meet Hooke's objections. This much of the reply was effective, and Newton might better have begun and ended with the elaboration of these arguments, for Hooke had challenged neither Newton's experiments nor the adequacy of his theory to resolve the experiments. But this is not what Newton did. In his lengthy and gratuitously caustic response, whose incongruity with Hooke's critique has escaped attention since the two have not before been printed together,[20] Newton at-

[18] Birch, *History of the Royal Society*, vol. 3, pp. 41 & 54.

[19] *Ibid.*, p. 295.

[20] Oldenburg, the secretary of the Royal Society and editor of the *Philosophical Transactions*, is known to have hated Hooke. This may well explain his failure to

tacked Hooke on three apparently incompatible grounds: Hooke had attributed to Newton a corpuscular theory that Newton had not developed; Hooke's impulse theory was not basically incompatible with the corpuscular theory (which Newton had disowned); and Hooke's impulse theory was incapable of accounting for the phenomena. Newton might have employed any of these three lines of attack alone—though only the third seems both relevant and accurate—but it is difficult to see how anything but consuming passion could have led him to employ them concurrently.

Newton was a man of passions. It is difficult to read many of his responses to criticism without concurring in a recent judgment of Newton's personality by the late Lord Keynes. After a lengthy examination of Newton's manuscripts Keynes wrote:

> For in vulgar modern terms Newton was profoundly neurotic of a not unfamiliar type, but—I should say from the records—a most extreme example. His deepest instincts were occult, esoteric, semantic—with profound shrinking from the world, a paralyzing fear of exposing his thoughts, his beliefs, his discoveries in all nakedness to the inspection and criticism of the world. "Of the most fearful, cautious and suspicious temper that I ever knew," said Whiston, his successor in the Lucasian Chair. The too well-known conflicts and ignoble quarrels with Hooke, Flamsteed, Leibnitz are only too clear an evidence of this. Like all his type he was wholly aloof from women. He parted with and published nothing except under the extreme pressure of friends.[21]

Newton's fear of exposure and the correlated compulsion to be invariably and entirely immune to criticism show throughout the controversial writings. They are apparent in both the tone and the substance of his reply to Hooke, where they are also combined with the beginning of that tendency to deny the apparent implications of earlier writings (rather than either defending them or ad-

print Hooke's critique with Newton's reply. The omission must have seemed a gratuitous insult to Hooke, particularly in view of the tone and substance of Newton's comments.

[21]J. M. Keynes, "Newton the Man," in the Royal Society's *Newton Tercentenary Celebrations* (Cambridge, 1947), p. 28. These documents can be put to other uses, however. Examine, for an opinion of the Hooke-Newton exchange directly opposed to the one given above, the analysis provided by Brewster, *Memoirs,* vol.1, pp. 86–92. But Brewster cannot avoid providing repeated illustrations of Newton's efforts to escape from controversy (for example, pp. 95–99).

mitting to a change of mind) which has so consistently misled subsequent students of his work. Did Hooke really misinterpret the
intent of Newton's remarks on the difficulties of constructing refracting telescopes? Is Newton honest in rejecting the corpuscular
hypothesis that Hooke ascribes to him? Or, to take a later and far
clearer example, is not Newton convicted of an irrationally moti-
vated lie in his reply to Huygens's remarks about the composition
of the color white? In his first paper Newton had said, in discussing
colors:

> But the most . . . wonderful composition is that of *Whiteness* . . . 'Tis
> ever compounded, and to its composition are requisite all the aforesaid
> primary Colours, mixed in a due proportion . . . Hence therefore it
> comes to pass, that *Whiteness* is the usual colour of *Light;* for Light is a
> confused aggregate of Rays indued with all sorts of Colours . . . if any
> one predominate, the Light must incline to that colour.

Yet when Huygens suggested that the combination of yellow and
blue might generate white, Newton admitted the possibility but
claimed that he had never meant anything else. The apparent
contradiction he reconciled by saying that Huygens's white would
be different from his own by virtue of its composition. Newton's
position was correct in the reply, but surely he had changed his
mind in reaching it.

The same defensiveness had more serious consequences in Newton's writings on telescopes. Here Newton's influence appears to
have been predominantly negative. His own work on telescopes was
of little practical importance, and his remarks on design were frequently wrong. Although he built the first working reflector, he
was never able to perfect the model sufficiently to enable it to compete with existing refractors, and so his position was not very different from that of the contemporary and independent designers,
James Gregory and Guillaume Cassegrain.[22] The reflecting telescope remained a curious toy on the shelves of the Royal Society

[22] James Gregory (1638–1675), a Scottish mathematician, described a reflecting
telescope in his *Optica Promota* (1633), and Newton had studied Gregory's design
when he started his own. Sieur Guillaume Cassegrain was a modeler and founder
of statues in the employ of Louis XIV. His design was surely independent of
Newton's and may have been independent of Gregory's. Both Gregory and
Cassegrain tried to build reflectors but were unable to polish adequate mirrors.

until, in 1722, James Hadley succeeded in grinding a parabolic mirror. But as soon as the reflector could compete with the refractor, Newton's design was discarded in favor of the designs by Gregory and Cassegrain that Newton had so vehemently criticized for essentially irrelevant reasons.[23]

Far more important in the development of telescopes were Newton's mistakes in the evaluation of optical aberrations. Having been led to the reflecting telescope by the discovery of the chromatic aberration caused by the variation of refractive index with color, Newton always insisted that chromatic rather than spherical aberration imposed the major limitation upon the power of refracting telescopes. Newton's theoretical comparisons of the two were both mathematically and optically correct, but, as Huygens pointed out in his comment, Newton's interpretation of the calculations was incompatible with the observed performance of spherical lenses. Newton explained the discrepancy correctly as due to the small effect on the eye of the widely dispersed red and blue rays, but he failed to notice that in practice this made chromatic aberrations little or no more important than spherical. So Newton continued to insist upon the practical superiority of reflectors.[24]

[23] On Newton's contributions to the development of telescopes see Louis Bell, *The Telescope* (New York, 1922).

[24] The study of Newton's most important and damaging error in his writings on the telescope is complicated rather than clarified by the papers reprinted below. In his *Opticks* (Book I, Part II, Experiment 8) Newton "proved" that it was impossible to build an achromatic lens, that is, a lens compounded from two or more materials so differing in dispersive power that they will refract a ray of white light without separating the colors in it. Newton claimed to have found by experiment that when a beam of light was passed through a succession of prisms of glass and water a spectrum was invariably generated unless the emergent and incident beams were parallel. He concluded that any combination of materials which could correct dispersion would also nullify refraction, so that no achromatic lens was possible. The error may well have hindered the development of achromatic lenses.

To get the experimental result Newton must either have shut his eyes, used sugar to raise the refractive index of his water, or employed a variety of glass with unusually low dispersive power. All three of these explanations have been advanced by subsequent historians, most of whom have also expressed surprise at Newton's readiness to draw so general a conclusion from such slight experimental evidence. For a full account of the development of achromatic lenses see N. V. E. Nordenmark and J. Nordstrom, "Om uppfinningen av den akromatiska och aplanatiska linsen," *Lychnos 4*, 1–52 (1938); *5*, 313–384 (1939). The second

Subsequent history bore out the judgment expressed by Huygens in his last letter of the optics controversy that until it became possible to grind nonspherical mirrors the future of practical telescopic observations would be associated with refractors of long focal length and consequently low aberrations.[25]

But among the aspects of Newton's thought that are illuminated by recognition of his dread of controversy, the most important is his attitude toward "hypotheses." Like most of his contemporaries, Newton was guided throughout his scientific career by the conception of the universe as a gigantic machine whose components are microscopic corpuscles moving and interacting in accordance with immutable laws.[26] Most of Newton's work in physics can be viewed appropriately as a part of a consistent campaign to discover the mathematical laws governing the aggregation and motion of the corpuscles of a mechanical "clock-work universe," and many of his specifically optical, chemical, or dynamical writings are difficult to comprehend without reference to the corpuscular metaphysic which played an active role in their creation.[27] Yet from most of his published writings Newton tried, never completely successfully,

portion of the article includes some appendices and an abstract in English.

It is apparent from the optical papers below that Newton's theorem concerning the relation of dispersion and refractive index was the best possible refutation for three of his early critics. It nullified the objections of Hooke and Huygens, who had urged that more attention be given to the perfection of refracting telescopes, and it made it certain that Lucas had erred in reporting the small dispersion of his prism. For this reason most historians have argued that the theorem developed in the *Opticks* was in Newton's mind, at least implicitly, from the beginning of his optical researches and that this is why he failed to consider more seriously the merits of his opponents' positions. But—and this is where the new complication enters—I can find no way of interpreting the text of Newton's response to Hooke without supposing that Newton is there proposing an achromatic lens made by compounding a water lens with two convexo-concave lenses of glass.

[25] The letters to and from Huygen's reprinted below are only a part of a larger correspondence, most of which was not published until recently. L. T. More discusses the complete correspondence more fully in his biography, *Isaac Newton* (New York, 1934). The letters themselves will be found in volume VII of the *Oeuvres complètes de Christiaan Huygens* (The Hague, 1888–1944).

[26] M. Boas, "The Establishment of the Mechanical Philosophy," *Osiris 10*, 412–541 (1952).

[27] For the role of the metaphysic in Newton's chemistry see the next section of this book. For its role in Newton's dynamics, see A. Koyré, "The Significance of the Newtonian Synthesis," *Archives internationales d'histoires des sciences 29*, 291–311 (1950), and T. S. Kuhn, *The Copernican Revolution* (Cambridge, Mass., 1957), chap. 7.

to eliminate just these hypothetical and therefore controversial elements.

In the notebook in which he recorded the progress of his early optical research Newton continually referred to light rays as composed of "globules," traveling with finite velocities and interacting in accordance with the known laws of impact.[28] But in his first published paper Newton omitted all explicit reference to particular corpuscular mechanisms which determine the behavior of light. He substituted geometrical entities ("rays") for physical entities (corpuscles moving in definite paths); and he contented himself with a retrospective argument showing that the experimentally determined properties of the rays must make light a substance rather than a quality. In his controversy with Hooke, who seems to have known more about the hypotheses than Newton had allowed to enter in his published discussion, he reneged on even this argument, and thus continued a retreat that had begun in his first paper and developed further in his letters to Pardies.

That this is a genuine retreat from the defense of metaphysical hypotheses which Newton believed and employed creatively is amply, if incompletely, attested by the inconsistencies in his discussions and use of hypotheses throughout the optical papers printed below. In the first paper light was a substance. In the letters to Pardies light was either a substance or a quality, but the definition of light rays in terms of "indefinitely small . . . inde-

---

[28] For example: "Though 2 rays be equally swift yet if one ray be lesse y^n y^e other that ray shall have so much lesse effect on y^e sensorium as it has lesse motion y^n y^e others &c.

"Whence supposing y^t there are loose particles in y^e pores of a body bearing proportion to y^e greater rays, as $9:12$ & y^e less globules is in proportion to y^e greater as $2:9$, y^e greater globulus by impinging on such a particle will loose $\frac{6}{7}$ parts of its motion y^e less glob. will loose $\frac{2}{7}$ parts of its motion & y^e remaining motion of y^e glob. will have almost such a proportion to one another as their quantity have viz. $\frac{5}{7} : \frac{1}{7} :: 9 : 1\frac{4}{5} w^{ch}$ is almost 2 y^e lesse glob. & such a body may produce blews and purples. But if y^e particles on wch y^e globuli reflect are equal to y^e lesse globulus it shall loose its motion & y^e greater glob. shall loose $\frac{2}{11}$ parts of its motion and such a body may be red or yellow." Hall, "Sir Isaac Newton's Note-Book," p. 248.

pendent" parts made light again corporeal. In the same letter
Newton proclaimed that his observations and *theories* could be
reconciled with the pressure *hypotheses* of either Hooke or Descartes,
but in the letter to Hooke he forcefully demonstrated the inadequacy of all pressure hypotheses to explain the phenomena of
light and colors. Newton denied his adherence to the corpuscular
hypothesis, and he stated that his credence was restricted to laws
that could be proved by experiment, but he returned to the pattern
of his notebook by employing implicitly the hypothetical scatter-
ings of corpuscles at points of focus to prove the disadvantages of
the Gregorian telescope.[29] In 1672 he denied the utility of hypotheses when presenting a theory which he believed could be made
independent of them, but in dealing with the colors of thin films
in the important letters of 1675/6 he employed explicit hypotheses,
presumably because the new subject matter of these letters could
not otherwise be elaborated. Significantly, it was just these later
letters, from which large segments of Books II and III of the *Opticks*
were transcribed, that Newton refused to publish until after
Hooke's death. Of all his optical writings, these letters best reflect
the procedures of Newton at work.[30]

Much of modern science inherits from Newton the admirable
pragmatic aim, never completely realized, of eliminating from the
final reports of scientific discovery all reference to the more speculative hypotheses that played a role in the process of discovery.
The desirability of this Newtonian mode of presenting theories is
well illustrated by the subsequent history of Newton's own hypoth-

[29] Brewster, *Memoirs,* p. 50 n.

[30] These critically important letters, reprinted below, deserve far more study
and discussion than they here receive. But such discussion necessarily assumes the
proportion of a critical analysis of the second and third books of the *Opticks* for
which these letters provided a draft, and the space for such an analysis is not here
available. For a discussion of the central ideas in these later letters, as they emerge
in the *Opticks,* see I. B. Cohen's introduction to the recent reissue of the *Opticks*
(New York, 1952).

Space limitations also prevent my discussing Newton's posthumously published
design of "An instrument for observing the Moon's Distance from the fixed Stars
at Sea." When written this paper contained important novelties of design, but
before it was published these new features had been independently incorporated
in practical navigational instruments by several designers. On these instruments
see Lloyd Brown, *The Story of Maps* (Boston, 1949), pp. 191 ff.

eses. The next great step in optics, the development of an adequate wave theory, was retarded by the grip of Newton's corpuscular hypotheses upon the scientific mind. But Newton's remarks about the role of hypotheses in science were dictated by personal idiosyncrasy as often as by philosophical acumen; repeatedly he renounces hypotheses simply to avoid debate. And so he has seemed to support the further assertion that scientific research can and should be confined to the experimental pursuit of mathematical regularity—that hypotheses which transcend the immediate evidence of experiment have no place in science. Careful examination of Newton's less systematic published writings provides no evidence that Newton imposed upon himself so drastic a restriction upon scientific imagination.

The achievements initiated by Newton's own imagination are unsurpassed, and it is primarily the magnitude of his achievements that directs attention to the man. If the resulting study displays error and idiosyncrasy in Newton's complex and difficult personality, it cannot lessen his unparalleled accomplishments. It can alter only our image of the requisites for preëminent scientific achievement. But this alteration is a goal worth pursuing: a true image of the successful scientist is a first condition for understanding science.

(3075)   Numb.80.

PHILOSOPHICAL
TRANSACTIONS.

February 19. 16$\frac{71}{72}$.

The CONTENTS.

A Letter of Mr.Iſaac Newton,*Mathematick Profeſſor in the Univerſi-*
ty of Cambridge ; containing his New Theory about Light *and* Colors : *Where* Light *is declared to be not Similar or Homogeneal , but*
conſiſting of diſform rays, ſome of which are more refrangible than o-
thers : And Colors *are affirm'd to be not Qualifications of Light, de-*
riv'd from Refractions of natural Bodies, (as *'tis generally believed* ;)
but Original and Connate properties, which in divers rays are divers :
Where ſeveral Obſervations and Experiments are alledged to prove the
ſaid Theory.   An Accompt of ſome Books : I. *A Deſcription of the*
EAST-INDIAN COASTS, MALABAR, COROMANDEL,
CEYLON,&c. in Dutch, *by* Phil.Baldæus. II. Antonii le Grand
*INSTITVTIO PHILOSOPHIÆ,*ſecundùm principia Renati
Des-Cartes ; *novâ methodo adornata & explicata.*   III. *An Eſſay*
to the Advancement of MVSICK; by Thomas Salmon *M. A.*
Advertiſement about Thæon Smyrnæus. *An* Index *for the Tracts*
of the Year 1671.

A Letter of Mr. Iſaac Newton, *Profeſſor of the Mathematicks in the*
Univerſity of Cambridge ; containing his New Theory about Light *and*
Colors : *ſent by the Author to the Publiſher from Cambridge,* Febr. 6.
16$\frac{71}{72}$; *in order to be communicated to the* R. Society.

SIR,

TO perform my late promiſe to you, I ſhall without further
ceremony acquaint you, that in the beginning of the Year
1666 (at which time I applyed my ſelf to the grinding of Optick
glaſſes of other figures than *Spherical,*) I procured me a Triangular glaſs-Priſme, to try therewith the celebrated *Phænomena* of

G g g g   *Colours.*

(3076)

Colours. And in order thereto having darkened my chamber, and made a small hole in my window-shuts, to let in a convenient quantity of the Suns light, I placed my Prisme at his entrance, that it might be thereby refracted to the opposite wall. It was at first a very pleasing divertisement, to view the vivid and intense colours produced thereby; but after a while applying my self to consider them more circumspectly, I became surprised to see them in an *oblong* form; which, according to the received laws of Refraction, I expected should have been *circular.*

They were terminated at the sides with streight lines, but at the ends, the decay of light was so gradual, that it was difficult to determine justly, what was their figure; yet they seemed *semicircular.*

Comparing the length of this coloured *Spectrum* with its breadth, I found it about five times greater; a disproportion so extravagant, that it excited me to a more then ordinary curiosity of examining, from whence it might proceed. I could scarce think, that the various *Thickness* of the glass, or the termination with shadow or darkness, could have any Influence on light to produce such an effect; yet I thought it not amiss, first to examine those circumstances, and so tryed, what would happen by transmitting light through parts of the glass of divers thicknesses, or through holes in the window of divers bignesses, or by setting the Prisme without so, that the light might pass through it, and be refracted before it was terminated by the hole : But I found none of those circumstances material. The fashion of the colours was in all these cases the same.

Then I suspected, whether by any *unevenness* in the glass, or other contingent irregularity, these colours might be thus dilated. And to try this, I took another Prisme like the former, and so placed it, that the light, passing through them both, might be refracted contrary ways, and so by the latter returned into that course, from which the former had diverted it. For, by this means I thought, the *regular* effects of the first Prisme would be destroyed by the second Prisme, but the *irregular* ones more augmented, by the multiplicity of refractions. The event was, that the light, which by the first Prisme was diffused into an *oblong* form, was by the second reduced into an *orbicular* one with as much regularity, as when it did not at all pass through them. So that, what ever was the cause of that length, 'twas not any contingent irregularity.

I

(3077)

I then proceeded to examin more critically, what might be effected by the difference of the incidence of Rays coming from divers parts of the Sun; and to that end, meafured the feveral lines
and angles, belonging to the Image.   Its diftance from the hole
or Prifme was 22 foot; its utmoft length 13¼ inches; its breadth
2⅝; the diameter of the hole ¼ of an inch; the angle, with the
Rays, tending towards the middle of the image, made with thofe
lines, in which they would have proceeded without refraction, was
44 deg. 56'.   And the vertical Angle of the Prifme, 63 deg. 12'.
Alfo the Refractions on both fides the Prifme, that is, of the Incident, and Emergent Rays, were as near, as I could make them,
equal, and confequently about 54 deg. 4'.   And the Rays fell perpendicularly upon the wall.   Now fubducting the diameter of the
hole from the length and breadth of the Image, there remains 13
Inches the length, and 2⅜ the breadth, comprehended by thofe
Rays, which paffed through the center of the faid hole, and confequently the angle of the hole, which that breadth fubtended,
was about 31', anfwerable to the Suns Diameter; but the angle,
which its length fubtended, was more then five fuch diameters,
namely 2 deg. 49'.

Having made thefe obfervations, I firft computed from them
the refractive power of that glafs, and found it meafured by the
ratio of the fines, 20 to 31.   And then, by that *ratio*, I computed
the Refractions of two Rays flowing from oppofite parts of the
Sun's *difcus*, fo as to differ 31' in their obliquity of Incidence, and
found, that the emergent Rays fhould have comprehended an
angle of about 31', as they did, before they were incident.

But becaufe this computation was founded on the Hypothefis
of the proportionality of the *fines* of Incidence, and Refraction,
which though by my own Experience I could not imagine to be
fo erroneous, as to make that Angle but 31', which in reality was
2 deg. 49'; yet my curiofity caufed me again to take my Prifme.
And having placed it at my window, as before, I obferved, that by
turning it a little about its *axis* to and fro, fo as to vary its obliquity to the light, more then an angle of 4 or 5 degrees, the Colours were not thereby fenfibly tranflated from their place on the
wall, and confequently by that variation of Incidence, the quantity of Refraction was not fenfibly varied.   By this Experiment
therefore, as well as by the former computation, it was evident,
that the difference of the Incidence of Rays, flowing from divers

(3078)

parts of the Sun, could not make them after decussation diverge at a sensibly greater angle, than that at which they before converged; which being, at most, but about 31 or 32 minutes, there still remained some other cause to be found out, from whence it could be 2 degr. 49'.

Then I began to suspect, whether the Rays, after their trajection through the Prisme, did not move in curve lines, and according to their more or less curvity tend to divers parts of the wall. And it increased my suspition, when I remembred that I had often seen a Tennis ball, struck with an oblique Racket, describe such a curve line. For, a circular as well as a progressive motion being communicated to it by that stroak, its parts on that side, where the motions conspire, must press and beat the contiguous Air more violently than on the other, and there excite a reluctancy and reaction of the Air proportionably greater. And for the same reason, if the Rays of light should possibly be globular bodies, and by their oblique passage out of one medium into another acquire a circulating motion, they ought to feel the greater resistance from the ambient Æther, on that side, where the motions conspire, and thence be continually bowed to the other. But notwithstanding this plausible ground of suspition, when I came to examine it, I could observe no such curvity in them. And besides (which was enough for my purpose) I observed, that the difference 'twixt the length of the Image, and diameter of the hole, through which the light was transmitted, was proportionable to their distance.

The gradual removal of these suspitions, at length led me to the Experimentum Crucis, which was this: I took two boards, and placed one of them close behind the Prisme at the window, so that the light might pass through a small hole, made in it for the purpose, and fall on the other board, which I placed at about 12 feet distance, having first made a small hole in it also, for some of that Incident light to pass through. Then I placed another Prisme behind this second board, so that the light, trajected through both the boards, might pass through that also, and be again refracted before it arrived at the wall. This done, I took the first Prisme in my hand, and turned it to and fro slowly about its Axis, so much as to make the several parts of the Image, cast on the second board, successively pass through the hole in it, that I might observe to what places on the wall the second Prisme would refract them.

And

(3079)

And I saw by the variation of those places, that the light, tending to that end of the Image, towards which the refraction of the first Prisme was made, did in the second Prisme suffer a Refraction considerably greater then the light tending to the other end. And so the true cause of the length of that Image was detected to be no other, then that *Light* consists of *Rays differently refrangible*, which, without any respect to a difference in their incidence, were, according to their degrees of refrangibility, transmitted towards divers parts of the wall.

When I understood this, I left off my aforesaid Glass works; for I saw, that the perfection of Telescopes was hitherto limited, not so much for want of glasses truly figured according to the prescriptions of Optick Authors, (which all men have hitherto imagined,) as because that Light it self is a *Heterogeneous mixture of differently refrangible Rays.* So that, were a glass so exactly figured, as to collect any one sort of rays into one point, it could not collect those also into the same point, which having the same Incidence upon the same Medium are apt to suffer a different refraction. Nay, I wondered, that seeing the difference of refrangibility was so great, as I found it, Telescopes should arrive to that perfection they are now at. For, measuring the refractions in one of my Prismes, I found, that supposing the common *sine* of Incidence upon one of its planes was 44 parts, the *sine* of refraction of the utmost Rays on the red end of the Colours, made out of the glass into the Air, would be 68 parts, and the *sine* of refraction of the utmost rays on the other end, 69 parts : So that the difference is about a 24*th* or 25*th* part of the whole refraction. And consequently, the object-glass of any Telescope cannot collect all the rays, which come from one point of an object so as to make them convene at its *focus* in less room then in a circular space, whose diameter is the 50*th* part of the Diameter of its Aperture ; which is an irregularity, some hundreds of times greater, then a circularly figured *Lens*, of so small a section as the Object glasses of long Telescopes are, would cause by the unfitness of its figure, were Light *uniform.*

This made me take *Reflections* into consideration, and finding them regular, so that the Angle of Reflection of all sorts of Rays was equal to their Angle of Incidence ; I understood, that by their mediation Optick instruments might be brought to any degree of perfection imaginable, provided a *Reflecting* substance could be found,

(3080)

found, which would polish as finely as Glass, and *reflect* as much light, as glass *transmits*, and the art of communicating to it a *Parabolick* figure be also attained. But there seemed very great difficulties, and I have almost thought them insuperable, when I further considered, that every irregularity in a reflecting superficies makes the rays stray 5 or 6 times more out of their due course, than the like irregularities in a refracting one : So that a much greater curiosity would be here requisite, than in figuring glasses for Refraction.

Amidst these thoughts I was forced from *Cambridge* by the Intervening Plague, and it was more then two years, before I proceeded further. But then having thought on a tender way of polishing, proper for metall, whereby, as I imagined, the figure also would be corrected to the last ; I began to try, what might be effected in this kind, and by degrees so far perfected an Instrument (in the essential parts of it like that I sent to *London*,) by which I could discern Jupiters 4 Concomitants, and shewed them divers times to two others of my acquaintance. I could also discern the Moon-like phase of *Venus*, but not very distinctly, nor without some niceness in disposing the Instrument.

From that time I was interrupted till this last Autumn, when I made the other. And as that was sensibly better then the first (especially for Day-Objects,) so I doubt not, but they will be still brought to a much greater perfection by their endeavours, who, as you inform me, are taking care about it at *London*.

I have sometimes thought to make a *Microscope*, which in like manner should have, instead of an Object-glass, a Reflecting piece of metall. And this I hope they will also take into consideration. For those Instruments seem as capable of improvement as *Telescopes*, and perhaps more, because but one reflective piece of metall is requisite in them, as you may perceive by the annexed diagram, where A B representeth the object metall, C D the eye glass, F their common Focus, and O the other focus of the metall, in which the object is placed.

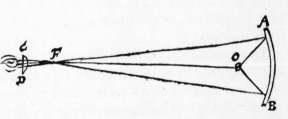

But

(3081)

But to return from this digreſſion, I told you, that Light is not ſimilar, or homogeneal, but conſiſts of *diſform* Rays, ſome of which are more refrangible than others : So that of thoſe, which are alike incident on the ſame medium, ſome ſhall be more refracted than others, and that not by any virtue of the glaſs, or other external cauſe, but from a prediſpoſition, which every particular Ray hath to ſuffer a particular degree of Refraction.

I ſhall now proceed to acquaint you with another more notable diſformity in its Rays, wherein the *Origin of Colours* is unfolded : Concerning which I ſhall lay down the *Doctrine* firſt, and then, for its examination, give you an inſtance or two of the *Experiments*, as a ſpecimen of the reſt.

The Doctrine you will find comprehended and illuſtrated in the following propoſitions.

1. As the Rays of light differ in degrees of Refrangibility, ſo they alſo differ in their diſpoſition to exhibit this or that particular colour. Colours are not *Qualifications of Light*, derived from Refractions, or Reflections of natural Bodies (as 'tis generally believed,) but *Original* and *connate properties*, which in divers Rays are divers. Some Rays are diſpoſed to exhibit a red colour and no other; ſome a yellow and no other, ſome a green and no other, and ſo of the reſt. Nor are there only Rays proper and particular to the more eminent colours, but even to all their intermediate gradations.

2. To the ſame degree of Refrangibility ever belongs the ſame colour, and to the ſame colour ever belongs the ſame degree of Refrangibility. The *leaſt Refrangible* Rays are all diſpoſed to exhibit a *Red* colour, and contrarily thoſe Rays, which are diſpoſed to exhibit a *Red* colour, are all the leaſt refrangible : So the *moſt refrangible* Rays are all diſpoſed to exhibit a deep *Violet Colour*, and contrarily thoſe which are apt to exhibit ſuch a violet colour, are all the moſt Refrangible. And ſo to all the intermediate colours in a continued ſeries belong intermediate degrees of refrangibility. And this Analogy 'twixt colours, and refrangibility, is very preciſe and ſtrict; the Rays always either exactly agreeing in both, or proportionally diſagreeing in both.

3. The ſpecies of colour, and degree of Refrangibility proper to any particular ſort of Rays, is not mutable by Refraction, nor by Reflection from natural bodies, nor by any other cauſe, that I could yet obſerve. When any one ſort of Rays hath been well
parted

(3082)

parted from thofe of other kinds, it hath afterwards obftinately retained its colour , notwithftanding my utmoft endeavours to change it. I have refracted it with Prifmes, and reflected it with Bodies, which in Day-light were of other colours; I have intercepted it with the coloured film of Air interceding two compref-fed plates of glafs ; tranfmitted it through coloured Mediums, and through Mediums irradiated with other forts of Rays, and diverfly terminated it; and yet could never produce any new colour out of it. It would by contracting or dilating become more brisk, or faint, and by the lofs of many Rays, in fome cafes very obfcure and dark; but I could never fee it changed *in fpecie.*

Yet feeming tranfmutations of Colours may be made, where there is any mixture of divers forts of Rays. For in fuch mixtures, the component colours appear not, but, by their mutual allaying each other, conftitute a midling colour. And therefore, if by refraction, or any other of the aforefaid caufes, the difform Rays, latent in fuch a mixture, be feparated, there fhall emerge colours different from the colour of the compofition. Which colours are not New generated, but only made Apparent by being parted; for if they be again intirely mix't and blended together, they will again compofe that colour, which they did before feparation. And for the fame reafon, Tranfmutations made by the convening of divers colours are not real; for when the difform Rays are again fevered, they will exhibit the very fame colours, which they did before they entered the compofition ; as you fee, *Blew* and *Yellow* powders, when finely mixed, appear to the naked eye *Green*, and yet the Colours of the Component corpufcles are not thereby really tranfmuted, but only blended. For, when viewed with a good Microfcope, they ftill appear *Blew* and *Yellow* interfperfedly.

5. There are therefore two forts of Colours. The one original and fimple, the other compounded of thefe. The Original or primary colours are, *Red, Yellow, Green, Blew*, and a *Violet-purple*, together with Orange, Indico, and an indefinite variety of Intermediate gradations.

6. The fame colours in *fpecie* with thefe Primary ones may be alfo produced by compofition : For, a mixture of *Yellow* and *Blew* makes *Green*; of *Red* and *Yellow* makes *Orange*; of *Orange* and *Yellowifh green* makes *yellow*. And in general, if any two Colours be mixed, which in the feries of thofe, generated by the Prifme, are

not

(3083)

not too far diftant one from another, they by their mutual alloy compound that colour, which in the faid feries appeareth in the mid-way between them. But thofe, which are fituated at too great a diftance, do not fo. *Orange* and *Indico* produce not the intermediate Green, nor Scarlet and Green the intermediate yellow.

7. But the moft furprifing,and wonderful compofition was that of *Whitenefs*. There is no one fort of Rays which alone can exhibit this. 'Tis ever compounded,and to its compofition are requifite all the aforefaid primary Colours, mixed in a due proportion. I have often with Admiration beheld, that all the Colours of the Prifme being made to converge, and thereby to be again mixed as they were in the light before it was Incident upon the Prifme, reproduced light, intirely and perfectly white, and not at all fenfibly differing from a *direct* Light of the Sun, unlefs when the glaffes, I ufed,were not fufficiently clear; for then they would a little incline it to *their* colour.

8. Hence therefore it comes to pafs,that*Whitenefs* is the ufual colour of *Light* ; for, Light is a confufed aggregate of Rays indued with all forts of Colors,as they are promifcuoufly darted from the various parts of luminous bodies. And of fuch a confufed aggregate,as I faid,is generated Whitenefs, if there be a due proportion of the Ingredients; but if any one predominate,the Light muft incline to that colour ; as it happens in the Blew flame of Brimftone; the yellow flame of a Candle ; and the various colours of the Fixed ftars.

9. Thefe things confidered, the *manner*, how colours are produced by the Prifme, is evident. For, of the Rays, conftituting the incident light, fince thofe which differ in Colour proportionally differ in Refrangibility, *they* by their unequall refractions muft be fevered and difperfed into an oblong form in an orderly fucceffion from the leaft refracted Scarlet to the moft refracted Violet. And for the fame reafon it is, that objects, when looked upon through a Prifme,appear coloured. For,the difform Rays, by their unequal Refractions, are made to diverge towards feveral parts of the *Retina*, and there exprefs the Images of things coloured, as in the former cafe they did the Suns Image upon a wall. And by this inequality of refractions they become not only coloured, but alfo very confufed and indiftinct

10. Why the Colours of the *Rainbow* appear in falling drops

Hhhh   of

(3084)

of Rain, is alſo from hence evident. For, thoſe drops, which refract the Rays, diſpoſed to appear purple, in greateſt quantity to
the Spectators eye, refract the Rays of other ſorts ſo much leſs,
as to make them paſs beſide it ; and ſuch are the drops on the inſide of the *Primary* Bow, and on the outſide of the *Secondary* or
Exteriour one. So thoſe drops, which refract in greateſt plenty
the Rays, apt to appear red, toward the Spectators eye, refract
thoſe of other ſorts ſo much more, as to make them paſs beſide it ;
and ſuch are the drops on the exteriour part of the *Primary*, and
interiour part of the *Secondary* Bow.

11. The odd Phænomena of an infuſion of *Lignum Nephriticum,*
Leaf gold, Fragments of coloured glaſs, and ſome other tranſparently
coloured bodies, appearing in one poſition of one colour, and of
another in another, are on theſe grounds no longer riddles. For,
thoſe are ſubſtances apt to reflect one ſort of light and tranſmit
another ; as may be ſeen in a dark room, by illuminating them
with ſimilar or uncompounded light. For, then they appear of
that colour only, with which they are illuminated, but yet in one
poſition more vivid and luminous than in another, accordingly
as they are diſpoſed more or leſs to reflect or tranſmit the incident
colour.

12. From hence alſo is manifeſt the reaſon of an unexpected
Experiment, which Mr. *Hook* ſomewhere in his *Micrography* re-
lates to have made with two wedg-like tranſparent veſſels, fill'd the
one with a red, the other with a blew liquor : namely, that though
they were ſeverally tranſparent enough, yet both together became
opake ; For, if one tranſmitted only red, and the other only blew,
no rays could paſs through both.

13. I might add more inſtances of this nature, but I ſhall conclude with this general one, that the Colours of all natural Bodies
have no other origin than this, that they are variouſly qualified to
reflect one ſort of light in greater plenty then another. And this
I have experimented in a dark Room by illuminating thoſe bodies
with uncompounded light of divers colours. For by that means
any body may be made to appear of any colour. They have
there no appropriate colour, but ever appear of the colour of the light caſt upon them, but yet with this difference,
that they are moſt brisk and vivid in the light of their own day-
light-colour. *Minium* appeareth there of any colour indifferently,
with which 'tis illuſtrated, but yet moſt luminous in red, and ſo

B ſ

(3085)

Bi/e appeareth indifferently of any colour with which 'tis illuftra-ted, but yet moft luminous in blew.   And therefore *Minium* re-flecteth Rays of any colour, but moft copioufly thcfe indued with red ; and confequently when illuftrated with day-light, that is, with all forts of Rays promifcuoufly blended, thofe qualified with red fhall abound moft in the reflected light, and by their preva-lence caufe it to appear of that colour.   And for the fame reafon *Bi/e*, reflecting blew moft copioufly, fhall appear blew by the ex-cefs of thofe Rays in its reflected light ; and the like of other bo-dies.   And that this is the intire and adequate caufe of their co-lours, is manifeft, becaufe they have no power to change or alter the colours of any fort of Rays incident apart, but put on all co-lours indifferently, with which they are inlightned.

Thefe things being fo, it can be no longer difputed, whether there be colours in the dark, nor whether they be the qualities of the objects we fee, no nor perhaps, whether Light be a Body. For, fince Colours are the *qualities* of Light, having its Rays for their intire and immediate fubject, how can we think thofe Rays *qualities* alfo, unlefs one quality may be the fubject of and fuftain another; which in effect is to call it *Subftance*.   We fhould not knowBodies for fubftances,were it not for their fenfible qualities, and the Principal of thofe being now found due to fomething elfe, we have as good reafon to believe that to be a Subftance alfo.

Befides, whoever thought any quality to be a *heterogeneous* ag-gregate, fuch as Light is difcovered to be.   But, to determine more abfolutely, what Light is, after what manner refracted,and by what modes or actions it produceth in our minds the Phan-tafms of Colours, is not fo eafie.   And I fhall not mingle con-jectures with certainties.

Reviewing what I have written, I fee the difcourfe it felf will lead to divers Experiments fufficient for its examination : And therefore I fhall not trouble you further, than to defcribe one of thofe,which I have already infinuated.

In a darkened Room make a hole in the fhut of a window, whofe diameter may conveniently be about a third part of an inch, to admit a convenient quanti y of the Suns light : And there place a clear and colourlefs Prifme, to refract the entring light towards the further part of the Room,which,as I faid,will thereby be diffufed into an oblong coloured Image.   Then place a *Lens* of

H h h h 2   about

(3086)

about three foot radius (fuppofe a broad Object-glafs of a three
foot Telefcope,) at the diftance of about four or five foot from
thence, through which all thofe colours may at once be tranfmitted, and made by its Refraction to convene at a further diftance
of about ten or twelve feet. If at that diftance you intercept this
light with a fheet of white paper, you will fee the colours converted into whitenefs again by being mingled. But it is requifite, that
the *Prifme* and *Lens* be placed fteddy, and that the paper, on
which the colours are caft, be moved to and fro; for, by fuch
motion, you will not only find, at what diftance the whitenefs is
moft perfect, but alfo fee, how the colours gradually convene, and
vanifh into whitenefs, and afterwards having croffed one another
in that place where they compound Whitenefs, are again diffipated, and fevered, and in an inverted order retain the fame colours, which they had before they entered the compofition. You
may alfo fee, that, if any of the Colours at the *Lens* be intercepted, the Whitenefs will be changed into the other colours. And
therefore, that the compofition of whitenefs be perfect, care muft
be taken, that none of the colours fall befides the *Lens*.

In the annexed defign of this Experiment, A B C expreffeth
the Prifm fet endwife to fight, clofe by the hole F of the window

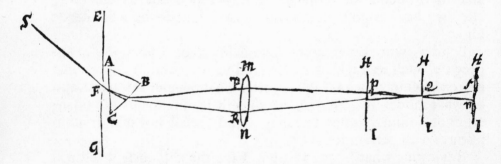

E G. Its vertical Angle A C B may conveniently be about 60
degrees: *M N* defigneth the *Lens*. Its breadth 2½ or 3 inches.
S F one of the ftreight lines, in which difform Rays may be conceived to flow fucceffively from the Sun. F P, and F R two of
thofe Rays unequally refracted, which the *Lens* makes to converge
towards Q, and after decuffation to diverge again. And H I the
paper, at divers diftances, on which the colours are projected:
which in Q conftitute *Whitenefs*, but are *Red* and *Yellow* in R, r, and
ꝛ, and *Blew* and *Purple* in P, p, and π.

                                                                    If

(3087)

If you proceed further to try the impoſſibility of changing any uncompounded colour (which I have aſſerted in the third and thirteenth Propoſitions,) 'tis requiſite that the Room be made very dark, leaſt any ſcattering light, mixing with the colour, diſturb and allay it, and render it compound, contrary to the deſign of the Experiment.   'Tis alſo requiſite, that there be a perfecter ſeparation of the Colours, than, after the manner above deſcribed, can be made by the Refraction of one ſingle Priſme, and how to make ſuch further ſeparations, will ſcarce be difficult to them, that conſider the diſcovered laws of Refractions.   But if tryal ſhall be made with colours not throughly ſeparated, there muſt be allowed changes proportionable to the mixture.   Thus if compound Yellow light fall upon Blew *Biſe*, the Biſe will not appear perfectly yellow, but rather green, becauſe there are in the yellow mixture many rays indued with green, and Green being leſs remote from the uſual blew colour of Biſe than yellow, is the more copiouſly reflected by it.

In like manner, if any one of the Priſmatick colours, ſuppoſe Red, be intercepted, on deſign to try the aſſerted impoſſibility of reproducing that Colour out of the others which are pretermitted ; 'tis neceſſary, either that the colours be very well parted before the red be intercepted, or that together with the red the neighbouring colours, into which any red is ſecretly diſperſed, (that is, the yellow, and perhaps green too) be intercepted, or elſe, that allowance be made for the emerging of ſo much red out of the yellow green, as may poſſibly have been diffuſed, and ſcatteringly blended in thoſe colours.   And if theſe things be obſerved, the new Production of Red, or any intercepted colour will be found impoſſible.

This, I conceive, is enough for an Introduction to Experiments of this kind ; which if any of the *R. Society* ſhall be ſo curious as to proſecute, I ſhould be very glad to be informed with what ſucceſs: That, if any thing ſeem to be defective, or to thwart this relation, I may have an opportunity of giving further direction about it, or of acknowledging my errors, if I have committed any.

So far this Learned and very Ingenious Letter ; which having been by that *Illuſtrious Company*, before whom it was read, with much applauſe committed to the conſideration of ſome of their Fellows, well verſed in this argument, the Reader may poſſibly in an other *Tract* be informed of ſome report given in upon this Diſcourſe.   *An*

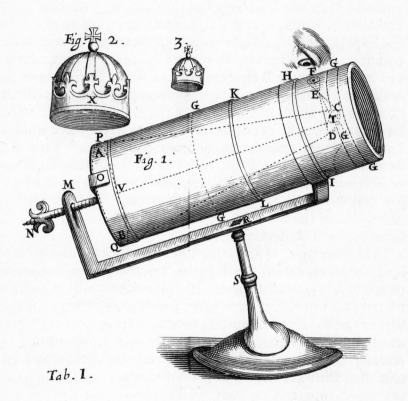

Fig. 2.

3.

Fig. 1.

Tab. 1.

(4004)

An Accompt of a New Catadioptrical Telescope invented by Mr. Newton, Fellow of the R.Society, and Professor of the Mathematiques in the University of Cambridge.

THis Excellent Mathematician having given us, in the Transactions of *February* laſt, an account of the cauſe, which induced him to think upon *Reflecting* Teleſcopes, inſtead of *Refracting* ones, hath thereupon preſented the Curious World with an *Eſſay* of what may be performed by ſuch Teleſcopes; by which it is found, that Teleſcopical Tubes may be conſiderably ſhortned without prejudice to their magnifying effect.

This new inſtrument is compoſed of two Metallin *ſpeculum's*, the one Goncave, (inſtead of an Object-glaſs) the other Plain; and alſo of a ſmall plano-convex Eye-Glaſs.

By *Figure* I. of *Tab.* I. the ſtructure of it may be eaſily imagined; viz. *That* the Tube of this Teleſcope is open at the end which reſpects the object; *that* the other end is cloſe, where the ſaid Concave is laid, and *that* near the open end there is a flat oval *ſpeculum*, made as ſmall as may be, the leſs to obſtruct the entrance of the rays of Light, and inclined towards the upper part of the Tube, where is a little hole furniſh't with the ſaid Eye-glaſs. So that the rays coming from the object, do firſt fall on the Concave placed at the bottome of the Tube; and are thence reflected toward the other end of it, where they meet with the flat ſpeculum, obliquity poſited, by the reflection of which they are directed to the little plano-convex Glaſs, and ſo to the ſpectators Eye, who looking downwards ſees the Object, which the Teleſcope is turned to.

To underſtand this more diſtinctly and fully, the Reader may pleaſe to look upon the ſaid *Figure*, in which

A B is the Concave *ſpeculum*, of which the *radius* or ſemidiameter is 12⅔ or 13 inches.

C D another metalline *ſpeculum*, whoſe ſurface is flat, and the circumference oval.

G D

(4005)

G D an Iron wire, holding a ring of brafs, in which the fpeculum *C D* is fixed.

F, a fmall Eye-glafs flat above, and convex below, of the twelfth part of an inch *radius*, if not lefs; forafmuch as the metal collects the Sun's rays at 6⅓ inches diftance, and the Eye-glafs at lefs than ⅐ of an inch diftance from its vertex : Befides that the Author (as he informs us) knew their dimenfions by the tools to which they were ground, and particularly meafuring the diameter of the hemi-fpherical Concave, in which the Eye-glafs was wrought, found it the *fixth* part of an inch.

G G G, the fore part of the Tube faftn'd to a brafs-ring *H I*, to keep it immoveable.

P 2 K L, the hind-part of the Tube, faftn'd to another brafs-ring *P Q*.

O, an Iron hook faftn'd to the Ring *P 2*, and furnifh't with a fcrew *N*, thereby to advance or draw back the hind-part of the Tube, and fo by that means to put the *fpecula* in their due diftance.

M 2 G I a crooked Iron fuftaining the Tube, and faft-ned by the nail *R* to the Ball and Socket *S*, whereby the Tube may be turned every way.

The Center of the flat *fpeculum* C D, muft be placed in the fame point of the Tube's Axe, where falls the perpendicular to this Axe, drawn to the fame from the center of the little Eye-glafs : which point is here marked at T.

And to give the Reader fome fatisfaction to underftand, in what degree it reprefents things diftinct, and free from colours, and to know the aperture by which it admits light ; he may compare the diftances of the *focus* E from the *vertex's* of the little Eye-glafs and the Concave *fpeculum*, that is, E F, ⅐ of an inch, and E T V, 6⅓ inches ; and the *ratio* will be found as 1 to 38 ; whereby it appears, that the Objects will be magnified about 38 times. To which proportion is very confentaneous, an Obfervation of the Crown on the weather-cock, about 300 feet diftant. For the fcheme X fig. 2. reprefents it bigger by 2½ times in diameter, when feen

through

(4006)

through this, than through an ordinary Telefcope of about 2 foot long. And fo fuppofing this ordinary one to magnifie 13 or 14 times, as by the defcription it fhould, this new one by the Experiment muft magnifie near as much as hath been affigned.

Thus far as to the ftrudure of this Telefcope. Concerning the Metalline matter, fit for thefe reflecting *Speculums*, the Inventor hath alfo confidered the fame, as may be feen by two of his Letters, written to the Publifher from Cambridge Jan. 18. and 29. 16$\frac{71}{72}$. to this effect, *viz*.

1. That for a fit metalline fubftance, he would give this Caution, that whileft men feek for a white, hard and durable metallin compofition, they refolve not upon fuch an one, as is full of fmall pores, only difcoverable by a Microfcope. For though fuch an one may to appearance take a good polifh, yet the edges of thofe fmall pores will wear away fafter in the polifhing than the other parts of the metal; and fo, however the Metal feem polite, yet it fhall not reflect with fuch an accurate regularity as it ought to do. Thus Tin-glafs mixt with ordinary Bell-metall makes it more white and apt to reflect a greater quantity of light; but withall its fumes, raifed in the fufion, like fo many aerial bubles, fill the metall full of thofe Microfcopical pores. But white Arfenick both blanches the Metall and leaves it folid without any fuch pores, efpecially if the fufion hath not been too violent. What the *Stellate Regulus* of *Mars* (which I have fometimes ufed) or other fuch like fubftance will do, deferves particular examination.

To this he adds this further intimation, that *Putty* or other fuch like powder, with which 'tis polifhed, by the fharp angles of its particles fretteth the metall, if it be not very fine, and fills it full of fuch fmall holes, as he fpeaketh of. Wherefore care muft be taken of that, before judgment be given, whether the metall be throughout the body of it porous or not.

2. He not having tried, as he faith, many proportions of the Arfenick and Metall, does not affirm, which is abfolutely beft, but thinks, there may conveniently be ufed

any

(4007)

any quantity of Arfenick equalling in weight between a fixt and eight part of the Copper, a greater proportion making the Metal brittle.

The way, which he ufed, was this. He firft melted the Copper alone, then put in the Arfenick, which being melted, he ftirred them a little together, bewaring in the mean time, not to draw in breath near the pernicious fumes. After this, he put in Tin, and again fo foon as that was melted (which was very fuddenly) he ftirred them well together, and immediately powred them off.

He faith, he knows not, whether by letting them ftand longer on the fire after the Tin was melted, a higher degree of fufion would have made the metall porous; but he thought that way he proceeded to be fafeft.

He adds, that in that metall, which he fent to *London*, there was no Arfenick, but a fmall proportion of Silver ; as he remembers, one fhilling in three ounces of metall. But he thought withall, that the Silver did as much harm in making the metall foft, and fo lefs fit to be polifh't, as good in rendring it white and luminous.

At another time he mixed Arfenick one ounce, Copper fix ounces, and Tin two ounces: And this an Acquaintance of his hath, as he intimates, polifh't better, than he did the other.

As to the *objection*, that with this kind of Perfpectives, objects are difficultly found, he anfwers in another letter of his to the Publifher, of Jan. 6. $16\frac{71}{72}$. that that is the inconvenience of all Tubes that magnifie much ; and that after a little ufe the inconvenience will grow lefs, feeing that himfelf could readily enough find any day-Objects, by knowing which way they were pofited from other objects that he accidentally faw in it ; but in the night to find Stars, he acknowledges it to be more troublefome ; which yet may, in his opinion, be eafily remedied by two fights affixed to the Iron rod, by which the Tube is fufteined ; or by an ordinary perfpective glafs faftn'd to the fame frame with the Tube, and directed towards the fame object, as Des-*Cartes* in his Dioptricks hath defcribed for remedying the fame inconvenience of his beft Telefcopes.

L l l   *So*

(4008)

So far the Inventors Letters touching this Instrument : of which
having communicated the defcription to Monfieur *Chriftian
Hugens de Zulichem,* we received from him an Anfwer to this
effect, in his Letter of Febr. 13. 1672. ft.n.

I fee by the Defcription, you have fent me of Mr. *Newtons*
admirable Telefcope, that he hath well confidered the advantage, which a *Concave fpeculum* hath above *Convex glaffes* in
collecting the parallel rays, which certainly according to the
calculation, I have made thereof, is very great. Hence it
is, that he can give a far greater aperture to that *fpeculum,*
than to an Object-glafs of the fame diftance of the *focus,* and
confequently that he can much more magnifie objects this
way, than by an ordinary Telefcope. Befides, by it he a-
voids an inconvenience, which is infeparable from convex
Object-Glaffes, which is the Obliquity of both their furfaces,
which vitiateth the refraction of the rays that pafs towards
the fides of the glafs, and does more hurt than men
are aware of. Again, by the meer reflection of the metallin
fpeculum there are not fo many rays loft, as in Glaffes, which
reflect a confiderable quantity by each of their furfaces, and
befides intercept many of them by the obfcurity of their
matter.

Mean time, the main bufinefs will be, to find a matter for
this *fpeculum* that will bear fo good and even a polifh as Glaffes, and a way of giving this polifh without vitiating the
fpherical figure. Hitherto I have found no *Specula,* that had
near fo good a polifh as Glafs ; and if M. *Newton* hath not
already found a way to make it better, than ordinarily I apprehend, his Telefcopes will not fo well diftinguifh objects,
as thofe with Glaffes. But 'tis worth while to fearch for a
remedy to this inconvenience, and I defpair not of finding
one. I believe, that M. *Newton* hath not been without confidering the advantage, which a *Parabolical fpeculum* would
have above a *Spherical* one in this conftruction ; but that he
defpairs, as well as I do, of working other furfaces than
fpherical ones with due exactnefs ; though elfe it be more
eafie to make a *Parabolical* than *Elliptical* or *Hyperbolical* ones,
by reafon of a certain propriety of the *Parabolick Conoid,* which

is,

(4009)

is, that all the Sections parallel to the Axis make the same Pa‐
rabola.

Thus far M. *Hugenius* his judicious Letter ; to the latter part
of which, concerning the grinding *Parabolical Conoids*, Mr.
Newton saith, in his Letter to the Publisher of Feb. 20. 71.
that though he with him despairs of performing that work by
Geometrical rules, yet he doubts not but that the thing may
in some measure be accomplished by Mechanical de‐
vises.

*To all which I cannot but subjoyn an Extract of a Letter , received
very lately, (March 19th) from the* Inventor *of this new Te‐
lescope, from* Cambridge, *viz.*

IN my last Letter I gave you occasion to suspect, that the
Instrument which I sent you, is in some respect or other
indisposed, or that the metals are tarnished. And by your
Letter of *March* 16. I am fully confirmed in that opinion. For,
whilest I had it, it represented the Moon in some parts of it as
distinctly, as other Telescopes usually do which magnifie as
much as that. Yet I very well know, that that Instrument
hath its imperfections both in the composition of the metall,
and in its being badly cast, as you may perceive by a scabrous
place near the middle of the metall of it on the polished side,
and also in the figure of that metall near that scabrous place.
And in all those respects that instrument is capable of further
improvement.

You seem to intimate, that the proportion of 38 to 1 holds
only for its magnifying Objects at small distances. But if for
such distances, suppose 500 feet, it magnifie at that rate, by
the rules of Opticks it must for the greatest distance imagi‐
nable magnifie more than $37\frac{3}{4}$ to 1 ; which is so considerable
a diminishing, that it may be even then as 38 to 1.

Here is made another Instrument like the former,
which does very well. Yesterday I compared it with a six
foot Telescope, and found it not only to magnifie more, but
also more distinctly. And to day I found, that I could read
in one of the *Philosophical Transactions*, placed in the Sun's

(4010)

light, at an hundred foot diftance, and that at an hundred and twenty foot diftance I could difcern fome of the words. When I made this tryal, its Aperture (defined next the Eye) was equivalent to more than an inch and a third part of the Object-metall. This may be of fome ufe to thofe that fhall endeavour any thing in *Reflexions* ; for hereby they will in fome meafure be enabled to judge of the goodnefs of their Inftruments, &c.

N. B. The Reader may expect in the *next Month* another Letter, which came fomewhat too late to be here inferted ; containing a *Table*, calculated by the fame Mr. *Newton*, about the feveral *Apertures* and *Charges* anfwering the feveral *Lengths* of thefe Telefcopes.

(4032)

Mr. Newton's *Letter to the Publisher of March* 26. 1672. *containing some more suggestions about his New Telescope, and a* Table *of* Apertures *and* Charges *for the several* Lengths *of that Instrument.*

SIR,

SInce my last Letter I have further compared the two Telescopes, and find that of Metal to represent as well the Moon, as neerer Objects, something distincter than the other. But I must tell you also, that I am not very well assured of the goodness of that other, which I borrowed to make the Comparison; and therefore desire, that the other Experiment should be rather confided in, of reading at the distance of between a 100 and 120 foot, at which I and others could read with it in the *Transactions*, as I found by measure : At which time the aperture was 1⅓- of an Inch ; which I knew by trying, that an obstacle of that breadth was requisite to intercept all the light, which came from one point of the object.

I should tell you also, that the little plain piece of metall, next the eye-glass, is not truly figured : whereby it happens, that objects are not so distinct at the middle as at the edges. And I hope, that by correcting its figure, (in which I find more difficulty than one would expect,) they will appear all over distinct, and distincter in the middle than at the edges. And I doubt not but that the performances will then be greater.

But yet I find, that there is more light lost by reflection of the metall which I have hitherto used, than by transmission through glasses : for which reason a shallower charge would probably do better for obscure objects ; suppose such an one, as would make it magnifie 34 or 32 times. But for bright objects at any distance, it seems capable of magnifying 38 or 40 times with sufficient distinctness. And for all objects, the same Charge, I believe, may with advantage be allowed, if the steely matter, imployed at *London*, be more strongly reflective than this which I have used.

The performances of one of these Instruments of any length being known, it will appear by this following *Table*, what may

be

(4033)

be expected from thofe of other Lengths by this way, if Art can accomplifh what is promifed by the Theory.   In the *firft* Column is expreffed the Length of the Telefcope in feet ; which doubled gives the femidiameter of the Sphere, on which the concave metall is to be ground.   In the *fecond* column are the proportions of the Apertures for thofe feveral Lengths. And in the *third* column are the Proportions of the *Charges*, or diameter of the fpheres, on which the convex fuperficies of the eye-glaffes are to be ground.

Lengths.	Apertures.	Charges.
$\frac{1}{2}$	100	100
1	168	119
2	283	141
3	383	157
4	476	168
5	562	178
6	645	186
8	800	200
10	946	211
12	1084	221
16	1345	238
20	1591	254
24	1824	263

The ufe of this Table will beft appear by example : Suppofe therefore a half foot Telefcope may diftinctly mag- nifie 30 times with an inch Aperture, and it being required to know, what ought to be the analogous conftitution and per- formance of a four foot Telefcope: By the fecond column, as 100 to 476 ; fo are the Apertures, as alfo the number of times which they magnifie.   And confequently fince the half foot Tube hath an inch aperture and magnifieth 30 times ; a four foot Tube proportionally fhould have $4\frac{76}{100}$ inches aper- ture, and magnifie 143 times.   And by the third column, as 100 to 168 ; fo are their Charges : And therefore if the dia- meter of the convexity of the eye-glafs for a half foot Telef- cope be $\frac{1}{7}$ of an inch, that for a four foot fhould be $\frac{168}{500}$, that is, about $\frac{1}{3}$ of an inch.

(4034)

In like manner, if a half foot Teleſcope may diſtinctly mag-nifie 36 times with $1\frac{1}{4}$ of an Inch Aperture; a four foot Te-leſcope ſhould with equal diſtinctneſs magnifie 171 times with 6 inches Aperture; and one of ſix foot ſhould magnifie 232 times with $8\frac{2}{3}$ inches Aperture; and ſo of other lengths. But what the event will really be, we muſt wait to ſee determined by experience. Only this I thought fit to inſinuate, that they which intend to make trials in other lengths, may more rea-dily know how to deſign their Inſtruments. Thus for a four foot Tube, ſince the Aperture ſhould be 5 or 6 inches, there will be required a piece of metal 7 or 8 inches broad at leaſt, becauſe the figure will ſcarcely be true to the edges. And the thickneſs of the metal muſt be proportional to the breadth, leaſt it bend in the grinding. The metalls being poliſhed, there may be tryals made with ſeveral eye-glaſſes, to find, what Charge may with beſt advantage be made uſe of.

An Extract of another Letter of the ſame to the Publiſher, dated March 30. 1672. by way of Anſwer to ſome Objections, made by an Ingenious French Philoſopher to the New Reflecting Teleſ-cope.

SIR,

I Doubt not but *M.A.* will allow the advantage of reflexion in the Theory to be very great, when he ſhall have infor-med himſelf of the different *Refrangibility* of the ſeveral rays of light. And for the practique part, it is in ſome meaſure manifeſt by the Inſtruments already made, to what degree of vivacity and brightneſs a metaline ſubſtance may be po-liſhed. Nor is it improbable but that there may be new ways of poliſhing found out for metal, which will far excell thoſe that are yet in uſe. And when a metal is once well poliſhed, it will be a long while preſerved from tarniſhing, if diligence be uſed to keep it dry and cloſe, ſhut up from Air: For the principal cauſe of tarniſhing ſeems to be, the condenſing of moiſture on its poliſhed ſurface, which by an Acid ſpirit, where-

(4035)

wherewith the Atmofphere is impregnated, corrodes and
rufts it; or at leaft, at its exhaling, leaves it covered o-
ver with a thin skin, confifting partly of an earthly fe-
diment of that moifture, and partly of the duft, which
flying to and fro in the Air had fetled and adhered to
it.

When there is not occafion to make frequent ufe of
the inftrument, there may be other waies to preferve
the metal for a long time; as perhaps by immerging
it in Spirit of wine or fome other convenient liquor.
And if they chance to tarnifh; yet their polifh may be
recovered by rubbing them with a foft piece of leather,
or other tender fubftance, without the affiftance of any
fretting powders, unlefs they happen to be rufty : for
then they muft be new polifhed.

I am very fenfible, that metal reflects lefs light than
glafs tranfmits; and for that inconvenience, I gave you
a remedy in my laft Letter, by affigning a fhallower
charge in proportion to the Aperture, than is ufed in o-
ther Telefcopes. But, as I have found fome metaline
fubftances to be more ftrongly reflective, and to polifh
better, and be freer from tarnifhing than others; fo I
hope there may in time be found out fome fubftance
much freer from thefe inconveniences, than any yet
known.

(4056)

Mr. Isaac Newton's *Considerations upon part of a Letter of Monsieur de* Bercé *printed in the Eight French* Memoire, *concerning the Cata drioptrical Telescope, pretended to be improv'd and refined by M.* Caffegrain.

That the Reader may be enabled the better to Judge of the whole, by comparing together the contrivances both of Mr. Newton *and* Mr. Caffegrain ; *it will be neceffary, to borrow from the faid* French Memoire *what is there faid concerning them : which is as followes.*

I Send you (faith M. de *Bercè* to the Publifher of the *Memoire,*) the Copy of the Letter, which M. *Caffagrain* hath written to me concerning the proportions of Sr. *Samuel Morelands* Trumpet. And as for the Telefcope of Mr. *Newton* it hath as much furprifed me, as the fame Perfon, that hath found out the proportions of the Trumpet. For 'tis now about three months that that perfon communicated to me the figure of a Telefcope, which was almoft like it, and which he had invented; but which I look upon as more witty. I fhall here give you the defcription of it in fhort.

ABCD. is a ftrong Tube, in the bottom of which there is a great concave *Speculum* CD, pierced in the midle E.

F. is a convex *Speculum,* fo difpofed, as to its convexity, that it reflects the *Species,* which it receives from the great *Speculum,* towards the hole E, where is an Eye-glafs, which one looketh through.

The advantage, which I find in this Inftrument above that of Mr. *Newton,* is firft, that the mouth or aperture AB of the Tube may be of what bignefs you pleafe; and confequently you may have many more rays upon the Concave *Speculum,* than upon that, of which you have given us the defcription. 2. The reflexion of the rays will be very natural, fince it will be made upon the *axis* it felf, and therefore more vivid. 3. The vifion of it will be fo much the more pleafing, in that you fhall not be incommoded by the great light, by reafon of the bottom CD, which hideth the whole face. Befides that

you'l

(4057)

you'l have lefs difficulty in difcovering the Objeᵭs, than in that of Mr. *Newtons.*

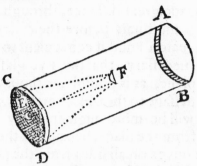

So far this French Author. To which we fhall now fubjoin the Confiderations of Mr. Newton *, as we received them from him in a Letter, written from* Cambridge *May* 4th 167 2, *as follows.*

SIR

I Should be very glad to   meet with any improvement of the Catadioptrical Telefcope; but that defign of it, which (as you informe me)Mr.*Caffegrain*hath communicated 3 months fince, and is now printed in one of the French *Memoires,* I fear will not anfwer Expeᶜtation. For, when I firft applied my-felf to try the effeᶜts of Reflexions, Mr. *Gregory's Optica Promota* (printed in the year 1663) being fallen into my hands, where there is an Inftrument (defcribed pag. 94) like that of Monfieur *Caffegrain's* with a hole in the midft of the Objeᶜt-Metal to tranfmit the Light to an Eye-glafs placed behind it ; I had thence an occafion of confidering that fort of conftructi-ons, and found their difadvantages fo great, that I faw it ne-ceffary, before I attempted any thing in the Praᶜtique, to al-ter the defign of them, and place the Eye glafs at the fide of the Tube rather than at the midle.

The difadvantages of it you will underftand by thefe parti-culars. 1. There will be more light loft in the Metal by reflexion from the little convex *fpeculum,* than from the Oval plane. For, it is an obvious obfervation, that Light is moft copioufly re-fleᶜted from any fubftance when incident moft obliquely. 2 The convex *fpeculum* will not refleᶜt the rays fo truly as the oval plane, unlefs it be of an Hyperbolique figure ; which is in-comparably more difficult to forme than a plane ; and if tru-

(4058)

ly formed, yet would only reflect thofe rays truly, which refpect the *axis*. 3 The errours of the faid convex will be much
augmented by the too great diftance, through which the rays ,
reflected from it , muft pafs before their arrival at the Eye-
glafs. For which reafon I find it convenient to make the Tube
no wider than is neceffary, that the Eye glafs be placed as
near to the Oval plane, as is poffible, without obftructing any
ufeful light in its paffage to the object metal. 4. The errors of
the object-metal will be more augmented by reflexion from
the convex than from the plane, becaufe of the inclination or
deflexion of the convex on all fides from the points, on which
every ray ought to be incident. 5. For thefe reafons there is requifite an extraordinary exactnefs in the figure of the little
convex, whereas I find by experience , that it is much more
difficult to communicate an exact figure to fuch fmall pieces of
Metal, than to thofe that are greater. 6 Becaufe the errors at
the perimeter of the concave Object-Metal , caufed by the
Sphericalnefs of its figure, are much augmented by the convex,
it will not with diftinctnefs bear fo large an aperture, as in the
other conftruction. 7. By reafon that the little convex conduces very much to the magnifying virtue of the inftrument,
which the Oval plane doth not, it will magnify much more in
proportion to the Sphere, on which the great concave is ground,
than in the other defign; And fo magnifying Objects much
more than it ought to do in proportion to its aperture, it muft
reprefent them very obfcure and dark; and not only fo, but
alfo confufed by reafon of its being overcharged. Nor is
there any convenient remedy for this. For, if the little convex be made of a larger Sphere , that will caufe a greater inconvenience by intercepting too many of the beft rayes ; or, if
the Charge of the Eye-glafs be made fo much fhallower as is
neceffary, the angle of vifion will thereby become fo little, that
it will be very difficult and troublefome to find an object, and
of that object, when found, there will be but a very fmall part
feen at once.

By this you may perceive, that the three advantages, which
Monfieur *Caffegrain* propounds to himfelf, are rather difadvantages. For, according to his defign, the aperture of the
iuftrument

(4059)

inftrument will be but fmall,the objeƈt dark and confufed,and alfo difficult to be found. Nor do I fee, why the reflexion is more upon the fame *axis*,and fo more natural in one cafe than in the other: fince the *axis* it felf is refleƈted towards the Eye by the Oval plain; and the Eye may be defended from external light as well at the fide, as at the bottome of the Tube.

You fee therefore, that the advantages of this defign are none, but the difadvantages fo great and unavoidable, thƹt I fear it will never be put in praƈtife with good effeƈt. And when I confider, that by reafon of its refemblance with other Telefcopes it is fomething more obvious than the other conftruƈtion; I am apt to believe, that thofe,who have attempted any thing in Catoptricks, have ever tryed it in the firft place, and that their bad fuccefs in that attempt hath been the caufe, why nothing hath been done in reflexions. For,Mr. *Gregory*,fpeaking of thefe inftruments in the aforefaid book pag 95, fayeth; *De mechanica horum fpeculorum & lentium , ab aliis fruftrà tentatâ, ego in mechanicis minus verfatus nihil dico.* So that there have been tryals made of thefe Telefcopes, but yet in vain. And I am infoimed,that about 7 or 8 years fince,Mr. *Gregory* himfelf, at *London,* caufed one of fix foot to be made by Mr. *Reive,* which I take to have been according to the aforefaid defign defcribed in his book ; becaufe, though made by a skilful Artift, yet it was without fuccefs.

I could wifh therefore, Mr. *Caffegrain* had tryed his defign before he divulged it: But if,for further fatisfaƈtion, he pleafe hereafter to try it, I believe the fuccefs will inform him, that fuch projeƈts are of little moment till they be put in praƈtife.

Some Experiments propos'd in relation to Mr. Newtons *Theory of light,printed in* Numb. 80; *together with the Obfervations made thereupon by the Author of that Theory; communicated in a Letter of his from* Cambridge, *April* 13. 1672.

I. TO contraƈt the beams of the Sun without the hole of the window, and to place the prifm between the focus of the *Lens* and the hole,fpoken of in M.*Newtons* theory of light,

II. To

(4060)

II. To cover over both Ends of the Prifm with paper at feveral diftances from the middle ; or with moveable rings,to fee,how that will vary or divide the length of the figure, infifted upon in the faid Theory.

III. To move the Prifm fo , as the End may turn about the middle being fteady.

IV. To move the prifm by fhoving it,till firft the one fide,than the midle, than the other fide pafs over the hole, obferving the fame Parallelifm.

The Obfervations, made upon thefe propofals.

I Suppofe the defign of the Propofer of thefe Experiments is, to have their events expreffed , with fuch obfervations as may occur concerning them. 1. Touching the *firft*, I have obferv'd, that the Solar image falling on a paper placed at the *focus* of the *Lens* , was by the interpofed Prifm drawn out in length proportional to the Prifms reflexion or diftance from that *focus*. And the chief obfervable here, which I remember, was, that the Streight edges of the oblong image were diftincter than they would have been without the *Lens*.

Confidering that the rays coming from the Planet *Venus* are much lefs inclined one to another , than thofe , which come from the oppofite parts of the Suns difque; I once tryed an experiment or two with *her* light. And to make it fufficiently ftrong, I found it neceffary to collect it firft by a broad *lens,* and then interpofing a Prifm between the *lens* and its *focus* at fuch diftance, that all the light might pafs through the Prifm; I found the *focus,* which before appeared like a lucid point, to be drawn out into a long fplendid line by the Prifms reflexion.

I have fometimes defigned to try,how a fixt *Star*,feen through a long Telefcope, would appear by interpofing a Prifm between the Telefcope and my eye. But by the appearance of *Venus,* viewed with my naked eye through a Prifm, I prefage the event.

2. Concerning the *fecond* experiment, I have occafionally obferved, that by covering both ends of the Prifm with Paper at feveral diftances from the midle, the breadth of the Solar image will be increafed or diminifhed as much , as is the aperture

(4061)

ture of the Prifm without any variation of the length : Or, if
the aperture be augmented on all fides, the image on all fides
will be fo much and no more augmented.

3. Of the *third* experiment I have occafion to fpeak in my
anfwer to another perfon ; where you'l find the effects of two
Prifms in all crofs pofitions of one to another defcribed. But
if one Prifm alone be turned about, the coloured image
will only be tranflated from place to place, defcribing a circle or fome other Conick Section on the wall, on which it is
projected, without fuffering any alteration in its fhape, unlefs
fuch as may arife from the obliquity of the wall or cafual change
of the Prifms obliquity to the Suns rays.

4. The effect of the *fourth* experiment I have already infinuated telling you(in pag. 3076 of the *Tranfactions*) that Light,
paffing through parts of the Prifm of divers thickneffes, did
ftill exhibit the fame Phænomena.

Note, that the long *axes* of the two Prifms in the experiment
defcribed in the faid pag. 3076 of the *Tranfactions*, were parallel one to another. And for the reft of their pofition, you will
beft apprehend it
by this Scheme ;
where let EG de-
fign the window ;
F the hole in it,
through which the
light arrives at the
Prifms ; ABC the
firft Prifm, which
refracts the light
towards P T, paint-
ing there the co-
lour in an oblong

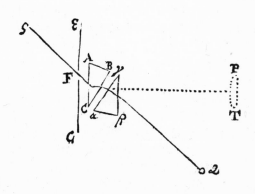

form ; and *αϐγ* the *fecond* Prifm, which refracts back again the
rays to Q where the long image PT is contracted into a round
one.

The plane *αγ* to BC, and *ϐγ* to AC, I fuppofe parallel, that
the rays may be equally refracted contrary ways in both Prifms.
And the Prifms muft be placed very near to one another ; For
if

(4062)

if their diftance be fo great, that colours begin to appear in the light before its incidence on the fecond Prifm , thofe colours will not be deftroyed by the contrary refractions of that Prifm.

Thefe things being obferved, the round image Q will appear of the fame bignefs, which it doth when both the Prifms are taken away, that the light may pafs directly towards Q from the hole without any refraction at all. And its diameter will equal the breadth of the long image PT, if thofe images be equally diftant from the Prifms.

If an accurate confideration of thefe refractions be defigned, it is convenient, that a *Lens* be placed in the hole F, or immediately after the Prifms, fo that its *focus* be at the image Q or PT. For, thereby the Perimeter of the image Q and the ftraight fides of the image PT will become much better defined than otherwife.

(4087)

A Latin Letter written to the Publisher *April* 9. 1672. n. st. by *Ignatius Gaston Pardies* P. Prof. of the Mathematicks in the Parisian Colledge of *Clermont*; containing some Animadversions upon Mr. *Isaac Newton*, Prof. of the Mathematicks in the University of *Cambridge*, his *Theory of Light*, printed in N°. 80.

Egi ingeniosissimam Hypothesin de Lumine & Coloribus *Clarissimi* Newtoni. *Et quia nonnullam Ego operam dedi in ista contemplatione atque Experimentis peragendis, perscribam ad Te pauca, quæ mihi circa novam istam doctrinam occurrerunt.*

Circa ipsam Luminis naturam illud profecto extraordinarium videtur, quòd ait vir eruditissimus, Lumen constare ex aggregatione infinitorum propemodum radiorum, qui suâpte indole suum quisque colorem referant retineantque, atque adeò nati apti sint certâ quadam & peculiari ratione, plus alij, alij minus, refringi: Radios ejusmodi, dum promiscui in aperto lumine confunduntur, nullatenus discerni, sed candorem potiùs referre; in refractione verò singulos unius coloris ab aliis alterius coloris secerni, & hoc modo secretos, sub proprio & nativo colore apparere: Ea corpora sub aliquo colore, v. g. rubro, videri, quæ apta sint reflectere aut transmittere radios solummodò rubros, &c.

Istæc tam extraordinaria Hypothesis, quæ, ut ipse observat, Dioptricæ fundamenta evertit, praxésque hactenus institutas inutiles reddit, tota nititur illo Experimento Prismatis Crystallini, ubi radij per foramen fenestræ intra obscurum cubiculum ingressi, ac deinde in parietem impacti, aut in charta recepti, non in rotundum conformati, ut ipsi, ad regulas refractionum receptas attendenti, expectandum videbatur, *sed in oblongam figuram extensi apparuerunt: Unde conclusit, oblongam ejusmodi figuram ex eo esse, quòd nonnulli radij minus, nonnulli magis refringerentur.*

Sed mihi quidem videtur juxta communes & receptas Dioptricæ leges figuram illam, non rotundam, sed oblongam esse oportere. Cùm enim radij ex oppositis disci Solaris partibus procedentes, variam habeant in ipso transitu Prismatis inclinationem, variè quoque refringi debent; ut cùm unorum inclinatio* 30 *saltem minutis major sit inclinatione aliorum, major quoque evadat illorum Refractio.*

X x x x *Igitur*

(4088)

Igitur Radii oppositi, ex altera superficie Prismatis emergentes magis divergunt & divaricantur, quàm si nullatenus, aut saltem æqualiter, omnes infracti processissent. Refractio autem ista radiorum fit solummodo versùs eas partes quæ fingi possunt in planis ad axem Prismatis rectis; nulla autem refractionis inæqualitas contingit versùs eas partes, quæ intelliguntur in planis axi parallelis; ut facilè demonstrari potest: superficies enim duæ Prismatis censeri possunt inter se parallelæ, ratione habita ad inclinationem axis, cùm singulæ ipsi axi parallelæ sint. Refractio autem per duas parallelas planas superficies nulla computatur, quia quantùm à prima superficie radius in unam partem torquetur, tantum ab altera in oppositam partem detorquetur. Igitur cùm radij solares è foramine per Prisma transmissi ad latera quidem non frangantur, procedunt ulterius, perinde ac si nulla Prismatis superficies obstitisset, (habitâ, inquam, ratione solùm ad lateralem illam divaricationem;) at verò cùm iidem radij ad superiores seu inferiores partes, alij quidem magis, alij verò minus, utpote inæqualiter inclinati, infringantur; necesse est eos magis inter se divaricari, adeóque & in longiorem figuram extendi.

Quin si calculus ritè obeatur; ut radij laterales inventi sunt à Cl. Newtono *in ea latitudine quæ subtendit arcum* 31', *qui arcus respondet diametro Solis; ita nullus dubito, quin illa inventa quoque altitudo imaginis, quæ* 2 gradus & 49' *subtendit, sit illa ipsa quæ eidem diametro Solis post inæquales refractiones in illo ipso casu respondeat.*

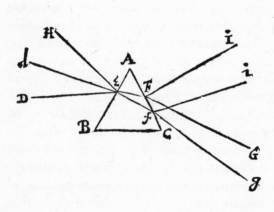

Et reverâ, posito Prismate ABC, *cujus angulus* A *sit* 60 grad. *Radio* DE, *qui faciat cum perpendiculari* EH *angulum* 30 grad. *Invenio illum, dum emergit per* FG, *facere cum perpendiculari* FI *angulum* 76 gr. 22'. *At verò posito alio radio* d E, *qui cum perpendiculari*

(4089)

culari E H *faciat angulum* 29°. 30', *invenio illum, dum emergit per* f g, *facere cum perpendiculari* f i, *angulum* 78°. 45'. *Unde isti duo radij* D E, d E, *qui procedere supponuntur ex oppositis partibus disci Solaris, faciuntque inter se angulum* 30', *iidem dum emergunt per lineas* F g, f g, *ita divergunt ut constituant angulum inter se* 2 *gr.* 23'. *Quod si duo alij radij assumerentur magis accedentes ad perpendicularem* E H, (*v.g. qui cum eadem perpendiculari facerent, unus quidem, angulum* 29°. 30', *alter verò,* 29°. 0';) *tunc iidem radij emergentes magis adhuc divergerent, constituerentque angulum majorem etiam aliquando plus quàm trium graduum. Et præterea augetur ulterius ista intercapedo refractorum radiorum ex eo, quòd duo radij* D E, d E, *concurrentes in* E, *illico incipiunt divaricari, atque impingunt in duo puncta disjuncta alterius superficiei, nempe in* F & *in* f. *Quapropter non sufficit ad obeundum rite calculum, ex longitudine imaginis impactæ in chartam subtrahere magnitudinem foraminis fenestræ* ; *quandoquidem etiam posito foramine indivisibili* E, *adhuc fieret aliud veluti foramen latum in alia superficie , nempe* F f.

Quod etiam vocat Experimentum crucis, *mihi quidem videtur quadrare cum vulgaribus & receptis Refractionum regulis. Nam, ut modo ostendi, radij solares, qui accedentes & convergentes faciunt angulum* 30', *egredientes deinde etiam post indivisibile foramen divergunt in angulum duorum & trium grad. Quapropter non mirum, si isti radij, sigillatim impingentes in alterum Prisma, perexiguo item apertum foramine, inæqualiter infringantur, cùm sit inæqualis illorum inclinatio. Neque refert , quòd isti radij attollantur aut deprimantur per conversionem primi Prismatis, manente immoto secundo Prismate,(quod tamen in omni casu fieri non potest) vel quòd manente primo immobili, secundum moveatur, ut succesivè radios coloratos totius imaginis excipiat & per proprium foramen transmittat ; utrolibet enim modo necesse est radios illos extremos, hoc est,* Rubrum & Violaceum, *incidere in secundum Prisma sub inæquali angulo, adeoque eorundem refractionem esse inæqualem, ut* Violaceorum *sit major.*

Cùm igitur manifesta causa appareat oblongæ ejusmodi figuræ radiorum, causaque illa ex ipsa natura Refractionis oriatur ; *non videtur necesse recurrere ad aliam Hypothesin, aut admittere diversam illam radiorum* frangibilitatem.

Quod

(4090)

Quod deinde excogitavit de Coloribus˙, *illud quidem egre-*
giè consequitur ex precedente Hypothesi ; veruntamen nonnullas
& ipsum patitur difficultates. Nam quod ait, nullum colorem,
sed potius candorem *apparere, ubi omnes omnium colorum*
radij promiscuè confunduntur, id verò non videtur conforme om-
nibus phænomenis. Certè quæ variationes cernuntur in permisti-
one diversorum corporum , diversis coloribus imbutorum , eà-
dem omninò observantur in permistione diversorum radiorum diversis
item coloribus imbutorum : Atque optimè ipse advertit, quòd quem-
admodum ex flavo & cæruleo corpore exsurgit viridis color ; ita ex
flavo & cæruleo radio viridis item color efficitur. Quare si omnes
omnium colorum radii simul confunderentur, necesse esset in ista hypo-
thesi, ut ille color appareret, qui revera apparet in permixtione om-
nium pigmentorum. Atqui si ista, hoc est, rubrum simul & flavum
unà cum cæruleo & purpureo aliisque omnibus , si quæ sint, conte-
rantur & confundantur, non jam candidus, sed obscurus & satur
color exsurget. Ergo similis color appareret in lumine ordinario,
quod constaret ex aggregatione omnium colorum.

Præterea nihil primo aspectu magis ingeniosum magisque aptum
videtur , quàm quod ait circa experimentum acutissimi Hookii,
quo duo diversi liquores, quorum alter rubeus, alter cæruleus, u-
terque sigillatim pellucidus, simul permixti, opaci evadunt. Id au-
tem ait Clarissimus Newtonus *ex eo oriri, quòd unus liquor solos*
rubeos natus sit transmittere, alter verò solos flavos ; unde per-
misti nullos transmittent. Hoc, inquam, videtur statim valdè
appositum ; nihilominus tamen ex eo conficeretur , quòd similis
opacitas fieret in permistione quorumcunque liquorum qui essent di-
versi coloris ; quod tamen verum non est.

Mr. *Newtons*

(4091)

Mr. *Newtons* Letter of *April* 13. 1672. ſt. v. written to the Publiſher, being an Anſwer to the fore-going Letter of P. *Pardies.*

_A*Ccepi Obſervationes Reverendi Patris* Ignatii Pardies *in Epiſtolam meam de Lucis Refractionibus & Coloribus ad Te conſcriptam : quo nomine me illi valde devinctum agnoſco ; atque hoc difficultatibus, quas propoſuit, eluendis reſcribo.   Imprimis ait, longitudinem ſolaris Imaginis à refractione Priſmatis effectam non alià indigere causâ,quàm diverſâ radiorum ab oppoſitis partibus ſolaris diſci profluentium incidentiâ, adeoque non probare diverſam refrangibilitatem diverſorum radiorum.   Et, quò aſſertionis ejus veritatem confirmet, oſtendit caſum, in quo ex* diverſa *incidentia* 30 *minutorum, differentia refractionis poteſt eſſe* 2 *grad.* 23. *min. vel etiam paulo major , prout exigit meum experimentum.   Sed hallucinatus eſt R. P. Nam refractiones à diverſa parte Priſmatis quantum poteſt inæquales ſtatuit, cùm tamen ego tum in experimentis, tum in calculo de experimentis iſtis inito, æquales adhibuerim,ut in Epiſtola præfata videre eſt.   Sit ergo A B C Priſmatis ſectio ad axem ejus perpendicularis, F L & K G radii duo in x (medio foraminis) decuſſantes & in Priſma illud incidentes ad G & L; ſintque eorum refracti G H & L m, ac denuò H I & m n.   Et*

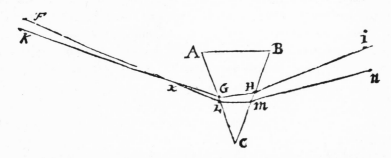

cùm refractiones ad latus A C æquales eſſe refractionibus ad latus B C quam proximè ſuppoſuerim ; Si A C & B C ſtatuantur æqualia, ſimilis erit radiorum G H & L m ad AB baſin Priſmatis inclinatio ; adeoque ang. C L m =ang. C H G & ang. C m L =ang. C G H. Quare etiam refractiones in G & m æquales erunt, ut & in L & H ;
atque

(4092)

*atque adeò ang. KGA= ang. n m B, & ang. FLA= ang. BHI ; &
proinde refractorum HI & m n eadem erit ad invicem inclinatio ac
est incidentium radiorum FL & KG. Sit ergo angulus F κ K 30 min.
æqualis nempe solari diametro, & erit angulus, quem HI & m n
comprehendunt, etiam 30 min. si modò radii FL & KG æqualiter refrangibiles statuantur. At mihi experienti prodiit angulus ille circiter
2 grad. 49. min. quem radius HI, extremum violaceum colorem, &
m n, cæruleum exhibens, constituêre ; ac proinde radios illos diversimodè refrangibiles esse, sive refractiones secundùm disparem sinuum
incidentiæ & refractionis rationem peragi necessariò concedendum est.*

*Addit præterea R. P. quòd non sufficit ad obeundum ritè calculum,
ex longitudine imaginis impactæ in Chartam subtrahere magnitudinem
foraminis fenestræ ; quandoquidem etiam posito foramine indivisibili,
adhuc fieret aliud veluti foramen latum in posteriori superficie prismatis. Mihi tamen videtur, his non obstantibus, quòd refractiones radiorum, in anteriori æquè ac in posteriori superficie Prismatis decussan-
tium, ex adhibitis principiis possint ritè computari. Sed si res secùs
esset, latitudo hiatûs in posteriori superficie, quod ad instar foraminis est, haud efficeret errorem duorum minutorum secundorum; & in
rebus practicis non operæ pretium duco ad minutias istas attendere.*

Illi insuper experimento, quod Crucis *vocaveram, nihil adversa-
tur R. P, dum contendit, inæquales radiorum, diversis coloribus imbutorum, refractiones ex inæqualibus incidentiis effectas fuisse. Nam
radiis per duo admodum parva, ab invicem distantia & immota foramina, transeuntibus, incidentiæ illæ, prout ego experimentum insti-
tui, omninò æquales erant, & tamen refractiones liquidò inæquales.
Sin ille de experimentis nostris dubitet, oro, ut radiorum diversis coloribus præditorum refractiones ex incidentiis paribus mensuret, &
sentiet inæquales esse. Si modus ille, quem ego ad hoc negotium ad-
hibui, minùs placeat (quo tamen nullus potest esse luculentior,) facile
est alios excogitare ; sicut & alios ipse haud paucos cum fructu ex-
pertus sum.*

Contra Theoriam de Coloribus *objicitur, quòd pulveres diversorum colorum permisti.non candidum sed subobscurum & fuscum colorem
exhibent. Mihi verò albus, niger, & omnes intermedii fusci, qui ab
albo & nigro permistis componi possunt, non specie coloris sed quantitate lucis tantùm differre videntur. Et cùm in mistione pigmentorum,
singula corpuscula non nisi proprium colorem reflectant, adeoq; maxima*

pars

(4093)

pars lucis incidentis supprimatur & retineatur ; lux reflexa subobscura evadet,& quasi cum tenebris permista,adeò ut non intensum alborem, sed qualem nigredinis permistio conficit,hoc est.fuscum,exhibere debeat.

Obijcitur deinde, quòd à liquoribus quibuscunque diversi coloris in eodem vase commistis,æquè ac in diversis vasis contentis,opacitas oriri debet ; quod tamen, ait, verum non esse. Sed non video consequentiam.   Nam plurimi liquores agunt in se invicem,& novam sibi mutuò partium contexturam secretò inducunt ; unde opaci, diaphani,vel variis coloribus, ex coloribus permistorum nullo modo oriundis,præditi evadere possunt.   Et hâc de causâ experimenta hujusmodi minùs apta semper existimavi, à quibus conclusiones deduci possint. Subnoto tamen, quòd ad hoc experimentum requiruntur liquores saturis & intensis coloribus præditi, qui perpaucos nisi proprii coloris radios transmittant ; quales rarò occurrunt, ut videbitur illuminando liquores cum diversis coloribus Prismaticis in obscurato cubiculo. Nam pauci reperientur, qui in propriis coloribus satis diaphani appareant, inque alienis opaci. Convenit præterea, ut adhibiti colores sint inter se oppositi, quales existimo fore rubrum & cæruleum, vel flavum & violaceum, vel etiam viridem & purpureum illum qui coccineo affinis est. Et ex hujusmodi liquoribus nonnulli (quorum partes tingentes non congredientur) fortasse permisti evadent opaciores. Sed de eventu nihil sum sollicitus, tum *quod luculentius est experimentum in liquoribus seorsim existentibus,* tum *quod experimentum illud (sicut & Iridis, Tincturæ Nephriticæ, & aliorum corporum naturalium phænomena) non ad probandam sed ad illustrandam tantùm doctrinam proposui.*

Quod R. P. *Theoriam nostram* Hypothesin *vocat, amicè habeo, siquidem ipsi nondum constet.   Sed alio tamen consilio proposueram,& nihil aliud continere videtur quàm* proprietates quasdem Lucis, *quas jam inventas probare haud difficile existimo, & quas si non veras esse cognoscerem, pro futili & inani speculatione mallem repudiare, quàm pro mea* Hypothesi *agnoscere.   Quid verò censeri mereatur,ex responsionibus ad animadversiones Domini* N.N.*fortasse* statim prodituris *clariùs* patebit. *Interea vale, & perge amare*

Tibi devinctissimum

J Newton

Some *Animadversions* on the Theory of Light of Mr. ISAAC NEWTON, Prof. of Mathematics in the University of Cambridge, printed in N°. 80. In a Letter of April 9, 1672, N. S. from IGNATIUS GASTON PARDIES,* P. Prof. of Mathematics in the Parisian College of Clermont. Translated from the Latin. N° 84, p. 4087.

I have read Mr. Newton's very ingenious hypothesis of light and colours.

---

* Ignatius Gaston Pardies, a French Jesuit, and professor of mathematics in the Parisian college of Clermont, was born in 1636. He entered the Jesuits order at 16, and after some time he devoted himself entirely to mathematics and natural philosophy. In this latter branch he followed the opinions of Descartes, though he feebly affected the contrary. He died at Paris in 1673, aged only 37, of a contagious disorder caught at the Bicêtre, where he officiated as a preacher and a confessor. He

And as I have given some attention to that subject, and also made experiments, I shall here inform you of what has occurred to me on that new doctrine.

It seems very extraordinary that the learned author should make light to consist of an almost infinite number of rays, endued with a natural disposition of retaining and exhibiting their own proper colours, and that are disposed in a certain peculiar way to be refracted, some in a greater, and others in a less degree : that these rays which, while promiscuously blended together in open daylight, are undiscernible, and exhibit only the colour of whiteness, should notwithstanding in refraction have rays of one colour separated from those of all others, and, thus separated, appear in their proper and native colours : and that bodies should appear of a certain colour, red for instance, which are adapted to reflect or transmit rays of that colour only.

This extraordinary hypothesis, which, as he observes, overturns the very basis of dioptrics, and renders useless the practice hitherto known, is founded entirely on the experiment of the prism, in which rays entering into a dark room through a hole in the window-shutter, and then falling on the wall, or received on a paper, did not form a round figure, as he expected according to the received rules of refraction, but appeared extended into an oblong form : whence he concluded, that this oblong figure was owing to the different refrangibility of the rays of light.

But it appears to me that, according to the common and received laws of dioptrics, the figure ought to be, not round but oblong. For since the rays proceeding from the opposite parts of the sun's disk, are variously inclined in their passage to the prism, they ought also to be variously refracted ; that since the inclination of some rays is at least 30′ more than that of others, their refraction must also be greater. Therefore the opposite rays, emerging from the other surface of the prism, become more diverging, than if they had proceeded without any refraction, or at least with an equal one. Now that refraction of the rays is made only towards those parts, which may be supposed to be in the planes perpendicular to the axis of the prism ; for there is no inequality of refraction towards those parts which are conceived to be in planes parallel to the axis, as may easily be demonstrated : for the two surfaces of the prism may be

was author of several ingenious works, which are written in a manner remarkably neat and clear, by which he acquired considerable credit, and by his talent as a teacher ; but, unfortunately for him, lost himself by the above imprudent attack on Sir I. Newton's theory of light and colours His works were chiefly, 1. Elements of Geometry, translated into English by Dr. John Harris, secretary of the Royal Society. 2. Discourse on the Knowledge of Beasts. 3. Statics, or the science of Moving Forces. 4. Two machines for drawing dials. 5. Discourse on Local motion. 6. Horologium Thaumanticum Duplex. 7. Dissertation on the Nature and Motion of Comets.

considered as parallel, with respect to the inclination to the axis, since they are both parallel to it. But the refraction through two parallel plane surfaces is accounted none, because by how much a ray is refracted one way by the first surface, by just so much is it refracted the contrary way by the other surface. Therefore since the solar rays, transmitted by a hole through a prism, are not refracted sideways, they proceed in that respect as if no prism at all stood in their way, that is with regard to the lateral divarication; but when the same rays on the superior and inferior parts, are refracted, some more, some less, as being unequally inclined, they must needs diverge more, and consequently be extended in an oblong figure.

But when a calculation is rightly made, as the lateral rays were found by Mr. Newton, of a breadth that subtended an arc of 31', which answers to the sun's diameter; so there is no doubt but the length of the image, which subtended 2° 49', would correspond with the same diameter after the unequal refractions. Thus, supposing the prism at ABC, (fig. 7, pl. 15,) having the angle A of 60°; and a ray DE making with the perpendicular EH an angle of 30°; after emerging in the line FG, I find it makes with the perpendicular FI an angle of 76° 22'. But taking another ray dE, which makes with the perpendicular EH an angle of 29° 30', I find that, when it emerges by fg, it makes with the perpendicular fi, an angle of 78° 45'. Hence those two rays DE, dE, which are supposed to proceed from opposite parts of the solar disk, and forming between them an angle of 30', where they emerge by the lines FG, fg, they diverge so as to form between them an angle of 2° 23'. And if two other rays were assumed approaching nearer the perpendicular EH, as suppose one of them forming with it an angle of 29° 30', and the other 29°; these rays, after emerging, would diverge still more, and form a greater angle, even sometimes more than 3°. And besides, this distance between the refracted rays is further increased, on this account, that the two rays DE, dE, meeting in E, begin immediately to diverge, and then fall on two distant points of the second surface, viz. in F and f. Therefore, in order to render the calculation just, it is not sufficient barely to subduct the diameter of the hole from the length of the image; for supposing the hole E to be invisible, or almost nothing, yet there would be formed a great hole as it were, in Ff, in the second surface of the prism.

What the author calls the Experimentum Crucis, seems also to agree with the commonly received laws of refraction. For, as was just now shown, the sun's rays, which approaching and converging from an angle of 30', coming from an invisible hole, do afterwards diverge in an angle of two or three degrees. It is not then to be wondered at, if these rays falling severally on a second prism, and having a very small hole in it, be unequally refracted, since their inclination is unequal. Nor does it alter the case, that those rays are raised or depressed by the rotation of the first prism, the second remaining immoveable, (which however cannot be done in all cases, or contrarywise, the second being turned while the first is fixed, that it may successively receive the coloured rays of the whole image, and transmit them through its proper hole; for in either case it is necessary that the extreme rays, viz. the red and the violet, should fall on the second prism under unequal angles, and consequently that their refraction be unequal, that of the violet being the greater.

Since then, here is an evident cause of that oblong figure of the rays, and that cause such as arises from the very nature of refraction; it seems needless to have recourse to another hypothesis, or to admit of that diverse refrangibility of the rays.

The author's notion of colours indeed follows very well from the preceding hypothesis; yet it is not without its difficulties. For when he says, that all the rays being promiscuously blended together, yield no colour, but rather a whiteness, this does not seem conformable to all the phænomena. Doubtless the same variations that are seen in the mixture of divers bodies of different colours, are also observed in the mixture of different rays of various colours: and the author himself has well observed, that as a green colour arises from a yellow and a blue body, so likewise a green colour is produced from a yellow and a blue ray. Therefore, if all the rays of the several colours be blended together, it is necessary in that hypothesis, that that colour should appear, which in reality arises on mixing together the several sorts of painters colours. That is, as the red, yellow, blue, purple, and all the others, when mixed together, produce, not a white, but an obscure sated colour. So also ordinary light should appear of the same colour, being a like aggregate of all the colours.

Indeed nothing can be more ingenious and proper, than what he says about Mr. Hook's experiment, in which are two different liquors, the one red, the other blue, and each apart transparent, yet when mixed together they become opaque: this the ingenious author thus explains: that the one liquor is disposed to transmit only the red rays, the other only the yellow; hence, both being mixed together, they transmit none at all. But it should seem that the like opacity should take place on the mixture of liquors of any other different colours: which however is far enough from the truth.

730   PHILOSOPHICAL TRANSACTIONS.   [ANNO 1672.

Mr. Newton's Letter of April 13, 1672, *O. S. written to the Editor, being an Answer to the foregoing Letter of F. Pardies. Translated from the Latin.* N° 84, *p.* 4091.

I received, Sir, the observations of the Rev. Father Ignatius Pardies, on my letter concerning the refractions and colours of light : for which I acknowledge myself much obliged to him ; and shall here clear up the difficulties he complains of. In the first place, he says that the length of the solar image produced by the refraction of the prism, requires no other cause to account for it, than the different incidence of the rays from opposite parts of the sun's disk ; and that therefore it does not prove a different refrangibility in the different rays. And, to prove the truth of his assertion, he states a case, in which from a difference of 30′ in the incidence, the difference of the refraction may be 2° 23′, or rather more, as my experiment requires. But the Rev. Father is under a mistake. For he has made the refractions by the different parts of the prism to be as unequal as possible, whereas in the experiments, and in the calculation from them, I employed equal refractions. Thus, let ABC (fig. 8, pl. 15,) be a section of the prism perpendicular to its axis ; FL and KG two rays crossing each other in x, the middle of the hole, and incident on the prism at G and L ; which let be first refracted into GH and Lm, and then into HI and mn. And since I supposed the refractions at the side AC are nearly equal to those at the side BC ; if AC and BC be equal, the inclination of the rays GH and Lm, to the base AB of the prism, will be similar ; and therefore the angle CLm=the angle CHG, and the angle CmL=the angle CGH. Therefore the refractions in G and m will be also equal, as well as those at L and H ; consequently the angle KGA=the angle nmB, and the angle FLA=the angle BHI ; and hence the inclination of the refracted rays HI and mn will be the same with that of the incident rays FL and KG. Therefore let the angle FxK of 30′ be equal to the sun's diameter, then the angle made by HI and mn will be also of 30′, provided the rays FL and KG be equally refrangible. But my experiment gave that angle about 2° 49′, which is constituted by the ray HI of the extreme violet colour, and by the ray mn which gives the blue ; and therefore those rays were differently refrangible, or the refractions were necessarily produced according to the unequal ratio of the sines of incidence and refraction.

The Rev. Father further adds, that to make a just calculation, it is sufficient to subtract the magnitude of the window hole from the length of the image on the paper ; since, even supposing the hole indivisible, yet there would be formed as it were a broad hole in the posterior surface of the prism. But yet it

VOL. VII.]   PHILOSOPHICAL TRANSACTIONS.   731

seems to me, that the refractions of rays crossing each other, both in the anterior and posterior surface of the prism, may be justly calculated from my principles. But if the case were otherwise, the breadth of the hole in the posterior surface, if such there be, would hardly produce an error of two seconds; and in practice such niceties may well be neglected.

What the Rev. Father contends is not inconsistent with what I called the Experimentum Crucis, viz. that the unequal refractions of rays endued with different colours, were produced by unequal incidences: for transmitting rays through two very small immoveable holes, and at a distance from each other, the incidences, as I made the experiment, were always equal, and yet the refractions were manifestly unequal. If he has any doubt of our experiment, I request that he may measure the refractions of the said rays of divers colours from equal incidences, and he will then see that they are unequal. But if he dislikes the manner in which I have performed this matter (than which however nothing can be clearer) it is easy to devise other ways; as indeed I myself have tried several other methods with advantage.

Against the theory of colours it is objected, that powders of divers colours mixed together, do not yield a white, but an obscure and dusky colour. But to me, white, black, and all the intermediate dusky colours, which can be compounded of mixtures of white and black, do not differ as to their species, but only as to their quantity of light. And since in the mixture of painters' colours, each corpuscle reflects only its own proper colour, and therefore the greatest part of the incident light is suppressed and retained; the reflected light will become obscure, and as if mixed with darkness, so that it exhibits not an intense whiteness, but an obscure dusky colour.

Again it is objected that an opacity ought equally to arise from a mixture of any liquors of different colours in the same vessel, as from the same liquors contained in different vessels; which however he says is not true. But I see no consequence in this. For many liquors act mutually on each other, and acquire a new texture of parts; hence they may become opaque, or diaphanous, or of various colours, in no manner owing to the colours of the compound. And on that account I have always esteemed experiments of this kind not so proper to draw conclusions from. It must also be noted that this experiment requires liquors of full and intense colours, which transmit very few rays besides those of their own colours; such as rarely occur, as will be seen by illuminating liquors with different prismatic colours in a dark room. For few will be found diaphanous enough in their own proper colours, and opaque in the others. Besides, it is proper that the colours employed be opposites, such as I count red and blue to be, or yellow and violet, or green, and that purple which approaches to scarlet.   And perhaps some of these liquors mixed together, whose tinging parts do not coalesce, will become more opaque.   But I am not solicitous about the event, both as the experiment is clearer in liquors apart, and as the experiment (like the phænomena of the iris, and the tincture of lignum nephriticum, and of other natural bodies) I proposed not to prove but only to illustrate the doctrine.

I do not take it amiss that the Rev. Father calls my theory an hypothesis, inasmuch as he was not acquainted with it.   But my design was quite different, for it seems to contain only certain properties of light, which, now discovered, I think easy to be proved, and which if I had not considered them as true, I would rather have them rejected as vain and empty speculation, than acknowledged even as an hypothesis.

(4004)

A Serie's of Quere's *propounded by Mr*. Iſaac Newton, *to be determin'd by Experiments , poſitively and directly concluding his
new Theory of Light and Colours ; and here recommended to the
Induſtry of the Lovers of Experimental Philoſophy, as they were
generouſly imparted to the Publiſher in a Letter of the ſaid Mr.*
Newtons *of* July 8. 1672.

IN the mean while give me leave, Sir, to inſinuate, that I cannot think it effectual for determining truth, to examin the
ſeveral waies by which Phænomena may be explained, unleſs
where there can be a perfect enumeration of all thoſe waies.
You know, the properMethod for *inquiring* after the properties
of things is, to deduce them from Experiments. And I told you,
that the Theory, which I propounded, was evinced to me, not
by inferring 'tis thus becauſe not otherwiſe, that is, not by
deducing it only from a confutation of contrary ſuppoſitions,
but by deriving it from Experiments concluding poſitively
and directly. The way therefore to examin it *is*, by conſi-
dering, whether the Experiments which I propound do prove
thoſe parts of the Theory, to which they are applyed; or by
proſecuting other Experiments which the Theory may ſug-
geſt for its examination. And this I would have done in a due
Method ; the Laws of *Refraction* being throughly inquired into and determined before the nature of *Colours* be taken into
conſideration. It may not be amiſs to proceed according to
the *Series* of theſe *Quæries* ; which I could wiſh were determined by the Event of proper Experiments ; declared by thoſe
that may have the curioſity to examin them.

1. Whether rays, that are *alike* incident on the ſame *Medium*, have *unequal* refractions ; and how great are the inequalities of their refractions at any incidence ?

2. What is the Law according to which each **ray** is more
or leſs refracted ; whether it be that the ſame ray is ever refracted according to the ſame *ratio* of the ſines of incidence
and refraction ; and divers rays, according to divers *ratio's* ; or
that the refraction of each ray is greater or leſs without any
certain rule ? *That is* , whether each ray have a certain degree of refrangibility according to which its refraction is performed ; or is refracted without that regularity?

3. Where-

(5005)

3. Whether rays, which are endued with particular degrees of refrangibility, when they are by any means separated, have particular colours conftantly belonging to them; *viz.* the leaft refrangible,*Scarlet*; the moft refrangible,*deep Violet*; the middle,*Sea-green*; and others,other colours? And on the contrary?

4. Whether the colour of any fort of rays apart may be changed by refraction?

5. Whether colours by coalefcing do really change one another to produce a new colour,or produce it by mixing only?

6. Whether a due mixture of rays, indued with all variety of colours, produces Light perfectly like that of the Sun,and which hath all the fame properties,and exhibits the fame *Phænomena*?

7. Whether the component colours of each mixture be really changed; or be only feparated when from that mixture various colours are produced again by Refraction?

8. Whether there be any other colours produced by refraction than fuch, as ought to refult from the colours belonging to the diverfly refrangible rays by their being feparated or mixed by that refraction?

To determine by Experiments thefe and fuch like *Quære's* which involve the propounded Theory, feems the moft proper and direct way to a conclufion. And therefore I could wifh all objections were fufpended, taken from *Hypothefes* or any other heads than thefe two; Of fhewing the infufficiency of Experiments to determine thefe *Quære's* or prove any other parts of my Theory, by affiguing the flaws and defects in my conclufions drawn from them; Or of producing other Experiments which directly contradict me, if any fuch may feem to occur. For if the Experiments, which I urge, be defective, it cannot be difficult to fhow the defects; but if valid, then by proving the Theory they muft render all Objections invalid.

So far this accurate Propofer; whofe Method appearing to be moft genuine and proper to the purpofe it is propounded for, and deferving therefore to be confidered and put to trial by Philofophers, abroad as well as at home; the Publifher, to invite and gratify Forraigners, was willing to deliver the above recited Extract of Mr. *Newtons* Letter in the language alfo of the Learned,as followeth;   Z z z z 2   *Ex-*

(5006)

Excerptum ex *Ifaaci Newtoni* Epiftola, nuper adEditorem fcript,quã ipfe genuinam fuggerit Methodum, doctrinam fuam d e *Luce* & *Coloribus*, antehac propofitam,evincendi , fubjectâ certorum *Quæfitorum*, debitis Experimentis folvendorum, ferie.

L*iceat mihi hac occafione tibi fignificare, nequaquam cenfere me, efficacem eam effe determinandæ veritatis rationem, quâ diverfi examinantur mc̃di, quibus Phænomena explicari poffunt, nifi ubi perfecta fuerit omnium iftorum modorum Enumeratio. Nofti, genuinam proprietates rerum inveftigandi Methodum effe, quâ illæ ab Experimentis deducuntur. Ac jam antè tibi dixeram* ; *Theoriam à me propofitam evictam mihi fuiffe,* non quidem inferendo rem ita fe habere quia haud fe habeat aliter, *i. e. non eam deducendo duntaxat à contrariarum fuppofitionum confutatione* ; fed ipfam ab Experimentis, pofitivè & directè concludentibus, derivando. *Vera itaque ratio eam examinandi hæc erit, fi confideremus fcilicet, num Experimenta à me propofita illas Theoria partes, quibus accommodantur, reverâ probent* ; *vel fi alia profequamur Experimenta, quæ ab ipfa Theoria ad examinandam eam fuggerantur. Atque hoc ipfum Methodo genuinâ fieri velim* ; *perveftigatis primum ac determinatis Legibus* Refractionis, *priufquam* Colorum *natura difquiratur. Præter rem itaque haud fore crediderim,difquifitionem hanc ex fequentium* Quæfitorum *ferie inftituere* ; *quæ quidem ut à folertibus fagacibufque naturæ Myftis,pronunciatis Experimentorum Eventibus,dirimantur,in votis quàm maximè habeo. Ea funt* ;

Primò, *Num radii, qui æquali incidentiâ in idem medium incidunt, Refractiones habeant* inæquales ; *quantæque fint refractionum,quas illi fubeunt, inæqualitates in quavis incidentia?*

Secundò, *Quænam ea Lex fit, juxta quam radius quilibet magis minúfve refringitur? fitne ,quòd idem radius femper refringatur fecundùm eandem rationem Sinuum Incidentiæ & Refractionis* ; *diverfi antem radii, fecundùm rationes diverfas? An verò, quòd cujuflibet radii refractio major minórve fit abfque ulla regula certa? Hoc eft, Utrum unufquifque radius certum habeat gradum Refrangibilitatis, juxta quem fiat ipfius refractio* ; *an verò refringatur fine ifta regularitate?*

Tertiò, *Num radii, certis gradibus refrangibilitatis præditi, quando,quodemum cumque modo,fecernuntur,certos obtineant colores ipfis proprios* ; *puta radii minimè omnium refrangibiles, Coccineum* ; *maximè refrangibiles, faturum Violaceum* ; *intermedii, fub-Viridem* ; *alii, alios? Et è contrà.*

Quartò, *Num color cujufvis generis radiorum feorfim exiftentium mutari poffint Refractione?*

Quintò, *Utrum colores coalefcendo reverà fe invicem mutent ad producendum colorem novum* ; *an verò eum producant nonnifi fe invicem commifcendo?*

Sextò, *Num debita radiorum mifcela, omnigenâ colorum varietate prædita, Lucem producat Solari luci fimillimam* ; *quæque eafdem omninò proprietates obtineat,eademque Phænomena exhibeat?*

Septimo

(5007)

Septimò, *Utrum componentes cujuſvis miſcela colores reverà mutentur ; an verò ſecernantur duntaxat, quando ex mixtura illa varii colores rurſum producuntur per Refractionem ?*

Octavò, *Denturne ulli alii colores Refractione producti præter eos, quos oriri oportet à Coloribus, ad radios diverſimodè refrangibiles pertinentibus, dum illi refractione iſtà ſecernuntur vel miſcentur ?*

Per Experimenta determinare hæc ſimiliave *Quæſita*, quæ propoſitam Theoriam involvunt, maximè genuina directaque videtur ad Concluſionem via: Proindéque omnes velim Objectiones ſuſpendi, quæ ab Hypotheſibus deſumuntur ulliſve Fontibus aliis, quàm his duobus; quibus nempe vel oſten‑datur Experimentorum ad determinanda hæc ζητήματα probandaſve ullas alias Theoriæ meæ partes inſufficientia, hallucinationes defectuſque in Concluſionibus meis inde deductis indigitando; vel alia producantur Experimenta, è diametro mihi oppoſita, ſi quæ talia occurrere videantur. Si enim Experimenta, quæ à me urgentur, laborant defectibus, difficile haud fuerit eos oſtendere ‑ ſi verò valida fuerint, eo ipſo dum Theoriam meam aſſerunt probantque omnes Objectiones convellunt.

(5012)

A Second Letter of P. *Pardies*, written to the Publisher from *Paris*
May 21. 1672. to Mr.*Newtons* Answer, made to his first Letter,
printed in *Numb.* 84.

R Edditæ mihi funt tuæ literæ cum Obfervationibus Clariffimi atque Inge-
nioffimi Newtoni, quibus ad meas difficultates respondit. Eas ego
legi non fine maxima voluptate : Et primùm, quod attinet ad ipfum Experimentum majoris Latitudinis colorum quàm exigeret vulgaris Theoria Refractionum; fateor, me inæquales refractiones in oppofitis Prifmatis facie-
bus fuppofuiffe, nec ulla tenus advertiffe in literis relatis in Tranfactionibus, obfervatam fuiffe à Newtono majorem illam latitudinem in eo cafu in
quo refractiones ponerentur reciprocè æquales, eo modo quo hîc in iftis obfervationibus dicitur.   Sed nec ab eo tempore in iifdem Tranfactionibus videre licuit, cùm eas non potuerim recuperare.   Cùm igitur nunc videam, etiam
in eo Cafu obfervatam majorem illam Colorum latitudinem; certè ex hoc capite nihil mihi ulterius reftat difficultatis : Ex hoc, inquam, capite; nam a-
liundè videtur poffe reddi ratio illius Phænomeni abfque ifta varia Radiorum
Refrangibilitate.   Etenim in ea Hypothefi, quam fusè explicat nofter Gri-
maldus, in qua fupponitur Lumen effe fubftantia quædam rapidiffimè mota,
poffet fieri aliqua diffufio luminis poft tranfitum foraminis & decuffationem
radiorum.   Item in ea Hypothefi, qua lumen ponitur progredi per certas quaf-
dam materiæ fubtilis Undulationes, ut explicat fubtiliffimus Hookius, poffunt explicari colores per certam quandam diffufionem atque expanfionem Undulationum, qua fiat ad latera radiorum ultra foramen, ipfo contagio ipfaque
materiæ continuatione.   Certe ego talem adhibeo hypothefin in Differtatione
de motu undulationis, quæ eft fexta pars meorum Mechanicorum; ut po-
nam, colores iftos apparentes fieri ex fola illa Communicatione motionis, qua
ab Undulationibus directè procedentibus ad latera effundatur : Ut, fi radii

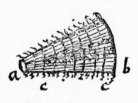

intrantes per foramen a progrediantur
versùs b, undulationes quidem directè
terminari deberent (habendo rationem ad
motum rectum & naturalem) ad lineam
rectam a b; nihilominus tamen, propter
continuitatem materiæ, fit aliqua commu-
nicatio commotionis verfus latera c c,
ubi tremula quædam & crifpans fuccuf-
fio excitatur : Atque fi in illa laterali
crifpatione confiftere colores fupponatur,
exiftimo omnia phænomena colorum ex-
plicari poffe, ut fufius in ea, quam dixi, Differtatione expono. Quibus
item pofitis apparet etiam, cur ultra quàm ferat radiorum ipforum divari-
catio, expandi colorum latitudinem neceffe fit. Verum ifta obiter hîc tantum
adnotaffe fufficiat.

2nd

(5013)

Quod annotat, errorem, qui oriri poffet in calculo, ex eo, quod dixeram, veluti foramine facto in posteriori facie prismatis; errorem, inquam, illum non poffe inducere senfibilem varietatem: id optimè annotatum eft; neque ego exiftimavi, inde multum augeri colorum latitudinem, fed tantummodò accuratam calculi rationem indicare volui: Quapropter etiam & ego in praxi negligendam hanc cautionem cenfeo.

Circa Experimentum crucis, *nequaquam dubito, quo minus in fuo experimento talem fitum adhibuerit, in quo æqualis inclinatio fuerit Radiorum incidentium; quandoquidem id ita à fe præftitum expreffe affirmat. Verùm id non ego poteram conijcere ex iis quæ in* Tranfactionibus *legeram, ubi ponuntur duo exigua & maximè diftantia foramina, & unum Prifma prope* primum *foramen quod eft in feneftra; per quod Prifma radij colorati erumpentes incidunt in alterum diftans foramen. Addebatur autem, quòd ad hoc ut omnes illi radii fucceffivè inciderent in* fecundum *illud foramen, convertebatur primum Prifma fupra axem: Atqui hoc modo neceffe eft mutari inclinationem radiorum qui incidunt in fecundum foramen: atque indicavi ego in literis, quòd perinde fe fe res haberet, five manente primo Prifmate immobili, fecundum foramen attolleretur aut deprimeretur, ut poffet fucceffivè radios omnes depictæ imaginis Solaris excipere; five manente ifto fecundo foramine immobili, primum prifma converteretur, ut ita eadem imago fitum mutaret, atque in foramen impingere fecundum omnes fucceffivè partes poffet. Sed alias fine dubio adhibuit cautiones folertiffimus* Newtonus.

Quæ circa Colores *objeceram, optimè foluta exiftimo. Quod autem* Theoriam *iftam, appellarim* Hypothefin *, id certè ego nullo adhibito confilio feci; atque nomen ufurpavi quod primum occurrit: quapropter velim ut ne per contemptum adhibitam vocem ejufmodi exiftimet. Præclara fanè inventa femper ego magni feci, Clariffimum verò* Newtonum *imprimis fufpicio ac veneror.*

Aaaaa 2   Mr. *Newtons*

(4014)

Mr. *Newtons* Anſwer to the foregoing Letter.

IN *Obſervationibus R. Patris* J. Pardies, *quas ad te denuò conſcripſit, an majus ſit Humanitatis argumentum quòd meis reſponſionibus vim omnem attribuit ; an Ingenii, quòd Objectiones proponit, quæ, ſi non probe tollantur, Doctrinam noſtram fruſtrari poſſint, vix dixerim. Utrumque ſanè ad determinandam veritatem optimè conducit, efficitque ut acceptis quàm lubentiſſimè reſpondeam.*

Ait R. P. quòd abſque *varia diverſorum radiorum refrangibilitate poſſibile ſit explicare longitudinem colorum ; puta ex Hypotheſi* P. Grimaldi, *per diffuſionem luminis, quod ſupponitur eſſe ſubſtantia quædam rapidiſſimè mota ; vel ex Hypotheſi* Hookii *noſtri, per diffuſionem vel expanſionem Undulationum, quas ſtatuit in æthere à lucidis corporibus excitatas quaquaverſum propagari. Addo, quòd ex Hypotheſi* Carteſiana *poteſt etiam effingi conſimilis diffuſio conatus vel preſſionis globulorum, perinde ut in explicatione* Caudæ Cometæ *ſupponitur. Et eadem diffuſio vel expanſio juxta aliam quamvis Hypotheſin, in qua lumen ſtatuitur eſſe vis, actio, qualitas, vel ſubſtantia qualibet à luminoſis corporibus undique emiſſa, effingi poteſt.*

Ut his reſpondeam, animadvertendum eſt, quòd Doctrina illa, quam de Refractione & Coloribus explicui, in quibuſdam Lucis Proprietatibus *ſolummodo conſtitit, neglectis* Hypotheſibus *per quas Proprietates illæ explicari debent. Optimus enim & tutiſſimus philoſophandi modus videtur, ut imprimis rerum proprietates diligenter inquiramus & per experimenta ſtabiliamus ; ac dein tardius contendamus ad Hypotheſes pro earum explicatione. Nam* Hypotheſes *ad explicandas rerum proprietates tantùm accommodari debent, & non ad determinandas uſurpari, niſi quatenus experimenta ſubminiſtrare poſſint. Et ſiquis ex ſola* Hypotheſium *poſſibilitate de veritate rerum conjecturam faciat, non video quo pacto quicquam certi in ulla ſcientia determinare poſſit ; ſiquidem alias atque alias Hypotheſes ſemper liceat excogitare, quæ novas difficultates ſuppeditare videbuntur. Quamobrem ab* Hypotheſium *contemplatione, tanquam improprio argumentandi loco, hîc abſtinendum eſſe cenſui, & vim Objectionis abſtrahendam, ut pleniorem & magis generalem reſponſionem accipiat.*

Itaque per Lumen *intelligo quodlibet Ens vel entis poteſtatem (ſive ſit ſubſtantia, ſive quavis ejus vis, actio, vel qualitas) quod à corpore lucido rectà pergens aptum ſit ad excitandam viſionem ; & per* radios Luminis *intelligo minimas vel quaslibet indefinitè parvas ejus partes, quæ ab invicem non dependent ; quales ſunt illi omnes radii, quos lucentia corpora vel ſimul vel ſucceſſivè ſecundùm rectas lineas emittunt. Nam illæ tum collaterales tum ſucceſſivæ partes luminis ſunt independentes ; ſiquidem unæ abſque aliis intercipi poſſint, & in quaslibet plagas ſeorſim reflecti vel refringi. Et hoc præcognito, Objectionis vis omnis in eo ſita erit ; Quòd colores per aliquam Luminis ultra foramen diffuſionem, quæ non oritur ab inæ-*

quali

(5015)

*quali diverforum radiorum (feu luminis independentium partium) refrangibi-
litate, in longum diduci poffint.*

Quòd autem non aliunde oblongentur, monftravi in Literis relatis in Phil.
Tranfactionibus, Num. 80. *Et ut rationes facilius percipiantur, non
gravabor jam fufius explicare.*

*Scilicet ex obfervatione, quòd radii poft refractionem non incurvabantur,
fed rectâ ad parietem progreffi fuêre, patuit, eandem fuiffe eorum ad fe mutuò inclinationem cùm modò exiêrunt Prifmate, atque cùm impegerunt in
parietem ; & proinde Longitudo colorum ex inclinatione radiorum emerfit quam
inter refringendum obtinuêre, hoc eft, ex quantitate refractionis quam fin-
guli radii in Prifmate patiebantur : Adeóque cùm colorum longitudo latitudinem aliquot vicibus ex obfervatione fuperavit, fequitur, majorem fuiffe in-
æqualitem refractionum quàm potuit oriri ex inæqualitate incidentiarum.
Quin imò ex figura imaginis coloratæ, quòd nempe non fuit Ovalis, fed ad
latera duabus parallelis rectis lineis terminata, patuit, eam ex indefinitè
multis imaginibus Solis, per inæqualem refractionem in longum diftractis, &
ferie continuâ difpofitis, conftitui ; adeoque radios à fingulis partibus folaris
Difci provenientes per totam ferè longitudinem colorum difpergi ; & proinde
fimiliter incidentium inæquales effe refractiones. Id quod aliis etiam indiciis
oftendi poffet.*

*Conftat itaque diverfas effe refractiones, ubi pares funt incidentiæ. Sed
amplius inquirendum eft, Unde oriatur illa diverfitas ; An fit à caufa aliqua incerta & irregulari, vel certâ lege, fecundùm quam radius quilibet
aptus eft determinatam aliquam refractionem pati. Per incertas & irregulares caufas intellige afperitates in fuperficie, vel venas diverfæ denfitatis in
interiori parte vitri ex quo Prifma conflatur; item irregularem fitum pororum,
quos nonnulli ob luminis tranfmiffionem directo tramite per vitrum omnifa-
riam traijci ftatuunt ; nec non tremores & inæquales commotiones partium
ætheris, aëris, vel vitri ; radiorum in refringente fuperficie fe mutuò for-
taffe comprimentium refulturam ab invicem ; ejufdem cujufque radii divifi-
onem ac diffipationem in partes divergentes, quas vel numero finitas vel indefinitè multas in fuperficie aliquâ continuatim jacentes imaginari liceat ; vel
quamvis aliam diffufionem & dilatationem Luminis quam poffumus excogitare,
non ortam ex diverfa prædifpofitione cujufque radii ad refractionem, in certo
aliquo & conftanti gradu patiendam.*

*Quod autem diverfa refractio non orta fit ex ullis ejufmodi caufis incertis
& irregularibus, probavi per Experimentum duorum confimilium Prifmatum
in contrario fitu juxta-pofitorum, itaut pofterius contrariâ fuâ refractione
retro-flecteret radios, & fic regulares effectus prioris deftrueret, fed per
iteratas refractiones augeret irregulares. Utpote fi prius Prifma diffunderet ac divergere faceret parallelos radios ; e.g. per afperam polituram, inæ-
quabilem denfitatem, aut irregularem fitum pororum Prifmatis ; vel per
tremulos motus partium ætheris, aëris aut vitri ; vel per dilatationem luminis
propter partium ejus (i.e. radiorum) fe mutuò comprimentium relaxationem
verfus adjacentia fpatia; quæ vel nullo vel minùs conftipato lumine irradiantur ;*

vel

(5016)

vel denique per cujusque radii dilatationem aut diffractionem in complures di-
vergentes radios : tum sanè posterius Prisma magis diffunderet ac dissiparet
radios per dictas irregularitates ætheris, aëris, aut vitri, vel per iteratam di-
latationem luminis à refringentis superficiei resistentia denuò constipati ac dif-
fusi, vel etiam per cujusque radii à priori diffractione orti iteratam diffractio-
nem ac divisionem in longe plures divergentes radios. Et sic Lumen magis
dispergeretur per refractionem secundi Prismatis, & in parietem projectam
Imaginem duplo longiorem minimùm exhiberet, quàm per solam refractionem
prioris Prismatis exhiberi potuisset. Quamobrem cùm, experientiâ teste,
refractio secundi Prismatis adeò non dispergat lumen ut contrahat & in pristi-
num statum reducat, efficiatque ut in forma Coni postea progrediatur, perinde
ac si nullam omnino refractionem passum fuisset ; concedendum est, Diffusionem
Luminis, à refractione anterioris Prismatis effectam, non oriri ab aliqua præ-
fatarum causarum, aut alia quavis irregularitate, sed diversa refrangibili-
tati diversorum radiorum solummodo tribuendam esse ; utpote quâ radius unus-
quisque, ex insita dispositione tantam refractionem in posteriori Prismate ac in
priori passus, reducitur in parallelismum cum seipso ; & sic omnes radii ad se
mutuò easdem inclinationes resumunt quas ante refractiones habuêre.

   Demum, ut hæc omnia summè confirmarem, adjeci Experimentum illud
quod jam nomine Crucis *passim insignitur : de cujus conditionibus cum R. P.*
dubitaverit, placuit jam designare Schemate. Sit B C anterior tabula, cui
Prisma A immediate præfigitur, sitque D E altera tabula, quasi duodecim
pedibus abinde distans, cui suffigitur alterum Prisma F. Tabulæ autem ad x
*& * y *ita perforentur, ut aliquantulum lucis ab anteriori Prismate refracta,*

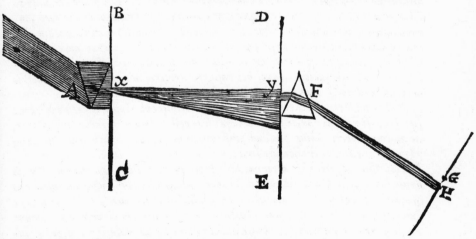

traijci possit per utrumque foramen ad secundum Prisma, inque eo denuò re-
fringi. Jam Prisma anterius circa axem reciproco motu convertatur, & co-
lores in Tabulam posteriorem D E procidentes, per vices attollentur ac depri-
mentur, eoque pacto alius atque alius color successivè pro arbitrio traijci potest
*per foramen ejus * y *ad posterius Prisma, dum cæteri colores in Tabulam im-*
pingunt : Et videbis, radios diversis coloribus præditos diversam pati refractio-
nem

(5017)

nem in illo posteriori Prismate, ex eo quòd ad diversa loca parietis vel cujusvis obstaculi G H, pedibus aliquot ulterius remoti, allabentur ; puta violacei *radii ad* H, rubri ad G, & intermedii *ad loca intermedia : & tamen propter determinatam positionem foraminum necesse est ut similis sit incidentia radiorum cujusque coloris per utrumque trajecti. Atque ita ex mensura constat radios, diversis coloribus affectos, habere diversas leges refractionum.*

Sed suspicor unde adductus sit R.P. in dubitationem ; nempe videtur collocasse primum Prisma A post *Tabulam B C, atque ita convertendo circa Axem, verisimile est inclinationem radiorum qui interjacent foramina propter intermediam refractionem fuisse mutatam.   At ex descriptione exposità in* Phil.
Transactionibus *debuit Tabula illa collocari* post   * Vid. Num.80. p.3078.
Prisma, ut radii inter foramina in directum jacerent,   *quæ verba Latinè ita so*
quemadmodum ex verbis ; I took two Boards and   *nant ;* Capiebam duas
placed one of them close behind the Prism   Tabulas ligneas, unamat the Window *, *constare potest.   Et usu Ex*   que earum immediatè
perimenti idem innuit.   collocabam post Prisma
     ad fenestram.

Ex abundanti placet observare, quòd in hoc Experimento colorata Lux ob refractionem secundi Prismatis longe minùs diffunditur ac divaricat, quàm cum alba existit, adeò ut imago ad G vel H sit penè circularis ; præsertim si Prismata statuantur parallela & in contrario situ angulorum, prout in Schemate designantur.   Quinetiam, si præterea diameter foraminis y adæquet latitudinem colorum, nulla erit ejusdem coloratæ lucis in longum diffusio ; sed imago, quæ à quopiam colore ad G vel H effingitur, (positis circularibus foraminibus, & refractione posterioris Prismatis non majori quàm prioris, radiisque ad obstaculum quàm proximè perpendicularibus,) erit planè circularis. Id quod arguit diffusionem, de qua supra egimus, non ex contagione vel continuitate materiæ undulantis aut celerrimè motæ vel similibus causis ortam esse, sed ex certa refractionum cujusque generis radiorum lege.   Cur autem Imago illa in uno casu sit circularis, & in aliis nonnihil oblongata, & quomodo diffusio lucis in longitudinem in quolibet casu pro arbitrio minui possit, à Geometris determinandum & cum experientia conferendum relinquo.

Postquam Proprietates Lucis *his & similibus experimentis satis exploratæ fuerint, spectando radios tanquam ejus sive collaterales sive successivas partes, de quibus experti simus per independentiam quod sint ab invicem distinctæ; Hypotheses exinde dijudicandæ sunt, & quæ non possunt conciliari reijciendæ. Sed levissimi negotii est, accommodare Hypotheses ad hanc Doctrinam.   Nam siquis Hypothesin* Cartesianam *defendere velit, dicendum est, globulos esse inæquales ; vel pressiones globulorum esse alias aliis fortiores, & inde diversimodè refrangibiles, & aptas ad excitandam sensationem diversorum colorum. Et sic juxta Hypothesin* Cl. Hookii *dicendum est, Undulationes ætheris esse alias majores sive crassiores aliis.   Atque ita in cæteris.   Hæc enim videtur esse summè necessaria Lex & Conditio* Hypothesium, *in quibus Naturalia corpora ponuntur constare ex quàm plurimis corpusculis acervatim contextis, ut à diversis lucentium corpusculis, vel ejusdem corpusculi diversis partibus (prout motu, figurâ, mole, aut aliis qualitatibus differunt) inæquales pressiones, motiones*

(5018)

aut mota corpufcula per æthera quaquaverfum traijciantur, ex quibus,confusè miftis, lux conftitui fupponetur.   Et nihil durius effe poteft in iftis Hypothe-fibus quàm contraria fuppofitio.

Ex apertura five dilatatione Lucis in pofteriori facie Prifmatis,quam R.P. dixit effe veluti foramen, fufficit, quod error non emerget fenfibilis fi modò aliquis emergeret.   Quòd fi calculus juxta Obfervationes præcisè ineatur, error erit nullus.   Nam diametro foraminis à longitudine Imaginis fubductâ, reftabit longitudo quam Imago haberet fi modò foramen ante Prifma effet indi-vifibile , idque non obftante præfatâ lucis dilatatione in pofteriori facie Prif-matis ; ut facile oftenditur.   Deinde ex data illa longitudine Imaginis,ac di-ftantia à foramine indivifibili, ut & pofitione & forma Prifmatis, & ad id inclinatione incidentium radiorum, ac angulo,quem refracti radii, ad medium Imaginis tendentes, cum à centro Solis incidentibus conftituunt, cætera omnia determinantur.   Et quæ determinant refractiones & pofitiones radiorum,fuf-ficiunt ad calculum iftarum refractionum rité ineundum.   Sed res non tanti effe videtur ut moram inferat.

Quòd R.P.Doctrinam noftram Hypothefin *vocaverit, non aliunde factum effe credo quàm quòd vocabulum ufurpavit quod primùm occurrit ; fiquidem mos obtinuit ut quicquid exponitur in Philofophia dicatur Hypothefis.   Et ego fane non alio confilio vocabulum iftud reprehendi quàm ut nè invalefceret ap-pellatio quæ rectè Philofophantibus præjudicio effe poffet.   R.Patris verò can-dor in omnibus confpicitur ; indeque modus efferendi Benevolentiam, qui mihi minimè convenit.   Quod tamen noftra non difplicent,vehementer gaudeo.Vale.* Dab. Cantabrig. 11ᵐᵒ Junii 1672.

*Hæc refponfio ad R.P.*Ignatium Pardies *mox tranfmiffa id effecit,ut ille die* 9. Julii 1672. *refcriberet Gallicè in hunc fenfum ;*
Omnino mihi fatisfecit noviffima refponfio,à Dn. *Newtono* ad meas Inftantias data.   Noviffimus fcrupulus, qui mihi hærebat circa *Ex-perimentum Crucis,*penitus fuit exemptus.   Atque nunc planè ex Figura ipfius intelligo quod non intellexeram ante.   Experimentum peractum cùm fuerit ifto modo, nil habeo quod in eo defiderem ampliùs.   Rem mihi pergratam feceris, fi ipfi fingularem meum ingenii & doctrinæ ejus cultum contefteris, & pro illo ftudio maximas gratias agas,quo voluit Annotationes meas examinare iifque refpondere.   Præter ex-iftimationem illam, quam jam ante de acumine ejus conceperam, af-fectus hic officiofus magnopere me ipfi devinxit.

*A second Letter of P. PARDIES, written to the Editor from Paris,
May 21, 1672, to Mr. NEWTON's Answer made to his first Letter,
printed in N°. 84. N°. 85, p. 5012. Translated from the Latin.*

I have received your letter, with the observations of the very ingenious Mr.
Newton, in which he answers my difficulties, which I have read with great
pleasure. And first, with respect to that experiment of the greater breadth of
the colours than what is required by the common theory of refractions; I confess that I supposed the refractions at the opposite sides of the prism unequal,
till informed by the letter in the Transactions, that the greater breadth was
observed by Newton in that case in which the refractions are supposed reciprocally equal, in the manner mentioned in those observations. But since I now see
that it was in that case that the greater breadth of the colours was observed, on
that head I find no further difficulty. I say on that head; for the greater
length of the image may be otherwise accounted for, than by the different
refrangibility of the rays. For according to that hypothesis, which is explained
at large by Grimaldi, and in which it is supposed that light is a certain substance
very rapidly moved, there may take place some diffusion of the rays of light
after their passage and decussation in the hole. Also on that other hypothesis,
in which light is made to proceed by certain undulations of a subtile matter, as
explained by Mr. Hook, colours may be explained by a certain diffusion and expansion of the undulations, made on the sides of the rays beyond the hole by

that there is no other channel by which the chyle is conveyed into the blood than that of the thoracic
duct, which generally opens into the left subclavian vein at the angle formed by it and the internal
jugular vein. Sometimes however it is inserted directly into the internal jugular.]

the influence and continuation of the subtile matter. Indeed I admit such an hypothesis in " the Dissertation on the Motion of Undulation," which is the sixth part of my mechanics, as I suppose that those apparent colours are the sole effect of that communication of motion which is diffused laterally by the direct undulations. As if the rays entering by the hole a, (fig. 9, pl. 15) should proceed towards b, the undulations ought indeed to terminate directly, with regard to their direct and natural motion, at the right line ab; yet nevertheless, because of the continuity of the matter, there is some communication of the motion towards the sides cc, where it becomes tremulous and undulatory. And if colours be supposed to consist in the lateral undulation, all their phænomena may be explained in this manner, as I have shown in the dissertation beforementioned; by which also the reason will appear, why the breadth of the colours must be expanded beyond the divergency of the rays themselves.

As to what he says of the error, which might arise in the calculation, from what I mentioned like a hole made in the posterior face of the prism, that that error could not cause any sensible variation; his remark is very proper : neither have I judged that hence the breadth of the colours would be much increased, but I wished only to indicate an accurate mode of calculation : and therefore I also think this caution may be neglected in practice.

As to the Experimentum Crucis, I make no doubt that the incident rays had an equal inclination, since the author expressly affirms it. But that is what I could not gather from what I read in the Transactions; where it is stated, that there are two small and very distant holes, and one prism near the first hole in the window; through which prism the coloured rays escaping, fall on the other distant hole. And it is added, that the first prism was turned round its axis, to cause all the rays to fall successively on the second hole. Now in this case the inclination of the rays which fall on the second hole, must necessarily be changed: and I hinted in my letter, that it would be the same thing, whether the second hole were raised or depressed, for all the rays pointing to the sun's image, to fall successively on it, while the first prism was invariable ; or whether, the second hole being immoveable, the first prism were turned round, so that the same image might change its situation, and all its parts successively fall on the second hole. But no doubt the sagacious Newton used other precautions.

As to what I objected about colours, I am well satisfied with the solutions. And as to my calling the author's theory an hypothesis, that was done without any design, having only used that word as first occurring to me ; and therefore request it may not be thought as done out of any disrespect. I have always esteemed ingenious discoveries, and the excellent Newton I very highly admire and honour.

740   PHILOSOPHICAL TRANSACTIONS.   [ANNO 1672.

Mr. NEWTON's *Answer to the foregoing Letter.* N° 85, *p.* 5014.
Translated from the Latin.

In the observations of the Rev. F. Pardies, one can hardly determine whether there is more of humanity and candour, in allowing my arguments their due weight, or penetration and genius in starting objections. And doubtless these are very proper qualifications in researches after truth. But to proceed, F. Pardies says, that the length of the coloured image can be explained, without having recourse to the divers refrangibility of the rays of light; as suppose by the hypothesis of F. Grimaldi, viz. by a diffusion of light, which is supposed to be a certain substance put into very rapid motion; or by Mr. Hook's hypothesis, by a diffusion and expansion of undulations; which, being formed in the æther by lucid bodies, is propagated every way. To which may be added the hypothesis of Descartes, in which a similar diffusion of *conatus,* or pression of the globules, may be conceived, like as is supposed in accounting for the tails of comets. And the same diffusion or expansion may be devised according to any other hypotheses, in which light is supposed to be a power, action, quality, or certain substance emitted every way from luminous bodies.

In answer to this, it is to be observed that the doctrine which I explained concerning refraction and colours, consists only in certain properties of light, without regarding any hypotheses, by which those properties might be explained. For the best and safest method of philosophizing seems to be, first to inquire diligently into the properties of things, and establishing those properties by experiments and then to proceed more slowly to hypotheses for the explanation of them. For hypotheses should be subservient only in explaining the properties of things, but not assumed in determining them; unless so far as they may furnish experiments. For if the possibility of hypotheses is to be the test of the truth and reality of things, I see not how certainty can be obtained in any science; since numerous hypotheses may be devised, which shall seem to overcome new difficulties. Hence it has been here thought necessary to lay aside all hypotheses, as foreign to the purpose, that the force of the objection should be abstractedly considered, and receive a more full and general answer.

By light therefore I understand, any being or power of a being, (whether a substance or any power, action, or quality of it, which proceeding directly from a lucid body, is apt to excite vision. And by the rays of light I understand its least or indefinitely small parts, which are independent of each other; such as are all those rays which lucid bodies emit in right lines, either successively or all together. For the collateral as well as the successive parts of light are inde-

VOL. VII.]   PHILOSOPHICAL TRANSACTIONS.   741

pendent; since some of the parts may be intercepted without the others, and be separately reflected or refracted towards different sides. This being premised, the whole force of the objection will lie in this, that colours may be lengthened out by some certain diffusion of light beyond the hole, which does not arise from the unequal refraction of the different rays, or of the independent parts of light. And that the image is no otherwise lengthened, was shown in my letter in Numb. 80 of the Transactions ; and to confirm the whole in the strictest manner, I added that experiment now known by the name Experimentum Crucis ; of the conditions of which, since the Rev. Father has some doubt, I have thought fit to represent it by a scheme. Let BC (fig. 10, pl. 15) then be the anterior board, to which the prism A is immediately prefixed, and let DE be the other board, at the distance of about 12 feet from the former, to which the other prism F is affixed. And let the boards be perforated at x and y in such a manner, that a little of the light refracted by the former prism may pass through both the holes to the second prism, and be there refracted again. Now let the former prism be turned about its axis with a reciprocal motion; then the colours falling on the latter board DE will be raised and depressed by turns : and thus the several colours may at pleasure be made to pass successively through the hole y to the latter prism, while all the other colours fall on the board. Then you will see that the said rays of different colours will be differently refracted at the latter prism, as they will be seen on different places of the opposite wall. or of any obstacle GH, at the distance of some feet from it; as suppose the violet rays at H, the red at G, and the intermediate rays at the intermediate places: and yet, because of the determinate position of the holes, the incidence of the rays of each colour through both must be similar. And thus it appears, by measuring, that the rays of different colours have different laws of refractions.

But I suspect what it was that caused the Rev. Father to doubt; viz. it seems he placed his first prism A behind the board BC, and thus by turning it about its axis, it is probable that the inclination of the rays intercepted between the two holes may have suffered some change by the intermediate refraction. But by the description before given in the Transactions, the first board ought to be placed after the prism, that the rays may pass in a straight direction between the holes, agreeably to my words ; " I took two boards, and placed one of them close behind the prism at the window." And the design of the experiment requires the same thing.

It may be further observed, that in this experiment, because of the refraction of the second prism, the coloured light is much less diffused and less divergent, than when it is quite white, so that the image at G or H is nearly circular ; especially if the prisms be placed parallel, and their angles in a contrary position, as in the present figure. And besides, if the diameter of the hole y be equal to the breadth of the colours, the coloured light will not be diffused lengthwise; but the image, which is formed by any colour at G or H, will be manifestly circular; supposing the holes to be circular, and the refraction of the latter prism not to be greater than that of the former, and the rays to be nearly perpendicular to the obstacle. This shows that the diffusion, above-mentioned, does not arise from the influence or continuity of the undulating matter, or matter put into a rapid motion, or any such like causes, but from a certain law of refractions for every species of rays. But why the image is in one case circular, and in others a little oblong, and how the diffusion of light lengthwise may in any case be diminished at pleasure, I leave to be determined by geometricians, and compared with experiments.

After the properties of light shall, by these and such like experiments, have been sufficiently explored, by considering its rays either as collateral or successive parts of it, of which we have found by their independence that they are distinct from one another; hypotheses are thence to be judged of, and those to be rejected which cannot be reconciled with the phænomena. But it is an easy matter to accommodate hypotheses to this doctrine. For if any one wish to defend the Cartesian hypothesis, he need only say that the globules are unequal, or that the pressures of some of the globules are stronger than others, and that hence they become differently refrangible, and proper to excite the sensation of different colours. And thus also according to Hook's hypothesis, it may be said, that some undulations of the æther are larger or denser than others. And so of the rest. For this seems to be the most necessary law and condition of hypotheses, in which natural bodies are supposed to consist of a multitude of corpuscules cohering together, and that from the different particles of lucid bodies, or from the different parts of the same corpuscule, (as they may happen to differ in motion, figure, bulk, or other qualities) unequal pressions, motions, or moved corpuscules, may be propagated every way through the æther, of the confused mixture of which light may be supposed to be constituted. And there can be nothing more difficult in these hypotheses than the contrary supposition.

As to that aperture or dilatation of the light in the posterior face of the prism, which the Rev. Father supposes to resemble a hole, it is sufficient that no sensible error can arise from it, if any at all. For if a calculation be made precisely according to the observations, the error will be found nothing. For by subtracting the diameter of the hole from the length of the image, there will remain that length which the image would have, if the hole before the prism were an indivisible point, and that notwithstanding the aforesaid dilatation of the light

1

VOL. VII.]   PHILOSOPHICAL TRANSACTIONS.   743

in the posterior face of the prism; as is easily shown. Then from that given length of the image, and its distance from the indivisible hole, as also from the position and form of the prism, and besides from the inclination of the incident rays, and from the angle which the refracted rays bending to the middle of the image make with those that are incident from the sun's centre, all other things may be determined. And the same data that determined the refractions and positions of the rays, are sufficient for an accurate calculation of these refractions. But this matter seems not to be of importance enough to be much regarded.

As to the Rev. Father's calling our doctrine an hypothesis, I believe it only proceeded from his using the word which first occurred to him, as a practice has arisen of calling by the name hypothesis whatever is explained in philosophy: and the reason of my making exception to the word, was to prevent the prevalence of a term, which might be prejudicial to true philosophy.

The above answer being sent to the Rev. Father Ig. Pardies, he returned his acknowledgement in a note as below.

I am quite satisfied with Mr. Newton's new answer to me. The last scruple which I had, about the Experimentum Crucis, is fully removed. And I now clearly perceive by his figure what I did not before understand. When the experiment was performed after his manner, every thing succeeded, and I have nothing further to desire.

Mr. Hooke's confiderations upon Mr. Newton's difcourfe on light and co-lours were read.   Mr. Hooke was thanked for the pains taken in bringing in fuch ingenious reflections ; and it was ordered, that this paper fhould be regiftred [r], and a copy of it immediately fent to Mr. Newton : and that in the mean time the printing of Mr. Newton's difcourfe by itfelf might go on, if he did not con-tradict it ; and that Mr. Hooke's paper might be printed afterwards, it not be-ing thought fit to print them together, left Mr. Newton fhould look upon it as a difrefpect, in printing fo fudden a refutation of a difcourfe of his, which had met with fo much applaufe at the Society but a few days before.

Mr. Hooke's paper was as follows :

" I have perufed the difcourfe of Mr. Newton about colours and refractions,
" and I was not a little pleafed with the nicenefs and curiofity of his obfervations.
" But, tho'. I wholly agree with him as to the truth of thofe he hath alledged,

[r] Letter-book, vol. v. p. 155.   [s] Regifter, vol. iv. p. 148.

" as

" as having, by many hundreds of trials, found them so ; yet as to his hypo-
" thesis of solving the phenomæna of colours thereby, I confess, I cannot see yet
" any undeniable argument to convince me of the certainty thereof. For all
" the experiments and observations I have hitherto made, nay, and even those
" very experiments, which he alledgeth, do seem to me to prove, that *white*
" is nothing but a pulse or motion, propagated through an homogeneous, uni-
" form, and transparent medium : and that colour is nothing but the disturb-
" ance of that light, by the communication of that pulse to other transparent me-
" diums, that is, by the refraction thereof :   that *whiteness* and *blackness* are no-
" thing but the plenty or scarcity of the undisturbed rays of light : and that
" the two colours (than the which there are not more uncompounded in nature)
" are nothing but the effects of a compounded pulse, or disturbed propagation
" of motion caused by refraction.

" But, how certain soever I think myself of my hypothesis (which I did not take
" up without first trying some hundreds of experiments) yet I should be very glad
" to meet with one *experimentum crucis* from Mr. NEWTON, that should divorce me
" from it. But it is not that, which he so calls, will do the turn ; for the same phæ-
" nomenon will be solved by my hypothesis, as well as by his, without any man-
" ner of difficulty or straining : nay, I will undertake to shew another hypothesis,
" differing from both his and mine, that shall do the same thing.

" That the ray of light is as it were split or rarified by refraction, is most cer-
" tain ; and that thereby a differing pulse is propagated, both on those sides, and
" in all the middle parts of the ray, is easy to be conceived : and also, that differ-
" ing pulses or compound motions should make differing impressions on the eye,
" brain, or sense, is also easy to be conceived : and that, whatever refracting me-
" dium does again reduce it to its primitive simple motion by destroying the ad-
" ventitious, does likewise restore it to its primitive whiteness and simplicity.

" But why there is a necessity, that all those motions, or whatever else it be
" that makes colours, should be originally in the simple rays of light, I do not
" yet understand the necessity of, no more than that all those sounds must be in
" the air of the bellows, which are afterwards heard to issue from the organ-
" pipes ; or in the string, which are afterwards, by different stoppings and strik-
" ings produced ; which string (by the way) is a pretty representation of the shape
" of a refracted ray to the eye ; and the manner of it may be somewhat imagined
" by the similitude thereof : for the ray is like the string, strained between the
" luminous object and the eye, and the stop or fingers is like the refracting sur-
" face, on the one side of which the string hath no motion, on the other a vi-
" brating one.   Now we may say indeed and imagine, that the rest or streight-
" ness of the string is caused by the cessation of motions, or coalition of all vi-
" brations ; and that all the vibrations are dormant in it : but yet it seems more
" natural to me to imagine it the other way.

" And

" And I am a little troubled, that this fuppofition fhould make Mr. NEWTON
" wholly lay afide the thoughts of improving telefcopes and microfcopes by re-
" fractions; fince it is not improbable, but that he, that hath made fo very good an
" improvement of telefcopes by his own trials upon reflection, would, if he had
" profecuted it, have done more by refraction.   And that reflection is not the
" only way of improving telefcopes, I may poffibly hereafter fhew fome proof
" of.   The truth is, the difficulty of removing that inconvenience of the fplit-
" ting of the ray, and confequently of the effect of colours, is very great; but
" yet not infuperable.   I have made many trials, both for telefcopes and mi-
" crofcopes by reflection, which I have mentioned in my Micrographia, but de-
" ferted it as to telefcopes, when I confidered, that the focus of the fpherical con-
" cave is not a point but a line, and that the rays are lefs true reflected to a
" point by a concave, than refracted by a convex; which made me feek that by
" refraction, which I found could not rationally be expected by reflection : nor
" indeed could I find any effect of it by one of fix foot radius, which, about fe-
" ven or eight years fince, Mr. REEVE made for Mr. GREGORY, with which I
" made feveral trials;   but it now appears it was for want of a good encheiria
" (from which caufe many good experiments have been loft) both which confi-
" derations difcouraged me from attempting further that way; efpecially fince I
" found the parabola much more difficult to defcribe, than the hyperbola or el-
" lipfis.   And I was wholly taken from the thoughts of it, by lighting on divers
" ways, which in theory anfwered all I could wifh for ; tho' having much more
" bufinefs, I could not attend to bring them into ufe for telefcopes; tho' for mi-
" crofcopes I have for a good while ufed it.   Thus much as to the preamble ; I
" fhall now confider the propofitions themfelves.

" Firft then, Mr. NEWTON alledgeth, that as the rays of light differ in re-
" frangibility, fo they differ in their difpofition to exibit this or that colour :
" with which I do in the main agree; that is, that the ray by refraction is, as it
" were, fplit or rarified, and that the one fide, namely that which is moft refracted,
" gives a *blue*, and that which is leaft a *red :* the intermediate are the dilutings
" and intermixtures of thofe two, which I thus explain.   The motion of light in
" an uniform medium, in which it is generated, is propagated by fimple and
" uniform pulfes or waves, which are at right angles with the line of direction ;
" but falling obliquely on the refracting medium, it receives another impreffion
" or motion, which difturbs the former motion, fomewhat like the vibration of a
" ftring : and that, which was before a line, now becomes a triangular fuperfi-
" cies, in which the pulfe is not propagated at right angles with its line of direc-
" tion, but afcew, as I have more at large explained in my Micrographia ; and
" that, which makes excurfions on the one fide, impreffes a compound motion on
" the bottom of the eye, of which we have the imagination of *red* ; and that,
" which makes excurfions on the other, caufes a fenfation, which we imagine a
" *blue* ; and fo of all the intermediate dilutings of thofe colours.   Now, that the
" intermediate are nothing but the dilutings of thofe two primary, I hope I have
" fufficiently proved by the experiment of the two wedge-like boxes, defcribed
" in my Micrographia.   Upon this account I cannot affent to the latter part of

2   " the

" the propofition, that colours are not qualifications of light, derived from refrac-
" tions, or refections of natural bodies, but original and connate properties, &c.

" The fecond propofition I wholly, allow, not exactly in the fenfe there meant,
" but with my manner of expreffing it; that is, that part of the fplit ray, which is
" moft bent, exhibits a blue, that which is leaft, a red, and the middle parts midling
" colours; and that thofe parts will always exhibit thofe colours till the com-
" pound motions are deftroyed, and reduced by other motions to one fimple and
" uniform pulfe as it was at firft.

" And this will eafily explain and give a reafon of the phænomena of the third
" propofition, to which I do readily affent in all cafes, except where the fplit ray
" is made by another refraction, to become intire and uniform, again to diverge
" and feparate, which explains his fourth propofition.

" But as to the fifth, that there are an indefinite variety of primary or original
" colours, amongft which are yellow, green, violet, purple, orange, &c. and
" an infinite number of intermediate gradations, I cannot affent thereunto, as
" fuppofing it wholly ufelefs to multiply entities without neceffity, fince I have
" elfewhere fhewn, that all the varieties of colours in the world may be made
" of two. I agree in the fixth, but cannot approve of his way of explicating
" the feventh. How the fplit ray being made doth produce a clear and uniform
" light, I have before fhewed; that is, by being united thereby from a fuperfi-
" cial motion, which is fufceptible of two, to a lineary, which is fufceptible of
" one only motion; and it is as eafy to conceive how all thofe motions again ap-
" pear after the rays are again fplit or rarified. He, that fhall but a little confider
" the undulations on the furface of a fmall river of water, in a gutter, or the
" like, will eafily fee the whole manner curioufly exemplified.

" The eighth propofition I cannot at all affent to, for the reafons above; and
" the reafons of the blue flame of brimftone, of the yellow of a candle, the
" green of copper, and the various colours of the ftars, and other luminous bo-
" dies, I take to proceed from quite another caufe, eafily explained by my for-
" mer hypothefis.

" I agree with the obfervations of the ninth, tenth, and eleventh, though not
" with his theory, as finding it not abfolutely neceffary, being as eafily and na-
" turally explained and folved by my hypothefis.

" The reafon of the phænomena of my experiment, which he alledgeth, is
" as eafily folvable by my hypothefis as by his; as are alfo thofe, which are men-
" tioned in the thirteenth. I do not therefore fee any abfolute neceffity to be-
" lieve his theory demonftrated, fince I can affure Mr. NEWTON, I cannot only
" folve all the phænomena of light and colours by the hypothefis I have for-
" merly printed, and now explicate them by, but by two or three other very dif-
" fering

" fering from it, and from this, which he hath defcribed in his ingenious dif-
" courfe.

" Nor would I be underftood to have faid all this againft his theory, as it is
" an hypothefis ; for I do moft readily agree with them in every part thereof, and
" efteem it very fubtil and ingenious, and capable of folving all the phænomena
" of colours : but I cannot think it to be the only hypothefis, nor fo certain as
" mathematical demonftrations.

" But grant his firft propofition, that light is a body, and that as many co-
" lours as degrees thereof as there may be, fo many forts of bodies there may
" be, all which compounded together would make white ; and grant further,
" that all luminous bodies are compounded of fuch fubftances condenfed, and
" that whilft they fhine, they do continually fend out an indefinite quantity there-
" of, every way in orbem, which in a moment of time doth difperfe itfelf to the
" utmoft and moft indefinite bounds of the univerfe ; granting thefe, I fay, I
" do fuppofe there will be no great difficulty to demonftrate all the reft of his
" curious theory : though yet, methinks, all the coloured bodies in the world
" compounded together fhould not make a white body, and I fhould be glad
" to fee an experiment of that kind done on the other fide. If my fuppofition
" be granted, that light is nothing but a fimple and uniform motion, or pulfe
" of a homogeneous and adopted (that is a tranfparent) medium, propagated from
" the luminous body in orbem, to all imaginable diftances in a moment of time,
" and that that motion is firft begun by fome other kind of motion in the lu-
" minous body ; fuch as by the diffolution of fulphureous bodies by the air, or
" by the working of the air, or the feveral component parts one upon another,
" in rotten wood, or putrifying fifh, or by an external ftroke, as in diamond, fu-
" gar, the fea-water, or two flints or cryftal rubbed together ; and that this
" motion is propagated through all bodies fufceptible thereof, but is blended or
" mixt with other adventitious motions, generated by the obliquity of the ftroke
" upon a refracting body ; and that, fo long as thofe motions remain diftinct in
" the fame part of the medium or propagated ray, fo long they produce the fame
" effect, but when blended by other motions, they produce other effects : and
" fuppofing, that by a direct contrary motion to the newly impreffed, that ad-
" ventitious one be deftroyed and reduced to the firft fimple motion ; I believe
" Mr. NEWTON will think it no difficult matter, by my hypothefis, to folve all the
" phænomena, not only of the prifm, tinged liquors, and folid bodies, but of
" the colours of plated bodies, which feem to have the greateft difficulty. It
" is true, I can, in my fuppofition, conceive the white or uniform motion of
" light to be compounded of the compound motions of all the other colours,
" as any one ftrait and uniform motion may be compounded of thoufands of
" compound motions, in the fame manner as DESCARTES explicates the reafon
" of the refraction ; but I fee no neceffity of it. If Mr. NEWTON hath any
" argument, that he fuppofes an abfolute demonftration of his theory, I fhould be

" very

" very glad to be convinced by it, the phænomena of light and colours being, in
" my opinion, as well worthy of contemplation, as any thing elfe in the world."

(5084)

Mr. Isaac Newtons *Answer to some Considerations upon his Doctrine of* Light *and* Colors ; *which Doctrine was printed in* Numb. 80. *of these Tracts.*

SIR, I have already told you, that at the perusal of the considerations, you sent me, on my Letter concerning *Refractions* and *Colors,* I found nothing, that, as I conceived, might not without difficulty be answer'd. And though I find the *Considerer* somewhat more concern'd for an *Hypothesis,* than I expected ; yet I doubt not, but we have one common design ; I mean, a sincere endeavour after knowledge, without valuing uncertain speculations for their subtleties, or despising certainties for their plainness : And on confidence of this it is, that I make this return to his discourse.*

* *Which* Discourse *was thought needless to be here printed at length, because in the body of this Answer are to be met with the chief particulars, wherein the* Answerer *was concern'd.*

1. *Of the Practique part of Optiques,*

The *first* thing that offers it self is less agreeable to me, and I begin with it because it is so. The considerer is pleased to reprehend me for laying aside the thoughts of improving Optiques by *Refractions.* If he had obliged me by a private Letter on this occasion, I would have acquainted him with my successes on the Tryals I have made of that kind, which I shall now say have been less than I sometimes expected, and perhaps than he at present hopes for. But since he is pleased to take it for granted, that I have let this subject pass without due examination, I shall refer him to my former Letter, * by which that conjecture will appear to be un-grounded. For, what I said

* *Printed in* Numb. 80. *of these Tracts.*

there, was in respect of Telescopes of the ordinary construction, signifying, that their improvement is not to be expected from the *well-figuring* of Glasses, as Opticians have imagin'd ; but I despaired not of their improvement by other constructions ; which made me cautious to insert nothing that might intimate the contrary. For, although successive refractions that are all made the same way, do necessarily more and more augment the errors of the first refraction ; yet it seem'd not impossible for *contrary* refractions so to correct each others inequalities, as to make their difference regular ; and, if that

could

(5085)

could be conveniently effected, there would be no further difficulty.   Now to this end I examin'd, what may be done not
only by *Glaſſes alone*, but more eſpecially by a Complication of
divers ſucceſſive *Mediums*, as by two or more Glaſſes or Cry-
ſtals with Water or ſome other fluid between them ; all which
together may perform the office of *one Glaſs*, eſpecially of the
Object-glaſs, on whoſe conſtruction the perfection of the inſtrument chiefly depends.   But what the reſults in Theory or
by Tryals have been, I may poſſibly find a more proper occaſion to declare.

     To the Aſſertion, that Rays are leſs true *reflected* to a point
by a *Concave*, than *refracted* by a Convex, I cannot aſſent ; nor
do I underſtand, that the *focus* of the latter is leſs a line than
that of the former.   The truth of the contrary you will rather
perceive by this following Table, computed for ſuch a *Reflecting Concave*, and *Refracting convex*, on ſuppoſition that they
have equal Apertures, and collect parallel rays at an equal diſtance from their *vertex* ; which diſtance being divided into
15000 parts, the Diameter of the Concave Sphere will be
60000 of thoſe parts, and of the Convex, 10000 ; ſuppoſing
the *Sines* of Incidence and Refraction to be, in round numbers, as 2 to 3.   And this Table ſhews, how much the exterior
rays, at ſeveral Apertures, fall ſhort of their principal *focus*.

The Diameter of the Aperture.	The parts of the Axis intercepted between the vertex and the rays.		The Error by	
	Reflected.	Refracted.	Reflexion.	Refraction.
2000	14991$\frac{2}{3}$	14865	8$\frac{1}{3}$	135 .
4000	14966	14449	33	551 .
6000	14924	13699	76	1301 .
8000	14865	12475	135	2525 .
10000	14787	9472	213	5528 .

     By this you may perceive, that the Errors of the *Refracting
convex* are ſo far from being *leſs*, that they are more than ſix-
teen times greater than the like errors of the *Reflecting Concave*,
eſpecially in great Apertures ; and that without reſpect to the
Heterogeneous conſtitution of light.   So that, however the
contrary ſuppoſition might make the Author of theſe Animad-
verſions reject *Reflections* as uſeleſs for the promoting of Op-

(5086)

tiques ; yet I muſt for this as well as other conſideratio ns pre fer them in the Theory before *Refractions*.

Whether the *Parabola* be more difficult to deſcribe than the *Hyperbola* or *Ellipſis*, may be a *Quære*: But I ſee no abſolute neceſſity of endeavouring after any of their deſcriptions. For, if Metals can be ground truly Spherical, they will bear as great Apertures, as I believe men will be well able to communicate an *exact* poliſh to. And for Dioptrique Teleſcopes, I told you, that the difficulty conſiſted not in the Figure of the glaſs, but in the Difformity of Refractions : Which if it did not, I could tell you a better and more eaſie remedy than the uſe of the *Conic Sections*.

2. Of the Theorique part. Thus much concerning the Praſtique part of Optiques. I ſhall now take a view of the Conſiderations on my *Theories*. And thoſe conſiſt in aſcribing an *Hypotheſis* to me, which is not mine; in Aſſerting an *Hypotheſis*, which, as to the principal parts, is not againſt me ; in Granting the greateſt part of my diſcourſe if explicated by that *Hypotheſis* ; and in Denying ſome things, the truth of which would have appear'd by an experimental examination.

3. Of an Hypotheſis miſtaken to be mine. Of theſe Particulars I. ſhall diſcourſe in order. And firſt of the *Hypotheſis*, which is aſcribed to me in theſe words : *But grant his firſt ſuppoſition, that light is a body, and that as many colours or degrees as there may be, ſo many bodies there may be ; all which componnded together would make White*, &c. This, it ſeems, is taken for my *Hypotheſis*. 'Tis true, that from my Theory I argue the *Corporeity* of Light ; but I do it without any abſolute poſitiveneſs, as the word *perhaps* intimates ; and make it at moſt but a very plauſible *conſequence* of the Doctrine, and not a fundamental *Suppoſition*, nor ſo much as any part of it ; which was wholly comprehended in the precedent Propoſitions. And I ſomewhat wonder, how the *Objector* could imagine, that, when I had aſſerted the Theory with the greateſt rigour, I ſhould be ſo forgetful as afterwards to aſſert the fundamental ſuppoſition it ſelf with no more than a *perhaps*. Had I intended any ſuch *Hypotheſis*, I ſhould ſomewhere have explain'd it. But I knew, that the *Properties*, which I declar'd of *Light*, were in

(5087)

fome meafure capable of being explicated not only by that, but by many other Mechanical *Hypothefes.* And therefore I chofe to decline them all, and to fpeak of *Light* in *general* terms, confidering it abftra&ly, as fomething or other propa. gated every way in ftreight lines from luminous bodies, with. out determining, what that Thing is; whether a confufed Mixture of difform qualities, or Modes of bodies, or of Bo= bies themfelves, or of any Virtues, Powers, or Beings what. foever. And for the fame reafon I chofe to fpeak of *Colours* according to the information of our Senfes, as if they were Qualities of Light *without* us. Whereas by that *Hypothefis* I muft have confidered them rather as *Modes* of Senfation, ex. cited in the mind by various motions, figures, or fizes of the corpufcles of Light, making various Mechanical impreffions on the Organ of Senfe; as I expreffed it in that place, where I fpake of the Corporeity of Light.

But fuppofing I had propounded that *Hypothefis,* I under-ftand not, why the Obje&or fhould fo much endeavour to op-pofe it. For certainly it has a much greater affinity with his own *Hypothefis,* than he feems to be aware of; the Vibrations of the *Æther* being as ufeful and neceffary in *this,* as in *his.*For, affuming the Rays of Light to be fmall bodies, emitted every way from Shining fubftances, thofe, when they impinge on any Refra&ing or Refle&ing fuperficies, muft as neceffarily excite Vibrations in the *æther,* as Stones do in water when thrown into it. And fuppofing thefe Vibrations to be of fe= veral depths or thickneffes, accordingly as they are excited by the faid corpufcular rays of various fizes and velocities;of what ufe they will be for explicating the manner of Refle&ion and Refraction, the production of Heat by the Sun-beams, the E= miffion of Light from burning putrifying, or other fubftances, whofe parts are vehemently agitated, the *Phænomena* of thin tranfparent Plates and Bubles, and of all Natural bodies, the Manner of Vifion, and the Difference of Colors, as alfo their Harmony and Difcord; I fhall leave to their confideration, who may think it worth their endeavor to apply this *Hypothefis* to the folution of *phænomena.*

(5088)

In the second place, I told you,that the Objectors *Hypothefis,* as to the fundamental part of it, is not againft me. That fundamental Suppofition is ; *That the parts of bodies, when briskly agitated, do ex- cite Vibrations in the Æther, which are* propagated every way from thofe bodies in ftreight lines, and caufe a Senfation of Light by beating and dafhing againft the bottom of the Eye, fomething after the manner that Vibrations in the Air caufe a Senfation of Sound by beating againft the Organs of Hearing. Now, the moft free and natural Application of this *Hypothefis* to the Solution of *phænomena* I take to be this : *That* the agitated parts of bodies, according to their feveral fizes, figures, and mo- tions, do excite Vibrations in the *æther* of various depths or bigneffes, which being promifcuoufly propagated through that *Medium* to our Eyes, effect in us a Senfation of Light of a *White* colour ; but if by any means thofe of unequal bigneffes be fe- parated from one another, the largeft beget a Senfation of a *Red* colour, the leaft or fhorteft, of a deep *Violet,* and the in- termediat ones, of intermediat colors ; much after the man- ner that bodies, according to their feveral fizes, fhapes, and motions, excite vibrations in the Air of various bigneffes, which, according to thofe bigneffes, make feveral Tones in Sound : *That* the largeft Vibrations are beft able to over- come the refiftance of a Refracting fuperficies, and fo break through it with leaft Refraction ; whence the Vibrations of feveral bigneffes, that is, the Rays of feveral Colors, which are blended together in Light, muft be parted from one ano- ther by Refraction, and fo caufe the *Phænomena* of *Prifmes* and other refracting fubftances : And *that* it depends on the thick- nefs of a thin tranfparent Plate or Buble, whether a Vibration fhall be *reflected* at its further fuperficies,or *tranfmitted* ; fo that, according to the number of vibrations, interceding the two fuperficies,they may be reflected or tranfmitted for many fuc- ceffive thickneffes. And fince the Vibrations which make *Blew* and *Violet,* are fuppofed fhorter than thofe which make *Red* and *Yellow,* they muft be reflected at a lefs thicknefs of the Plate : Which is fufficient to explicate all the ordinary *phæno- mena* of thofe Plates or Bubles, and alfo of all natural bodies, whofe

4. *Of the Objector's* Hypothefis, *and that the moft free and genuine Con- ftitution of that and all other Mecha- nical Hypothefes is conformable to my* Doctrine.

(5089)

whofe parts are like fo many fragments of fuch Plates.

Thefe feem to be the moft plain, genuine and neceffary conditions of this *Hypothefi*: And they agree fo juftly with my Theory, that if the *Animadverfor* think fit to apply them, he need not, on that account, apprehend a divorce from it. But yet how he will defend it from other difficulties, I know not. For, to me, the Fundamental Suppofition it felf feems impoffible ; namely, That the *Waves* or Vibrations of any Fluid,can, like the Rays of Light, be propagated in *Streight* lines,without a continual and very extravagant fpreading and bending every way into the quiefcent Medium, where they are terminated by it. I miftake, if there be not both Experiment and De-monftration to the contrary. And as to the other two or three *Hypothefes*, which he mentions, I had rather believe them fub-ject to the like difficulties,than fufpect the *Animadverfor* fhould felect the worft for his own.

What I have faid of this, may be eafily applied to all other *Mechanical Hypothefes*, in which Light is fuppofed to be caufed by any Preffion or Motion whatfoever, excited in the *æther* by the agitated parts of Luminous bodies.For,it feems impoffible, that any of thofe Motions or Preffions can be propagated in *Streight* lines without the like fpreading every way into the fhadow'd Medium, on which they border. But yet, if any man can think it poffible, he muft at leaft allow,that thofe Mo-tions or Endeavors to motion, caufed in the *æther* by the feve-ral parts of any Lucid body that differ in fize, figure, and agi-tation, muft neceffarily be unequal : Which is enough to de-nominate Light an Aggregat of *difform* rays, according to any of thofe Hypothefes. And if thofe Original inequalities may fuffice to difference the Rays in Colour and Refrangibility, I fee no reafon, why they, that adhere to any of thofe *hypothefes*, fhould feek for other Caufes of thefe Effects, unlefs (to ufe the *Objectors* argument) they will multiply entities without ne-ceffity.

The *third* thing to be confidered is, the Condition of the *Animadverfor's* Conceffions, which is, that I would explicate my *Theo-ries* by his *Hypothefis*:And if I could comply with him in that point,

5. *Of the* Animadverfor's *Conceffi-ons, and their limitation to his Hypo-thefis.*

there

(5090)

there would be little or no difference between Us. For he grants, that without any respect to a different Incidence of rays there are different Refractions; but he would have it explicated, not by the different Refrangibility of several Rays, but by the Splitting and Rarefying of æthereal pulses. He grants my *third, fourth* and *sixth* Propositions; the sense of which is, That Un-compounded Colors are unchangeable, and that Compounded ones are changeable only by resolving them into the colors, of which they are compounded ; and that all the Changes, which can be wrought in Colours, are effected only by variously mixing or parting them : But he grants them on condition that I will explicate Colors by the two sides of a split pulse, and so make but two *species* of them, accounting all other Colors in the world to be but various degrees and dilutings of those two. And he further grants, that *Whiteneſſe* is produced by the Convention of all Colors; but then I muſt allow it to be not only by Mixture of those Colors, but by a farther Uniting of the parts of the Ray ſuppoſed to be formerly split.

If I would proceed to examine theſe his Explications, I think it would be no difficult matter to ſhew, that they are not only *inſufficient*, but in ſome reſpects to me (at leaſt) *un-intelligible*. For, though it be eaſie to conceive, how *Motion* may be dilated and ſpread, or how parallel motions may become diverging; yet I underſtand not, by what artifice any *Linear* motion can by a refracting ſuperficies be *infinitely* dilated and rarefied, ſo as to become *Superficial*: Or, if that be ſuppoſed, yet I underſtand as little, why it ſhould be ſplit at ſo ſmall an angle only, and not rather ſpread and diſperſed through the whole angle of Refraction. And further, though I can eaſily imagine, how Unlike motions may croſs one another ; yet I cannot well conceive, how they ſhould coaleſce into one *uniform* motion, and then part again, and recover their former Unlikeneſs ; notwithſtanding that I conjecture the ways, by which the *Animadverſor* may endeavour to explain it. So that the Direct, uniform and undiſturbed Pulſes ſhould be ſplit and diſturbed by Refraction ; and yet the Oblique and diſturbed Pulſes perſiſt without ſplitting or further diſturbance by following Refractions, is (to me) as unintelligible. And there is

as

(5089)

as great a difficulty in the Number of Colours; as you will see hereafter.

But whatever be the advantages or difadvantages of this *Hypothefis*, I hope I may be excufed from taking it up, fince I do not think it 6.*That it is not neceffary, to limit or explain my Doctrine by any* Hypothefis. needful to explicate my Doctrine by any *Hypothefis* at all. For if *Light* be confider'd abftractedly without refpect to any *Hypothefis*, I can *as* eafily conceive, that the feveral parts of a fhining body may emit rays of differing colours and other qualities, of all which Light is conftituted, *as* that the feveral parts of a falfe or uneven ftring, or of uneavenly agitated water in a Brook or Cataract, or the feveral Pipes of an Organ infpired all at once, or all the variety of Sounding bodies in the world together, fhould produce founds of feveral Tones, and propagate them through the Air confufedly intermixt.   And, if there were any natural bodies that could *reflect* founds of one tone, and ftifle or *tranfmit* thofe of another; then, as the *Echo* of a confufed Aggregat of all Tones would be that particular Tone, which the Echoing body is difpofed to reflect; fo, fince (even by the *Animadverfor's* conceffions) there are bodies apt to *reflect* rays of one colour, and ftifle or *tranfmit* thofe of another; I can as eafily conceive, that thofe bodies, when illuminated by a mixture of all colours, muft appear of that colour only which they reflect.

But when the *Objector* would infinuate a difficulty in thefe things, by alluding to Sounds in the ftring of a Mufical inftrument before percuffion, or in the Air of an Organ Bellowes before its arrival at the Pipes; I muft confefs, I underftand it as little, as if one had fpoken of Light in a piece of Wood before it be fet on fire, or in the oyl of a Lamp before it afcend up the match to feed the flame.

You fee therefore, how much it is befides the bufinefs in hand, to difpute about *Hypothefes*. For 7. *The difficulties of the* Animadverfors *difcourfe abftracted from* Hypothefes, *and confider'd more generally.* which reafon I fhall now in the laft place, proceed to abftract the difficulties in the *Animadverfor's* difcourfe, and, without having regard to any *Hypothefis*, confider them in general terms. And they may be reduced to thefe 3 *Quæres:* L l l l l   1. Whe-

(5092)

1. Whether the unequal Refractions, made without refpect to any inequality of incidence, be caufed by the different Refrangibility of feveral Rays; or by the fplitting, breaking or diffipating the fame Ray into diverging parts?

2. Whether there be more than two forts of Colours?

3. Whether Whitenefs be a mixture of all Colours?

3. That the Ray is not fplit, or any otherwife dilated.

The *Firft* of thefe *Quæres* you may find already determin'd by an Experiment in my former Letter; the defign of which was to fhew, That the length of the colour'd Image proceeded not from any unevennefs in the Glafs, or any other *contingent* Irregularity in the Refractions. Amongft other Irregularities I know not, what is more obvious to fufpect, than a fortuitous dilating and fpreading of Light after fome fuch manner, as *Des-Cartes* hath defcribed in his Æthereal Refractions for explicating the *Tayle* of a *Comet*; or as the *Animadverfor* now fuppofes to be effected by the Splitting and Rarifying of his Æthereal fpulfes. And to prevent the fufpicion of any fuch Irregularities, I told you, that I refracted the Light contrary ways with two Prifmes fucceffively, to deftroy thereby the *Regular* effects of the *firft* Prifme by the *fecond*, and to difcover the *Irregular* effects by augmenting them with iterated refractions. Now, amongft other Irregularities, if the *firft* Prifme had fpread and diffipated every ray into an indefinit number of diverging parts, the *fecond* fhould in like manner have fpread and diffipated every one of thofe parts into a further indefinite number, whereby the Image would have been ftill more dilated, contrary to the event. And this ought to have hapned, becaufe thofe Linear diverging parts depend not on one another for the manner of their Refraction, but are every one of them as truly and compleatly Rays as the whole was before its Incidence; as may appear by intercepting them feverally.

The reafonablenefs of this proceeding will perhaps better appear by acquainting you with this further circumftance. I fometimes placed the *fecond* Prifme in a pofition Tranfverfe to the *firft*, on defign to try, if it would make the long Image become four-fquare by refractions croffing thofe that had drawn the round Image into a long one. For, if amongft other Irregularities the Refraction of the *firft* Prifme, did by Splitting dilate

(5093)

dilate a Linear ray into a Superficial, the Crofs refractions of that *second* Prifme ought by further fplitting to dilate and draw that Superficial ray into a Pyramidal folid. But, upon tryal, I found it otherwife ; the Image being as regularly Ob· long as before, and inclin'd to both the Prifmes at an angle of 45. degrees.

I tryed alfo all other Pofitions of the fecond Prifme, by turning the Ends about its middle part; and in no cafe could ob ferve any fuch Irregularity. The Image was ever alike incli ned to both Prifmes, its Breadth anfwering to the Suns Dia meter, and its length being greater or lefs accordingly as the Refractions more or lefs agreed, or contradicted one ano ther.

And by thefe Obfervations, fince the Breadth of the Image was not augmented by the Crofs refraction of the *fecond*Prifme, that refraction muft have been perform'd *without* any fplitting or dilating of the ray ; and therefore at leaft the Light inci dent on that Prifme muft be granted an Aggregat of Rays *un equally refrangible* in my fenfe. And fince the Image was e qually inclin'd to both *Prifmes*, and confequently the Refra ctions alike in both, it argues, that they were perform'd accor ding to fome *Conftant Law* without any irregularity.

To determine the *fecond* Quæ re, the *Animadverfor* referrs to an Experiment made with two *9. That there are more than two Original Colors.* *Wedge-like boxes,* recited in the *Micrography* of the Ingenious Mr. Hook Obferv. 10. pag. 73. the defign of which was to produce *all* Colours out of a mixture of *two*. But there is, I conceive, a double defect in this inftance. For, it appears not, that by this Experiment all colours can be produced out of two ; and, if they could, yet the Inference would not fol low.

That *all* Colours cannot by that Experiment be produced out of two, will appear by confidering, that the Tincture of *Aloes*, which afforded one of thofe Colours, was not all over of one uniform colour, but appear'd *yellow* near the edge of the Box, and *red* at other places where it was thicker: affording all variety of colours from a *pale yellow* to a *deep red* or Scarlet, according to the various thicknefs of the liquor. And fo the

(5c88)

folution of *Copper*, which afforded the other colour, was of various B*lews* and *Indigo's*. So that inftead of *two* colours, here is a great variety made ufe of for the produ&ion of all o-thers. Thus, *for inftance*, to produce all forts of *Greens*, the fe-veral degrees of *Yellow* and *pale Blew* muft be mixed ; but to compound *Purples*, the *Scarlet* and *deep Blew* are to be the In-gredients.

Now, if the *Animadverfor* contend, that all the *Reds* and *Yel-lows* of the one Liquor, or *Blews* and *Indigo's* of the other, are only various degrees and dilutings of the fame Colour, and not divers colours, that is a Begging of the Queftion : And I fhould as foon grant, that the two *Thirds* or *Sixths* in Mufick are but feveral degrees of the fame found, and not divers founds. Certainly it is much better to believe our Senfes, in-forming us, that *Red* and *yellow* are divers colours, and to make it a Philofophical *Quære*, Why the fame Liquor doth, accor-ding to its various thicknefs, appear of thofe divers colours, than to fuppofe them to be the fame colour becaufe exhibited by the fame liquor ? For, if that were a fufficient reafon, then *Blew* and *Yellow* muft alfo be the fame colour, fince they are both exhibited by the fame Tin&ure of *Nephritick Wood*. But that they are *divers* colours, you will more fully underftand by the reafon, which, in my Judgment, is this : The Tin&ure of *Aloes* is qualified to tranfmit *moft eafily* the rays indued with *red*, *moft difficultly* the rays indued with *violet*, and with *intermedi-at degrees of facility* the rays indued with *intermediat* colours. So that where the liquor is very thin, it may fuffice to intercept moft of the *violet*, and yet tranfmit moft of the other colours ; all which together muft compound a middle Colour, that is, a *faint yellow*. And where it is fo much thicker as alfo to inter-cept moft of the *Blew* and *Green*, the remaining *Green*, *Yellow*, and *Red*, it muft compound an *Orenge*. And where the thick-nefs is fo great, that fcarce any rays can pafs through it be-fides thofe indued with *Red*, muft appear of that colour, and that fo much the deeper and obfcurer, by how the liquor is thicker. And the fame may be underftood of the various de-grees of *Blew*, exhibited by the Solution of *Copper*, by reafon of its difpofition to intercept *Red* moft eafily, and tranfmit a *deep Blew* or *Indigo* Colour moft freely.

But

(5089)

But, suppofing that *all* Colours might, according to this ex`periment, be produced out of *two* by mixture ; yet it follow^s not, that thofe two are the only *Original* colours, and that fo^r a double reafon. *Firft*, becaufe thofe two are not themfelve^s Original colours, but compounded of others ; there being no liquor nor any other body in nature, whofe colour in Day-light is wholly un-compounded. And *then*, becaufe, though thofe two were Original, and all others might be compounded of them, yet it follows not, that they cannot be otherwife produced. For I faid, that they had a double Origin, the fame Colours to fenfe being in fome cafes compounded and in others un compounded ; and fufficiently declar'd in my *third* and *fourth* Propofitions, and in the Conclufion, by what Properties the one might be known and diftinguifh't from the other. But, becaufe I fufpect by fome Circumftances, that the *Diftinction* might not be rightly apprehended, I fhall once more declare it, and further explain it by Examples.

That Colour is *Primary* or *Original*, which cannot by any Art be changed, and whofe Rays are not *alike* refrangible : And that *Compounded*, which is changeable into other colours, and whofe Rays are *not alike* refrangible. *For inftance*, to know, whether the colour of any *Green* object be compounded or not, view it through a Prifme, and if it appear *confufed*, and the edges tinged with *Blew*, *Yellow*, or any variety of other colours, then is that *Green* compounded of fuch colours as at its edges emerge out of it : But if it appear *diftinct*, and well defin'd, and entirely Green to the very edges, without any other colours emerging, it is of an Original and un-compounded Green. In like manner, if a refracted beam of light, being caft on a white wall, exhibit a *Green* colour, to know whether that be compounded, refract the beam with an interpofed Prifme ; and if you find any Difformity in the refractions, and the *Green* be transform'd into *Blew*, *Yellow*, or any variety of other colours, you may conclude, that it was compounded of thofe which emerge : But if the Refractions be uniform, and the *Green* perfift without any change of colour, then is it Original and un compounded. And the reafon why I call it fo, is, becaufe a *Green* indued with fuch properties cannot be produced by any mixing of other colours.

Now

(5097)

Now, if two *Green* Objects may to the naked eye appear of the same colour, and yet one of them through a prisme seem *confused* and variegated with other colours at the edges, and the other *distinct* and entirely Green ; or, if there may be two Beams of Light, which falling on a white wall do to the naked eye exhibit the same *Green* colour, and yet one of them, when transmitted through a Prisme, be uniformly and *regularly* refracted, and retain its colour unchanged, and the other be *irregularly* refracted and to divaricate into a multitude of other colours ; I suppose, these two *greens* will in both cases be granted of a different Origin and constitution. And if by mixing colours, a *green* cannot be compounded with the properties of the *Unchangeable* Green, I think, I may call *that* an *Un-compounded* colour, especially since its rays are alike refrangible, and uniform in all respects.

The same rule is to be observ'd in examining, whether *Red*, *Orenge*, *Yellow*, *Blew*, or any other colour be compounded or not. And, by the way, since all *White* objects through the Prisme appear confus'd and terminated with colours, *Whiteness* must, according to this distinction, be ever compounded, and that the most of all colours, because it is the most confus'd and changed by Refractions.

From hence I may take occasion to communicate a way for the improvement of *Microscopes* by Refraction. The way is, by illuminating the Object in a darkned room with Light of any convenient colour not too much compounded: for by that means the Microscope will with distinctness bear a deeper Charge and larger Aperture, especially if its construction be such, as I may hereafter describe ; for, the advantage in Ordinary Microscopes will not be so sensible.

10. *That Whiteness is a mixture of all Colours.*

There remains now the *third* Quære to be consider'd, which is, Whether *Whiteness* be an Uniform Colour, or a dissimilar Mixture of all colours ? The Experiment which I brought to decide it, the *Animadversor* thinks may be otherwise explain'd, and so concludes nothing. But he might easily have satisfied himself by trying, what would be the result of a Mixture of all colours. And that very Experiment might have satisfied him, if he had pleased to examine it by the

(5096)

the various circumstances. One circumstance I there declared, of which I see no notice taken; and it is, That if any colour at the *Lens* be intercepted, the *Whitenes* will be changed
into the other colours : If all the colours but *red* be intercepted, that Red alone in the concourse or crossing of the Rays
will not constitute Whiteness, but continues as much Red as
before; and so of the other colours. So that the business is
not only to shew, how rays, which before the concourse exhibit colours, do in the concourse exhibit *White* ; but to shew,
How in the same place, where the several sorts of rays apart
exhibit several colours, a Confusion of all together make White.
For instance, if red alone be first transmitted to the paper at
the place of concourse, and then the other colours be let fall
on that Red, the *Question* will be, Whether they convert it in-
t ﹥ White, by mixing with it only, as Blew falling on Yellow |false
light is suppos'd to compound Green ; or, Whether there be
some further change wrought in the colours by their mutual
acting on one another, untill, like contrary *Peripatetic* qualities, they become assimilated. And he that shall explicate this
last Case *mechanically*, must conquer a double impossibility.
He must *first* shew, that many unlike motions in a Fluid can by
clashing so act on one another, and change each other, as to
become one Uniform motion ; and *then*, that an Uniform motion can of it self, without any new unequal impressions, de-
part into a great variety of motions regularly un-equal. And
after this he must further tell me, Why all Objects appear
not of the same colour, that is, why their colours in the Air,
where the rays that convey them every way are confusedly
mixt, do not assimilate one another and become Uniform before they arrive at the Spectators eye ?
     But if there be yet any doubting,'tis better to put the Event
on further Circumstances of the *Experiment*, than to acquiesce
in the possibility of any *Hypothetical* Explication. As, for instance, by trying, What will be the apparition of these colours
in a very quick Consecution of one another. And this may be
easily perform'd by the rapid gyration of a Wheel with {many
Spoaks or coggs in its perimeter, whose Interstices and thicknesses may be equal and of such a largeness, that, if the Wheel
be interposed between the Prisme and the white concourse

of

(5084)

of the colours, one half of the Colours may be intercepted by a fpoake or cogg, and the other half pafs through an inter-ftice.   The Wheel being in this pofture, you may firft turn it flowly about, to fee all the colours fall fucceffively on the fame place of the paper, held at their aforefaid concourfe ; and if you then accelerate its gyration, until the Confecution of thofe colours be fo quick, that you cannot diftinguifh them feverally, the refulting colour will be a Whitenefs per-fectly like that, which an an-refracted beam of Light exhibits, when in like manner fucceffively interrupted by the fpoaks or coggs of that circulating Wheel.   And that this *Whitenefs* is produced by a fucceffive Intermixture of the Colours, with-out their being affimilated , or reduc'd to any Unifor-mity, is certainly beyond all doubt, unlefs things that exift not at the fame time may notwithftanding act on one a-nother.

There are yet other Circumftances, by which the Truth might have been decided; as by viewing the White concourfe of the Colours through another Prifme plac'd clofe to the eye, by whofe Refraction that whitenefs may appear again tranf-form'd into Colours : And then, to examine their Origin, if an Affiftant intercept any of the colours at the *Lens* before their arrival at the Whitenefs, the fame colours will vanifh from a-mongft thofe, into which that Whitenefs is converted by the *fecond* Prifme.   Now, if the rays which difappear be the fame with thofe that are intercepted, then it muft be acknowled-ged, that the *fecond* Prifme makes no new colours in any rays, which were not in them *before* their concourfe at the paper. Which is a plain indication, that the rays of feveral colours re-main diftinct from one another in the Whitenefs, and that from their *previous* difpofitions are deriv'd the Colours of the *fecond* Prifme.   And, by the way, what is faid of their Colors may be applied to their Refrangibility.

The aforefaid *Wheel* may be alfo here made ufe of ; and, if its gyration be neither too quick nor two flow, the fuc-cefsion of the colours may be difcern'd through the Prifme, whilft to the naked eye of a Byftander they exhibit white-nefs.

There is fomething ftill remaining to be faid of this Experi-

ment

(5099)

ment. But this, I conceive, is enough to enforce it, and so to decide the controversy. How-ever, I shall now proceed to shew some
other ways of producing *Whiteness by mixtures*, since I perswade my
self, that this Assertion above the rest appears Paradoxical, and is
with most difficulty admitted. And because the *Animadversor* desires
an instance of it in Bodies of divers colours, I shall begin with that.
But in order thereto it must be consider'd, that such colour'd Bodies
reflect but some part of the Light incident on them ; as is evident
by the 13 *Proposition* : And therefore the Light reflected from an Aggregat of them will be much weakned by the loss of many rays.
Whence a perfect and *intense* Whiteness is not to be expected, but
rather a Colour between those of Light and Shadow, or such a
Gray or Dirty colour as may be made by mixing White and Black
together.

And that such a Colour will result, may be collected from the
colour of *Dust* found in every corner of an house, which hath been
observ'd to consist of many colour'd particles. There may be also
produced the like Dirty colour by mixing several *Painters colours*
together. And the same may be effected by Painting a *Top* (such
as Boys play with) of divers colours. For, when it is made
to circulate by whipping it, it will appear of such a dirty colour.

Now, the Compounding of these colours is proper to my purpose, because they differ not from Whiteness in the *Species* of colour, but only in *degree* of Luminousness : which (did not the *Animadversor* concede it) I might thus evince. A beam of the Suns
Light being transmitted into a darkned room, if you illuminate a
sheet of White Paper by that Light, reflected from a body of a-
ny colour, the paper will always appear of the colour of that body, by whose reflected light it is illuminated. If it be a red body, the paper will be red; if a green body, it will be green; and so
of the other colours. The reason is, that the fibers or threds, of
which the paper consists, are all transparent and specular ; and such
substances are known to reflect colours without changing them. To
know therefore, to what *Species* of colour a *Grey* belongs, place a-
ny Gray body(suppose a Mixture of *Painters colours*,)in the said Light,
and the paper, being illuminated by its reflexion, shall appear White.
And the same thing will happen, if it be illuminated by reflexion
from a *black* substance.

These therefore are all of one *Species* ; but yet they seem distin-
guisht not only by *degrees* of Luminousness, but also by some other
Inequalities, whereby they become more harsh or pleasant. And the
distinction seems to be, that *Greys* and perhaps *Blacks* are made by an
uneven defect of Light, consisting as it were of many little veins
or streams, which differ either in Luminousness or in the Unequal di-

M m m m m   stribution

(5100)

ftribution of diverfly colour'd rays ; fuch as ought to be caus'd by Reflexion from a Mixture of white and black, or of diverfly co. lour'd corpufcles. But when fuch imperfectly mixt Light is by a *fecond* Reflexion from the paper more evenly and uniformly blended, it becomes more pleafant, and exhibits a *faint* or fhadow'd Whitenefs. And that fuch little irregularities as thefe may caufe thefe differences, is not improbable, if we confider, how much variety may be caufed in *Sounds* of the fame tone by irregular and uneven jarrings. And befides, thefe differences are fo little, that I have fometimes doubted, whether they be any at all, when I have confider'd that a Black and White Body being plac'd together, the one in a ftrong light, and the other in a very faint light, fo proportion'd that they might appear equally luminous ; it has been difficult to diftinguifh them, when view'd at diftance, unlefs when the Black feem'd more blewifh ; and the White body in a light ftill fainter, hath, in comparifon of the Black body, it felf appear'd Black.

This leads me to another way of *Compounding Whitenefs* ; which is, That, if four or five Bodies of the more eminent colours, or a Paper painted all over, in feveral parts of it, with thofe feveral colours in a due proportion, be placed in the faid Beam of Light ; the Light, reflected from thofe Colours to another White paper, held at a convenient diftance, fhall make that paper appear White. If it be held too near the Colours, its parts will feem of thofe colours that are neareft them ; but by removing it further, that all its parts may be equally illuminated by all the colours, they will be more and more diluted, until they become perfectly White. And you may further obferve, that if any of the colours be intercepted, the Paper will no longer appear White, but of the other colours which are not intercepted. Now, that this *Whitenefs* is a Mixture of the feverally colour'd rays, falling confufedly on the paper, I fee no reafon to doubt of ; becaufe, if the Light became Uniform and Similar before it fell confufedly on the paper, it muft much more be Uniform, when at a greater diftance it falls on the Spectators eye, and fo the rays, which come from feveral colours, would in no qualities differ from one another, but all of them exhibit the fame colour to the Spectator, contrary to what he fees.

Not much unlike this Inftance it is, That, if a polifht piece of Metal be fo placed, that the colours appear in it as in a Looking-glafs, and then the Metal be made rough, that by a confus'd reflexion thofe apparent colours may be blended together, they fhall difappear, and by their mixture caufe the Metall to look White.   But

(5101)

But further to enforce this *Experiment* ; if, inftead of the Paper, any White *Froth*, confifting of fmall bubles, be illuminated by reflexion from the aforefaid Colours, it fhall to the naked eye feem White, and yet through a good Microfcope the feveral Colours will appear diftinct on the bubles, as if feen by reflexion from fo many fpherical furfaces. With my naked eye, being very near, I have alfo difcern'd the feveral colours on each buble ; and yet at a greater diftance, where I could not diftinguifh them apart, the Froth hath appear'd entirely White. And at the fame diftance, when I look'd intently, I have feen the colours diftinctly on each buble ; and yet, by ftraining my eyes as if I would look at fomething far off beyond them, thereby to render the Vifion confus'd, the Froth has appear'd without any other colour than Whitenefs. And what is here faid of Froths, may eafily be underftood of the Paper or Metal in the foregoing Experiments. For, their parts are fpecular bodies, like thefe Bubles : And.perhaps with an excellent Microfcope the Colours may be alfo feen intermixedly reflected from them.

In proportioning the feverally Colour'd bodies to produce thefe effects, there may be fome nicenefs ; and it will be more convenient, to make ufe of the colours of the Prifme, caft on a Wall, by whofe reflexion the Paper, Metal, Froth, and other White fubftances may be illuminated. And I ufually made my Tryals this way, becaufe I could better exclude any fcattering Light from mixing with the colours to dilate them.

To this way of Compounding Whitenefs may be referr'd that other, by Mixing light after it hath been trajected through tranfparently colour'd fubftances. *For inftance,* if no Light be admitted into a room but only through Colour'd glafs, whofe feveral parts are of feveral colours in a pretty equal proportion; all White things in the room fhall appear White, if they be not held too near the Glafs. And yet this light, with which they are illuminated, cannot poffibly be uniform, becaufe, if the Rays, which at their entrance are of divers colours, do in their progrefs through the room fuffer any alteration to be reduced to an Uniformity; the Glafs would not in the remoteft parts of the room appear of the very fame colour, which it doth when the Spectators eye is very near it : Nor would the rays, when tranfmitted into another dark room through a little hole in an oppofite door or partition-wall, project on a Paper the *Species* or reprefentation of the glafs in its proper colours.

And, by the by, this feems a very fit and cogent Inftance of fome other parts of my *Theory*, and particularly of the 13 *Propofition*. For, in this room all natural Bodies whatever appear in their proper colours. And all the *Phænomena* of colours in nature, made either by Refraction or without it, are here the fame as in the Open Air. Now, the Light in this room being fuch a Diffimilar mixture, as

M m m m m 2   I

(5102)

I have defcrib'd in my *Theory*, the Caufes of all thefe *Phænomena* muſt be the fame that I have there aſſign'd. And I fee no reafon to fufpeԁ, that the fame *Phænomena* ſhould have other caufes in the O-pen Air.

The fuccefs of this Experiment may be eafily conjeԁur'd by the appearances of things in a Church or Chappel, whofe windores are of colour'd glafs ; or in the Open Aɪr, when it is illuſtrated with Clouds of various colours.

There are yet other ways, by which I have produced *Whitenefs* ; as *by* caſting feveral Colours from two or more Prifmes upon the fame place ; *by* Refraԁing a Bɩ a n of Lɪght with two or three Prifmes fuc-ceſſively, to make the diverging colours converge again ; *by* Refle-ԁing one colour to another ; and *by* looking through a Prifme on an Objeԁ of many colours ; and, (which is equivalent to the above men-tion'd way of mixing colours by concave *Wedges* fill'd with colour'd liquors,) I have obferv'd the ſhadows of a painted Glafs-window to become White, where thofe of many colours have at a great diſtance interfered. But yet, for further fatisfaԁion, the *Animadverfor* may try, if he pleafe, the effeԁs of four or five of fuch *Wedges* filled with liquors of as many feveral colours.

Befides all thefe, the Colours of *Water-bubbles* and other thin pellu-cid fubſtances afford feveral inſtances of Whitenefs produced by their mixture ; with *one* of which I ſhall conclude this particular. Let fome Water, in which a convenient quantity of Soap or waſh-ball is diſſolv'd, be agitated into Froth, and, after that froth has ſtood a while without further agitation, till you fee the bubbles, of which it conſiſts, begin to break, there will appear a great variety of colours all over the top of every bubble, if you view them neaɾ at hand ; buƭ if you view them at fo great a diſtance that you cannot diſtinguiſh the colours one from another, the Froth will appear perfeԁly White.

Thus much concerning the defign 11. *That the* Experimentum crucis and fubſtance of the *Animadverfor's* *is fuch.* Confiderations. There are yet fome particulars to be taken notice of, be-fore I conclude ; as the denyal of the *Experimentum Crucis*. On *this* I chofe to lay the whole ſtrefs of my difcourfe ; which therefore was the principal thing to hɪve been objeԁed againſt. But I cannot be convinced ot its infufficiency by a bare denyal without affigning a Reafon for it. I am apt to believe, it has been mifunderſtood ; for otherwife it would have prevented the difcourfes about Rarifying and Splitting of rays ; becaufe the defign of it is, to ſhew, that Rays of divers colours, confider'd a part, do at *Equal* Incidences fuffer *Un-equal* Refraԁions, without being fplit, rarified, or any wayɪ diʒ lated.

In

(5103)

In the Confiderations of my firft and
fecond Propofitions, the *Animadverfor*   12. *Some particulars recommended to*
hath rendred my Doctrine of *Un-equal*   *further confideration.*
Refrangibility very imperfect and maim-
ed, by explicating it wholly by the Splitting of rays ; whereas I chiefly
intended it in thofe Refractions that are perform'd without that fuppos'd Irregularity ; fuch as the *Experimentum Crucis* might have inform'd him of.   And, in general I find, that, whilft he hath endeavour'd to explicate my Propofitions *Hypothetically*, the more material
fuggeftions, by which I defign'd to recommend them, have efcap'd
his confideration ; fuch as are, The Unchangeablenefs of the degree
of Refrangibility peculiar to any fort of rays; the ftrict Analogy between the degrees of Refrangibility and Colours ; the Diftinction
between compounded and un-compounded colours ; the Unchangeablenefs of un-compounded colours; and the Affertion, that if any one
of the Prifmatique colours be wholly intercepted, that colour cannot
be new produced out of the remaining Light by any further Refraction or Reflexion whatfoever.   And of what ftrength and efficacy
thefe Particulars are for enforcing the *Theory*, I defire therefore may
be now confider'd.

(6086)

An Extraɛt of a Letter lately written by an ingenious perſon ſrom Paris, *containing ſome Conſiderations upon* Mr. Newtons *Ɛrine of* Colors, *as alſo upon the effeɛts of the different Refraɛtions of the Rays in Teleſcopical Glaſſes.*

I Have ſeen, how Mr. *Newton* endeavours to maintain his new Theory concerning *Colours.* Me thinks, that the moſt important Objeɛtion, which is made againſt him by way of *Quære,* is that, Whether there be more than two ſorts of Colours. For my part, I believe, that an *Hypotheſis,* that ſhould explain mechanically and by the nature of motion the Colors *Jellow* and *Blew,* would be ſufficient for all the reſt, in regard that thoſe others, being only more deeply charged (as appears by the Priſmes of Mr. *Hook.*) do produce the dark or deep-Red and Blew; and that of theſe four all the other colors may be compounded. Neither do I ſee, why Mr. *Newton* doth not content himſelf with the two Colors, Yellow and Blew; for it will be much more eaſy to find an *Hypotheſis* by Motion, that may explicate theſe two differences, than for ſo many diverſities as there are of others Colors. And till he hath found this *Hypotheſis,* he hath not taught us, what it is wherein conſiſts the nature and difference of Colours, but only this accident (which certainly is very conſiderable,) of their *different Refrangibility.*

As for the compoſition of *White* made by all the Colors together, it may poſſibly be, that *Yellow* and *Blew* might alſo be ſufficient for that: Which is worth while to try; and it may be done by the Experiment, which Mr. *Newton* propoſeth, by receiving againſt a wall of a darkn'd room the Colours of the Priſme, and to caſt their refleɛted light upon white paper. Here you muſt hinder the Colors of the extremities, *viz.* the Red and Purple, from ſtriking againſt the wall, and leave only the intermediate Colors, yellow, green and blew, to ſee, whether the light of theſe alone would not make the paper appear white, as well as when they all give light. I even doubt, whether the lighteſt place of the yellow color may not all alone produce that effeɛt, and I mean to try it at the firſt conveniency; for this thought never came into my mind but juſt now

(6087)

now. Mean time you may fee, that if thefe Experiments do fucceed, it can no more be faid, that all the Colors are neceffary to compound White, and that 'tis very probable, that all the reft are nothing but degrees of *Yellow* and *Blew*, morè or lefs charged.

Laftly, touching the Effect of the different Refractions of the Rays in Telefcopical Glaffes, 'tis certain, that Experience agrees not with what Mr. *Newton* holds. For to confider only a picture, which is made by an object-glafs of 12 feet in a dark room, we fee, it is too diftinct and too well defined to be produced by rayes, that fhould ftray the 50*th*. part * of the Aperture. So that, (as I believe I have told you heretofore) the difference of the Refrangibility doth not, it may be, alwayes follow the fame proportion in the great and fmall inclinations of the Rayes upon the furface of the Glafs.

Compare herewith what Mr. New-ton, *faith in* Numb. 80. *of thefe Tracts,* pag. 3079.

Mr. Newtons *Anfwer to the foregoing Letter further explaining his Theory of Light and Colors, and particularly that of White-nefs ; together with his continued hopes of perfecting Telefcopes by Reflections rather than Refractions.*

Concerning the bufinefs of Colors ; in my faying that when Monfieur N. hath fhewn how *White* may be produced out of two uncompounded colors, I will tell him, why he can conclude nothing from *that* ; my meaning was, that fuch a White, (were there any fuch,) would have different properties from the White, which I had refpect to, when I defcribed my Theory, that is, from the White of the Sun's immediate light, of the ordinary objects of our fenfes, and of all white *Phænomena* that have hitherto faln under my obfervation. And thofe different properties would evince it to be of a different conftitution : Infomuch that fuch a production of white would be fo far from contradicting, that it would rather illuftrate and confirm my Theory ; becaufe by the difference of that from other whites it would appear, that other Whites are not compounded of only two colours like that. And therefore if Monfieur N. would prove any thing, it is requifite that he do not only produce out of two primitive Co-

lors,

(6088)

lors a white which to the naked eye shall appear like other whites, but also shall agree with them in all other properties.

But to let you underſtand wherein ſuch a white would differ from other whites and why from thence it would follow that other whites are otherwiſe compounded, I ſhall lay down this poſition.

That a compounded color can be resolved into no more ſimple colors then thoſe of which it is compounded.

This ſeems to be ſelf evident, and I have alſo tryed it ſeveral ways, and particularly by this which follows. Let *a* repreſent an oblong piece of white-paper about ½ or ¼ of an inch broad, and illuminated in a dark room with a mixture of two colours caſt upon it from two Priſms, ſuppoſe a deep blew and ſcarlet, which muſt ſeverally be as uncompounded as they can conveniently be made. Then at a convenient diſtance, ſuppoſe of ſix or eight yards, view

it through a clear triangular glaſs or cryſtal Priſm held parallel to the paper, and you ſhall ſee the two colors parted from one another in the faſhion of two images of the paper, as they are repreſented at *c* and *γ*, where ſuppoſe *β* the ſcarlet and *γ* the blew, without green or any other color between them.

Now from the aforeſaid Poſition I deduce theſe two concluſions. 1. That if there were found out a way to compound white of two ſimple colors only, that white would be again reſolvable into no more than two. 2. That if other whites (as that of the Suns light, *&c.* be reſolvable into more than two ſimple colours (as I find by Experiment that they are) then they muſt be compounded of more than two.

To make this plainer, ſuppoſe that A repreſents a white body illuminated by a direct beam of the Sun tranſmitted through a ſmall hole into a dark room, and *a* ſuch another body illuminated by a mixture of two ſimple colors, which if poſſible may

(6089)

may make it also appear of a white color exactly like A. Then
at a convenient diftance view thefe two whites through a
Prifm,and A will be changed into a feries of all colors, Red,
Yellow, Green, Blew, Purple,with their intermediate degrees
fucceeding in order from B to C. But *a*, according to the a-
forefaid Experiment, will only yield thofe two colors of
which 'twas compounded, and thofe not conterminate like
the colors at BC,but feparate from one another as at *c* and *γ*,
by means of the different refrangibility of the rays to which
they belong. And thus by comparing thefe two whites, they
would appear to be of a different conftitution, and A to confift of more colors then *a*. So that what Monfieur N. contends
for, would rather advance my Theory by the accefs of a new
kind of white than conclude againft it. But I fee no hopes.
of compounding fuch a white.

As for Monfieur N.his expreffion,that I maintain my doctrine
with fome concern, I confefs it was a little ungrateful to me
to meet with objections which had been anfwered before,
without having the leaft reafon given me why thofe anfwers
were infufficient. The anfwers which I fpeak of are in the
Tranfactions from *pag.* 5093 to *pag.* 5102. And particularly in
pag. 5095 ; to fhew that there are other fimple colors befides
blew and yellow, I inftance in a fimple or homogeneal Green,
fuch as cannot be made by mixing blew and yellow or any o-
ther colours. And there alfo I.fhew why, fuppofing that all
colors might be produced out of two, yet it would not follow that thofe two are the only Original colors. The reafons
I defire you would compare with what hath been now faid of
White. And fo the neceffity of all colors to produce white
might have appear'd by theExperiment *pag.* 5097,where I fay,
that if any color at the *Lens* be intercepted, the whitenefs
(which is compounded of them all) will be changed into (the
refult of) the other colors.

However, fince there feems to have happened fome mif-
underftanding between us, I fhall endeavor to explain myfelf
a little further in thefe things according. to the following method.

Defini

(6090)

Definitions.

1 I call that Light homogeneal, fimilar or uniform, whofe rays are equally refrangible.

2. And that heterogeneal, whofe rays are unequally refrangible.

Note. There are but three affections of Light in which I have obferved its rays to differ. *viz.* Refrangibility, Reflexibility, and Color; and thofe rays which agree in refrangibility agree alfo in the other two, and therefore may well be defined homogeneal, efpecially fince men ufually call thofe things homogeneal, which are fo in all qualities that come under their knowledg, though in other qualities that their knowledg extends not to there may poffibly be fome heterogeneity.

3. Thofe colors I call fimple, or homogeneal, which are exhibited by homogeneal light.

4. And thofe compound or heterogeneal, which are exhibited by heterogeneal light.

5. Different colors I call not only the more eminent fpecies, red, yellow, green, blew, purple, but all other the minuteft gradations; much after the fame manner that not only the more eminant degrees in Mufick, but all the leaft gradations are efteemed different founds.

Propofitions.

1. The Sun's light confifts of rays differing by indefinite degrees of Refrangibility.

2. Rays which differ in refrangibility, when parted from one another do proportionally differ in the colors which they exhibit. Thefe two Propofitions are matter of fact.

3. There are as many fimple or homogeneal colors as degrees of refrangibility. For, to every degree of refrangibility belongs a different color, by *Prop.* 2. And that color is fimple by *Def.* 1. and 3.

4. Whitenefs in all refpects like that of the Sun's immediate light and of all the ufual objects of our fenfes cannot be compounded of two fimple colors alone. For fuch a compofition muft be made by rays that have only two degrees of refrangibility, by *Def.* 1. and 3; and therefore it cannot be like that of the Suns light, by *Prop.* 1; Nor, for the fame reafon, like that of ordinary white objects.

5. Whitenefs

(6091)

5. Whiteneſs in all reſpects like that of the Sun's immediate light cannot be compounded of ſimple colors without an
indefinite variety of them. For to ſuch a compoſition there
are requiſite rays indued with all the indefinite degrees of refrangibility, by *Prop.* 1. And thoſe infer as many ſimple colors,
by *Def.* 1. and 3. and *Prop.* 2. and 3.

To make theſe a little plainer, I have added alſo the Propoſitions that follow.

6. The rays of light do not act on one another in paſſing
through the ſame Medium. This appears by ſeveral paſſages
in the *Tranſactions* pag. 5097, 5098, 5100, and 5101. and is
capable of further proof.

7. The rays of light ſuffer not any change of their qualities
from refraction.

8. Nor afterwards from the adjacent quiet *Medium*. Theſe
two Propoſitions are manifeſt *de facto* in homogeneal light,
whoſe color and refrangibility is not at all changeable either
by refraction or by the contermination of a quiet *Medium*.
And as for heterogeneal light, it is but an aggregate of ſeveral
ſorts of homogeneal light, no one ſort of which ſuffers any
more alteration than if it were alone, becauſe the rays act not
on one another, by *Prop.* 6. And therefore the aggregate can
ſuffer none. Theſe two *Propoſitions* alſo might be further proved apart by Experiments, too long to be here deſcribed.

9. There can no homogeneal colors be educed out of light
by refraction which were not commixt in it before : Becauſe,
by *Prop.* 7, and 8, Refraction changeth not the qualities of the
rays, but only ſeparates thoſe which have divers qualities, by
meanes of their different Refrangibility.

10. The Sun's light is an aggregate of an indefinite varie-
ety of homogeneal colors ; by *Prop.* 1, 3, and 9. And hence
it is, that I call homogeneal colors alſo primitive or original.
And thus much concerning Colors.

Monſieur N. has thought fit to inſinuate, that the aberration
of rays (by their different refrangibility) is not ſo conſiderable a diſadvantage in glaſſes as I ſeemed to be willing to
make men believe, when I propounded concave mirrors as the
only hopes of perfecting Teleſcopes. But if he pleaſe to take
his pen and compute the errors of a Glaſs and Speculum that

Ooo ooo   collect

(6092)

colle&ct; rays at equal diftances, he will find how much he is miftaken, and that I have not been extravagant, as he imagins, in preferring Reflexions. And as for what he fays of the difficulty of the praxis, I know it is very difficult, and by thofe ways which he attempted it I believe it unpracticable. But there is a way infinuated in the *Tranfactions pag.*3080. by which it is nct improbable but that as much may be done in large Telefcopes, as I have thereby done in fhort ones, but yet not without more then ordinary diligence and curiofity.

(6108)

An Extract of Mr. Ifaac Newton's *Letter, written to the Publifher from* Cambridge April 3. 1673. *concerning the Number
of* Colors, *and the Neceffity of mixing them all for the production of* White; *as alfo touching the Caufe why a Picture caft
by Glaffes into a darkned room appears fo diftinct notwithftanding its Irregular refraction: (Which Letter, being an Imme-
diat anfwer to that from* Paris, *printed* N°.96.p.6086. *of thefe
Tracts, fhould alfo, if it had not been mif-laid, have immediately followed the fame.)*

IT feems to me, that N. takes an improper way of examining
the nature of *Colors*, whilft he proceeds upon compounding
thofe that are already compounded; as he doth in the former
part of his Letter. Perhaps he would fooner fatisfie himfelf
by refolving Light into Colors, as far as may be done by Art,
and then by examining the properties of thofe colors apart,
and afterwards by trying the effects of re-conjoining two or
more or all of thofe; and laftly, by feparating them again to
examine, what changes that re-conjunction had wrought in
them. This, I confefs, will prove a tedious and difficult task
to do it as it ought to be done; but I could not be fatisfied,
till I had gone through it. However, I only propound it, and
leave every man to his own method.

As to the Contents of his Letter, I conceive, my former Anfwer to the *Quære* about the *Number* of *Colors* is fufficient, which
was to this effect; That all Colors cannot practically be derived out of the *Yellow* and *Blew*, and confequently that thofe
Hypothefes are groundlefs which imply they may. If you ask,
What colors cannot be derived out of *yellow* and *blew*? I anfwer, none of all thofe which I defin'd to be Original; and if
he can fhew by experiment, how they may, I will acknowledge
my felf in an error. Nor is it eafier to frame an *Hypothefis* by
affuming only two Original colors rather than an indefinit
variety; unlefs it be eafier to fuppofe, that there are but two
figures, fizes and degrees of velocity or force of the Æthereal
corpufcles or pulfes, rather than indefinit variety; which certainly would be a harfh fuppofition. No man wonders at the
indefinit variety of Waves of the Sea, or of fands on the fhore;
but,

(6109)

but, **were they** all but two fizes, it would be a very puzling *phænomenon.* And I fhould think it as unaccountable, if the feveral parts or corpufcles, of which a fhining body confifts, which muft be fuppos'd of various figures, fizes and motions, fhould imprefs but two forts of motion on the adjacent Æthe- real *medium,* or any other way beget but two forts of Rays. But to examine, how Colors may be explain'd *hypothetically,* is befides my purpofe. I never intended to fhew, wherein con- fifts the Nature and Difference of colors, but only to fhew, that *de facto* they are Original and Immutable qualities of the Rays which exhibit them ; and to leave it to others to explicate by Mechanical *Hypothefes* the Nature and Difference of thofe qualities: which I take to be no difficult matter. But I would not be underftood, as if their Difference confifted in the Dif- ferent Refrangibility of thofe rays ; for, that different Refran- gibility conduces to their production no otherwife, than by feparating the Rays whofe qualities they are. Whence it is, that the fame Rays exhibit the fame Colors when feparated by any other means ; as by their different *Reflexibility,* a quality not yet difcourfed of.

In the next particular, where N. would fhew, that it is not neceffary to mix all Colors for the production of *White* ; the mixture of *Yellow, Green* and *Blew,* without *Red* and *Violet,* which he propounds for that end, will not produce *White,* but *Green* ; and the brighteft part of the Yellow will afford no o- ther colour but Yellow, if the Experiment be made in a room well darkn'd, as it ought ; becaufe the Colour'd light is much weaken'd by the Reflexion, and fo apt to be diluted by the mixing of any other fcattering light. But yet there is an Ex- periment or two mention'd in my Letter in the *Tranfactions Numb.* 88, by which I have produced *White* out of two colors alone, and that varioufly, as out of *Orange* and a *full Blew,* and out of *Red* and *pale Blew,* and out of *Yellow* and *Violet,* as alfo out of other pairs of Intermediat colors. The moft conveni- ent Experiment for performing this, was that of cafting the co- lors of one Prifme upon thofe of another, after a due manner. But what N. can deduce from hence, I fee not. For the two colors were compounded of all others, and fo the refulting White, (to fpeak properly,) was compounded of them all,

(6110)

and only de-compounded of thofe two. For *inftance*, the *Orange* was compounded of Red, Orange, Yellow and fome Green ; and the *Blew*, of Violet, full Blew, light Blew, and fome Green, with all their Intermediat degrees ; and confequently the Orange and Blew together made an Aggregate of all colors to conftitute the White. Thus, if one mix red, orange and yellow Powders to make an Orange ; and green, blew and violet colors to make a Blew ; and laftly, the two mixtures, to make a Grey ; that Grey, though de-compounded of no more than two Mixtures, is yet compounded of all the fix Powders, as truly as if the powders had been all mixt at once.

This is fo plain, that I conceive there can be no further fcruple ; efpecially to them who know how to examine, whether a colour be fimple or compounded, and of what colors it is compounded ; which having explained in another place, I need not now repeat. If therefore N. would conclude any thing, he muft fhew, how White may be produced out of two *Uncompounded* colors ; which when he hath done, I will further tell him, why he can conclude nothing from that. But I believe, there cannot be found an Experiment of that kind ; becaufe, as I remember, I once tryed, by gradual fucceffion, the mixture of all pairs of Un-compounded colors ; and, though fome of them were paler, and nearer to White, than others, yet none could be truly call'd White. But it being fome years fince this tryal was made, I remember not well the circumftances, and therefore recommend it to others to be tryed again.

In the laft place, had I thought, the Diftinctnefs of the Picture, which (for *inftance*) a Twelf foot Object glafs cafts into a darken'd room, to be fo contrary to me as N. is pleafed to affirm, I fhould have waved my Theory in that point before I propounded it. For, that I had thought on that difficulty, you may eafily guefs by an expreffion, fomewhere in my firft Letter *, to this purpofe; That I wonder'd, how Telefcopes could be brought to fo great perfection by Refractions which were fo Irregular. But, to take away the difficulty, I muft acquaint you *firft*, That, though I put the greateft Lateral error of the rays from one another to be about ⅟₅₀ of the Glaffes diameter ; yet their greater error from the Points on which they ought to fall, will be but

(6111)

but $\frac{1}{100}$ of that diameter : And *then*, that the rays, whofe error is fo great, are but very few in comparifon to thofe, which are refracted more Juftly ; for, the rays which fall upon the middle-parts of the Glafs, are refracted with fufficient exactnefs, as alfo are thofe that fall near the *perimeter* and have a *mean* degree of Refrangibility ; So that there remain only the rays, which fall near the perimeter and are *moft* or *leaft* refrangible to caufe any fenfible confufion in the Picture. And thefe are yet fo much further weaken'd by the greater fpace, through which they are fcatter'd, that the Light which falls on the due point, is infinitely more denfe than that which falls on any other point round about it. Which though it may feem a *Paradox*, yet is certainly demonftrable. Yea, although the Light, which paffes through the middle parts of the Glafs, were wholly intercepted, yet would the remaining light convene infinitely more denfe at the due points, than at other places. And by this excefs of Denfity, the Light, which falls *in* or invifibly *near* the juft point, may, I conceive, ftrike the *fenforium* fo vigoroufly, that the imprefs of the weak light, which errs round about it, fhall, in comparifon, not be ftrong enough to be animadverted, or to caufe any more fenfible confufion in the Picture than is found by Experience.

This, I conceive, is enough to fhew, Why the Picture appears fo diftinct, notwithftanding the Irregular refraction. But, if this fatisfie not, *N.* may try, if he pleafe, how diftinct the Picture will appear, when all the *Lens* is cover'd excepting a little hole next its edge on one fide only : And, if in this cafe he pleafe to meafure the breadth of the colors thus made at the edge of the Suns picture, he will perhaps find it to approach nearer to my proportion than he expects.

An

(6112)

An Anſwer (to the former Letter,) written to the Publiſher June
*10.1673. by the ſame Pariſian Philoſopher,that was lately ſaid to
have written the Letter already extant in* N°. 96. p. 6086.

Touching the Solutions,given by M. *Newton* to the
ſcruples by me propos'd about his Theory of Colors,there were matter to anſwer them, and to form new difficulties ; but ſeeing that he maintains his opinion with ſo much
concern,I liſt not to diſpute.   But what means it,I pray, that
he ſaith ; *Though I ſhould ſhew him,that the White could be produced of only two Un-compounded colors,yet I could conclude nothing
from that.*   And yet he hath affirm'd in *p. 3083.* of the *Tranſactions,* that to compoſe the White, all primitive colors are
neceſſary.

As to the manner,whereby he reconciles the effect of Convex glaſſes for ſo well aſſembling the rays, with what he eſta-
bliſhes concerning the different refrangibility, I am ſatisfied
with it ; but then he is alſo to acknowledge,that this aberration of the rays is not ſo diſadvantagious to Optic glaſſes as he
ſeems to have been willing to make us believe, when he propoſed *Concave ſpeculums* as the only hopes of perfecting Teleſcopes.   His invention certainly was very good ; but,as far as
I could perceive by experience, the defect of the Matter renders it as impoſſible to execute, as the difficulty of the Form
obſtructs the uſe of the *Hyperbole* of M. *Des-Cartes* : So that, in
my opinion,we muſt ſtick to our Spheric Glaſſes,whom we are
already ſo much obliged to,and that are yet capable of greater perfection,as well by increaſing the length of Teleſcopes,as
by correcting the nature of Glaſs it ſelf.   *So far He.*

To this Letter is to be referr'd that, which is already extant in
N.96.p.6087. *as being an Anſwer thereto.*

(217)   *Numb.*110.

PHILOSOPHICAL
TRANSACTIONS.

Januar. 25. 16$\frac{74}{75}$.

The CONTENTS.

A Letter *of the Learn'd* Franc. Linus, *to a Friend of his in* London,
animadverting upon Mr. Iſaac Newton's *Theory of Light and Co-*
lors, formerly printed in theſe Tracts.

Honoured Sir,

UNderſtanding, that things of the nature I now write, are always welcom unto you,from what hand ſoever they come,I
thought good,though unknown to you,to give you notice,That per-
uſing lately the *Philoſophical Tranſactions*, to ſee what I could find
therein,in order to a little Treatiſe ofOpticks I have in hand;I lighted in page 3075.upon a Letter of Mr.*Iſaac Newton*,Profeſſor of Mathematicks in the Univerſity of *Cambridge*,wherein he ſpeaks of an

                                                                        Ex-

(218)

Experiment he tryed, by letting the Sun-beams through a little hole into a dark chamber; which paffing through a glafs ,Prifm to the oppofite wall, exhibited there a *Spectrum* of divers colours, but in a form much more long then broad: whereas according to the received Laws of Refraction, it fhould rather have appeared in a circular form. Whereupon conceiving a defect in thofe ufual Laws of Refraction, he frames his new Theory of Light, giving to feveral rays, feveral refrangibilities, without refpect to their Angles of Incidence, *&c.*

Truly, Sir, I doubt not of what this learned Author here affirms ; and have my felf fometimes in like circumftances obferved the like difference between the length and breadth of this coloured *Spectrum* ; but never found it fo when the sky was clear and free from clouds, near the Sun: but then only appeared this difference of length and breadth, when the Sun either fhined through a white cloud, or enlightned fome fuch clouds near unto it. And then indeed it was no marvel, the faid *Spectrum* fhould be longer then broad ; fince the cloud or clouds, fo enlightned, were in order to thofe colours like to a great Sun, making a far greater Angle of Interfection in the faid hole, then the true rays of the Sun do make; and therefore are able to enlighten the whole length of the Prifm, and not only fome fmall part thereof, as we fee enlightned by the true Sun-beams coming through the fame little hole. And this we behold alfo in the true Sun-beams, when they enlighten the whole Prifm: for, although in a clear Heaven, the rays of the Sun, paffing through the faid hole, never make a *Spectrum* longer then broad, becaufe they then occupy but a fmall part of the Prifm ; yet if the hole be fo much bigger as to enlighten the whole Prifm, you fhall prefently fee the length of the *Spectrum* much exceed its breadth ; which excefs will be always fo much the greater, as the length of the Prifm exceeds its breadth. From whence I conclude, that the *Spectrum*, this learned Author faw much longer then broad, was not effected by the true Sun-beams, but by rays proceeding from fome bright cloud, as is faid; and by confequence, that the Theory of Light grounded upon that Experiment cannot fubfift.

What I have here faid, needs no other confirmation than meer experience, which any one may quickly try; neither have I only tryed the fame upon this occafion, but near 30 years ago fhewed the fame, together with divers other Experiments of Light, to that worthy Promoter of Experimental Philofophy, Sr. *Kenelm Digby*, who coming into thefe parts to take the Spaw-Waters, reforted oftentimes

to

(219)

to my darkned Chamber, to fee thofe various Phænomena of Light made by divers Refractions and Reflexions, and took Notes upon them; which induftry if they alfo had ufed, who endeavour to explicate the aforefaid difference between the length and breadth of this coloured *Spectrum*, by the received Laws of Refraction, would never have taken fo impoffible a task in hand.

The reft is, Honoured Sir, that it is far from my intent, that the miftake here mentioned do any way derogate from that learned perfon: Which truly might have happened to my felf, if at my firft tryal thereof, the Sun had been in a white cloud, as it feems, it happened to him. Wherefore ceafing further to trouble you, I reft,

Yours to command,   Francis Linus.
6 Octob. 1674.

Sir,   *An Anfwer to this Letter.*

THE Letter you thought fit to write by way of Animadverfion upon Mr. *Newton's* new Theory of Light and Colors, grounded upon an Experiment of letting the Sun-beams through a little hole into a dark chamber, feems to need no other Anfwer but this, That you would be pleafed to look upon and confider the Scheme in Mr. *Newton's* 2ᵈ Anfwer to *P. Pardies* in *Numb.* 85. of the *Ph. Tranfactions*; and reft affured, that the Experiment, as it is reprefented, was tryed in clear days, and the Prifm placed clofe to the hole in the window, fo that the Light had no room to diverge, and the colour'd Image made not parallel (as in that conjecture) but tranfverfe to the axis of the Prifm.

London, Decemb. 17. 1674.

(499)

A Letter of Mr. Franc. Linus, *written to the Publisher from* Liege
the 25th *of* Febr. 1675. ft.n. *being a Reply to the Letter printed
in* Numb. 110. *by way of Answer to a former Letter of the same
Mr.* Linus, *concerning Mr.* Isaac Newton's *Theory of Light and
Colours.*

Honoured Sir,

IN yours of *Dec.* 17. which I received about the end of *Jan.* you
say, I may reft affured, *First*, that the Experiment was made in
clear days. *Secondly*, that the Prifm was placed clofe to the hole,
fo that the light had no room to diverge : And *thirdly*, that the I-
mage was not Parallel (as I conjectured) but Tranfverfe to the
Axis of the Prifm.   Truly, Sir, if thefe Affertions be admitted,
they do indeed directly cut off what I faid of Mr. *Newton's* being
deceived by a bright cloud.   But if we compare them with Mr.
Newton's Relation of the Experiment in the *Phil. Tranfactions, N.*
80 *p.* 3076. it will evidently appear, they cannot be admitted as
being directly contrary to what is there delivered.   For there he
tells us, the ends of the coloured Image , he faw on the oppofit
wall, near five times as long as broad, *feemed to be Semicircular.*
Now thefe Semicircular Ends are never feen in a clear day, as Experience fhews.   From whence follows againft the *first* Affertion,
That the Experiment was not made in a clear day. Neither are thofe
Semicircular Ends ever feen, when the Prifm is placed clofe to
the Hole ; which contradicts the *fecond* Affertion.   Neither are
they ever feen, when the Image is Tranfverfe to the length or Axis
of the Prifm ; which directly oppofes the *third* Affertion. But if
in any of thefe three Cafes, the Image be made fo much longer than
broad (as eafily it may, by turning the Prifm a little about its Axis) near five times as long as broad, than the one End thereof will run
out into a fharp Cone or Pyramis like the flame of a Candle, and the
other into a Cone fomewhat more blunt ; both which are far from
feeming Semicircular : Whereas, if the Image be made not in a
clear day, but with a bright cloud, and the Prifm not placed clofe
to the Hole, but in a competent diftance from the fame (as you fee
it placed in the Scheme of the Experiment in *N.* 84. *p.* 4091.)
then thefe Semicircular Ends always appear with the fides thereof ftraight lines juft as Mr. *Newton* there defcribes them. Neither

T t t   is

(501)

is the length of the Image Tranfverfe, but Parallel to the length of the Prifm. Out of all which evidently follows, that the Experiment was not made in a clear day ; nor with the Prifm clofe to the Hole ; nor yet with the Image Tranfverfe(as is now affirmed,) but by a bright Cloud, and a Parallel Image (as I conjectured ;) and I hope you will alfo now fay, I had good reafon fo to conjecture, fince it fo well agrees with the Relation. And Experience will alfo fhew you, if you pleafe to make tryal, as it was made, in a dark Chamber, and obferve the difference between fuch an Image made by a bright Cloud, and another made by the immediate rayes of the Sun: For, the former you fhall always find Parallel, with the Ends Semicircular ; but the latter you fhall find Tranfverfe, with the Ends Pyramidical, as aforefaid, whenfoever it appears fo much longer than broad.

More might be faid out of the fame Relation, to fhew that the Image was not Tranfverfe. For, if it had been Tranfverfe, Mr. *Newton*, fo well skilled in Opticks, could not have been furprifed (as he fays he was) to fee the length thereof fo much to exceed the breadth ; it being a thing fo obvious and eafie to be explicated by the ordinary Rules of Refraction. That other place alfo , in the next *page* 3077.(where he fays,the Incident Refractions were made in the Experiment equal to the Emergent,) proves again that the faid oblong Image was not Tranfverfe, but Parallel. For it is impoffible, the Tranfverfe Image fhould be fo much longer than broad, unlefs thofe two Refractions be made very unequal, as both the computation according to the common Rules of Refraction, and Experience teftifie. Wherefore Mr. *Newton* had no reafon to tax (in *pag.* 4091.) P. *Pardies* of Hallucination,for making in *page* 4088. thofe two Refractions very unequal: For , that learned Optike very well faw, that in a clear day fo great an inequality of length and breadth could not be made, unlefs thofe two Refractions were alfo made very unequal. Thefe places, I fay, might be added to the former, and further here explicated if need were ; but there being no need, I ceafe to detain you any longer herein.

Mr.

(500)

Mr. Isaac Newton's *Confiderations on the former Reply ; together with further Directions, how to make the Experiments controverted aright: Written to the Publifher from* Cambridge, Novemb. 13. 1675.

SIR,

WHen you fhew'd me Mr. *Line*'s fecond Letter, I remember I told you, that I thought an anfwer in writing would be infignificant, becaufe the difpute was not about any Ratiocination, but my veracity in relating an Experiment, which he denies will fucceed as it is defcribed in my printed Letters : For this is to be decided not by difcourfe, but new tryal of the Experiment. What it is that impofes upon Mr. *Line* I cannot imagin; but I fufpect he has not tryed the Experiment fince he acquainted himfelf with my Theory, but depends upon his old notions taken up before he had any hint given to obferve the figure of the coloured Image. I fhall defire him therefore, before he returns any anfwer, to try it once more for his fatisfaction, and that according to this manner.

Let him take any Prifme, and hold it fo that its Axis may be perpendicular to the Sun's rays, and in this pofture let it be placed as clofe as may be to the hole through which the Sun fhines into a dark room, which hole may be about the bignefs of a Peafe. Then let him turn the Prifm flowly about its Axis, and he fhall fee the colours move upon the oppofite wall firft towards that place to which the Sun's direct light would pafs, if the Prifm were taken away, and then back again. When they are in the middle of thefe two contrary motions, that is, when they are neareft that place to which the Sun's direct ray tends, there let him ftop ; for then are the rays equally refracted on both fides the Prifm. In this pofture of the Prifm let him obferve the figure of the colours, and he fhall find it not round as he contends, but oblong, and fo much the more oblong as the Angle of the Prifm, comprehended by the refracting plains, is bigger, and the wall, on which the colours are caft, more diftant from the Prifm ; the colours red, yellow, green, blew, purple, fucceeding in order not from one fide of the figure to the other, as in Mr. *Line*'s conjecture, but from one end to the other; and the length of the Figure being not parallel but tranverfe to the Axis of the Prifm. After this manner I ufed to try the Experi-

Ttt 2   ment

(502)

ment : For I have try'd it often ; fometimes to obferve the circumftances of it, fometimes in order to further Experiments,and fometimes to fhow it to others, and in all my tryals the fuccefs was the
fame. But whereas Mr. *Line* thinks,I tryed it in a cloudy day,and
placed the Prifm at a great diftance from the hole of the window;
the Experiment will not fucceed well if the day be not clear , and
the Prifm placed clofe to the hole, or fo near at leaft, that all the
Sun's light that comes from the hole may pafs through the Prifm
alfo, fo as to appear in a round form if intercepted by a paper immediately after it has paft the Prifm.

When Mr. *Line* has tryed this, I could wifh,he would proceed
a little further to try that which I call'd the *Experimentum Crucis*,
feeing (if I mif-remember not) he denies that as well as the other.
For when he has tryed them (which by his denying them , I know
he has not done yet as they fhould be tryed)I prefume he will reft
fatisfied.

Three or four days after you gave me a fight of Mr. *Line*'s fecond
Letter, I remember I thereupon fhow'd the firft of thefe two Experiments to that Gentleman whom you found with me,when you gave
me that vifit,and whilft I was fhewing it to him, *A. H.* (a member of
the *R. Society)* came in and I fhewed it to him alfo. And you may remember,that *R. H.* two or three years agoe in a Letter read before
the *R. Society*,and tranfmitted to me,gave teftimony not only to the
Experiments queftioned by Mr. *Line*,but to all thofe fet down in
my firft Letter about Colours, as having tryed them himfelf; and
when you read Mr. *Line*'s Letter at a meeting of the faid *Society*,
and was pleafed to do me the favour to propound the Experiment to be tryed in their prefence , *R. H.* fpake of it to them as
a thing not to be queftioned. But if it have not yet been tryed before them, and any of them, upon Mr. *Line*'s confidence,doubt of
it, I promife when I fhall have the happinefs to be at any more of
their Affemblies, upon the leaft hint, to fhew 'em the tryal of it ;
and I hope, I fhall not be troublefome, becaufe it may be tryed
(though not fo perfectly)even without darkning a room, or the
expence of any more time than half a quarter of an hour ; although,
if Mr. *Line* perfift in his denyal of it , I could wifh it might be
tryed fooner there , than I fhall have an opportunity to be among
them.

An

(503)

An Extract of another Letter of Mr. Newton, *written to the Publisher the* 10th *of* January 167⅚, *relating to the same Argument.*

——. BY Mr. *Gascoin's* Letter* one might suspect, that Mr. *Linus* tryed the Experiment some other way than I did; and therefore I shall expect, till his friends have tryed it according to my late Directions. In which tryal it may possibly be a further guidance to them, to acquaint them, that the Prism casts from it several Images: *One* is, that *Oblong* one of *Colours* which I mean; and this is made by two Refractions only. *Another* there is, made by two Refractions and an intervening Reflexion; and this is *Round* and *Colourless*, if the Angles of the Prism be exactly equal; but if the Angles at the Reflecting base be not equal, it will be *colour'd,* and that so much the more, by how much unequaller the Angles are, but yet not much *unround*, unless the angles be very unequal. A *third* Image there is, made by one single Reflexion, and this is always *round* and *colourless*. The only danger is in mistaking the *second* for the *first*. But they are distinguishable not only by the Length and Lively colors of the *first*, but by it's different Motion too: For, whilst the Prism is turned continually the same way about it's *axis*, the *second* and *third* move swiftly, and go always on the same way till they disappear; but the *first* moves slow, and grows continually slower till it be stationary, and then turns back again, and goes back faster and faster, till it vanish in the place where it began to appear.

If without darkning their Room they hold the Prism at their window in the Sun's open Light, in such a posture that it's *axis* be

perpen.

(504)

perpendicular to the Sun-beams, and then turn it about its *axis*, they cannot mifs of feeing the *firft* Image; which having found, they may double up a paper once or twice, and make a round hole in the middle of it about ¼ or ¾ of an inch broad, and hold the paper immediately before the Prifm, that the Sun may fhine on the Prifm through that hole ; and the Prifm being ftay'd, and held fteddy in that pofture which makes the Image Stationary ; if the Image then fall directly on an oppofite wall, or on a fheet of paper placed at the wall, fuppofe 15 or 20 foot from the Prifm, or further off; they will fee the Image in fuch an *Oblong* figure as I have defcribed, with the *Red* at one end, the *Violet* at the other, and a *Blewifh green* in the middle : And if they obfcure their Room, as much as they can, by drawing curtains or otherwife, it will make the Colours the more confpicuous.

This direction I have fet down, that no body, into whofe hands a Prifm fhall happen, may find difficulty or trouble in trying it. But when Mr. *Linus*'s friends have tryed it thus, they may proceed to repeat it in a dark Room with a *lefs* hole made in their window fhut. And then I fhall defire, that they will fend you a full and clear defcription, How they tryed it, expreffing the length, breadth and angles of the Prifm; its pofition to the Incident rays and to the window fhut ; the bignefs of the hole in the window fhut through which the Sun fhined on the Prifm ; what fide of the Prifm the Sun fhin'd on ; and at what fide the light came out of it again ; the diftance of the Prifm from the oppofite paper or wall on which the Refracted light was caft perpendicularly ; and the length, breadth, and figure of the fpace there illuminated by that light, and the fcituation of each colour within that figure. And, if they pleafe to illuftrate their defcription with a Scheme or two, it will make the bufinefs plainer. By this means, if there be any difference in our way of experimenting, I fhall be the better enabled to difcern it, and give them notice, where the failure is, and how to rectifie it. I fhould be glad too, if they would favour me with a defcription of the Experiment, as it hath been hitherto tryed by Mr. *Linus*, that I may have an opportunity to confider, what there is in that which makes againft me.

So far Mr. Newton; which was thought fit to make publick with the reft, that fo the Curious every where, who have a mind to try the Experiment, may find the fuller directions for their tryal.

An

(556)

A particular Anſwer of Mr. Iſaak Newton *to Mr.* Linus *his Letter, printed in* Numb. 121. p.499. *about an Experiment relating to the New Doctrine of Light and Colours: This Anſwer ſent from Cambridge in a Letter to the Publiſher Febr.* 29. 167⁵⁄₆ .

Sir ,

BY reading Mr. *Linus*'s Letter when you ſhew'd it to me at *London*, I retained only a general remembrance, that Mr. *Linus* deny'd what I affirmed, and ſo could lately ſay nothing in particular to it ; but having the opportunity to read it again in *Numb.* 121. of the *Tranſactions*, I perceive he would perſwade you, that the information you gave him about the Experiment is as inconſiſtent with my printed Letters as with experience ; and therefore, left any who have not read thoſe Letters ſhould take my ſilence in this point for an acknowledgment, I thought it not amiſs, to ſend you ſomething in anſwer to this alſo.

He

(557)

He tells you that, *Whereas you assure him, First, that the Experiment was made in clear days; secondly, that the Prism was placed close to the hole, so that the light had no room to diverge; and thirdly, that the Image was not parallel but transverse to the axis of the Prism: If these Assertions be compared with my Relation of the Experiment in the Phil. Transaction N. 80. p. 3076. it will evidently appear, they cannot be admitted as being directly contrary to what is there delivered.* His reasons are these:

First, that I said, *the ends of the long Image seemed semicircular, which,* saies he, *never happens in any of the three cases above-said.* But this is not to set me at odds with my self, but with the experiment; for it is there described to happen in them all; and I still say, it doth happen in them. Let others try the Experiment, and judge.

Further he saies, that *the Prism is placed at a distance from the hole in the Scheme of the Experiment in* N. 84. p 4091. But, what if it were so *there?* For, that is the Scheme of a *demonstration,* not of the *experiment,* and would have served for the demonstration, had the distance been put twenty times greater than it is. In the Schemes of the Experiment *N. 80. p.* 3086, and *N. 82. p.* 5016. it is represented close, and close enough in the Scheme, *N. 83. p.4061:* But Mr. *Linus* thought fit to wink at these, and pitch upon the Scheme of a Demonstration, and such a Scheme too as hath no hole at all represented in it. For, the Scheme † *Numb.* 84. *p.* 491 is this;

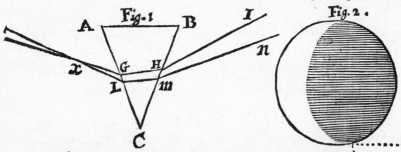

in which the rays are not so far distant from one another at G L, but that the hole, had I exprest it, might have been put there, and yet have comprehended them. But if we should put the hole at *x,* their decussation; yet will it not be any thing to his purpose; the distance *x* G or *x* L being but about half the breadth of a side of the Prism ($\frac{1}{2}$AC) which I conceive is not the twentieth part of the distance requisite in his conjecture.

† *See Fig. 1.*

Thirdly,

(558)

3. He fays, that *more might be faid out of my relation to fhew, that the Image was not tranfvers, for if it had been tranfvers, I could not have been furprized (as I faid I was) to fee the length thereof fo much exceed the breadth, it being a thing fo obvious & eafie to be explicated by the ordinary rules of Refraction.* But on the contrary, it may rather be faid, that if the Image had been parallel, I could not have been furprized to fee the length thereof fo much exceed the breadth, it being a thing fo extreamly obvious as not to need any explication. For who that had but common fenfe, and faw the whole Prifm or a good part of it illuminated, could not expect the light fhould have the fame long figure upon the wall that it had when it came out of the Prifm?   Mr. *Linus* therefore, while he would ftrengthen his argument by reprefenting me well skilled in Opticks, does but over-throw it. But whereas he fayes, *I could not have been furprized at the length, had the Image been parallel, it being a thing fo obvious and eafy to be explicated by the ordinary rules of refraction:* Let any Man take the Experiment intire as I have there delivered it, that is, with this condition, that *the refractions on both fides the Prifm were equal*, and try if he can reconcile it with the ordinary rules of refraction. On the contrary, he may find the impoffibility of fuch a reconciliation, demonftrated in my Anfwer to *P. Pardies N.* 84, *p.* 4091.

In the laft place, he objects, that my faying in *N.* 80, *p.* 3077, *that the incident refractions were in the Experiment equal to the emergent*, proves again, that the long Image was parallel. And yet that very faying is a fufficient argument, that I meant the contrary, becaufe it becomes wholly impertinent, if apply'd to a parallel image; but in the o her cafe is a very neceffary circumftance. What is added therefore of *P. Pardies*, might have been fpared, efpecially fince that Learned Perfon underftood my difcourfe to be meant of a tranfvers Image, and acquiefced in my Anfwers.

This in anfwer to Mr. *Linus*'s Letter: And now to take away the like fufpicions from his Friends, if my declaration of my meaning fatisfie not, I fhall note fome further paffages in my Letters, whereby they may fee, how I was to be underftood from the beginning, as to the aforefaid three circumftances.

For the *Day*; I exprefs every where that the Experiment was tried in the Sun's light, and in *N.* 80. *p.* 3077, that the breadth of the Image by meafure anfwered to the Sun's diameter: But becaufe it is pretended, I was impofed upon, I would ask, what the Experiment as it is advanced to that which I called the *Experimentum*

(559)

tum Crucis, can have to do with a cloudy day ? For, if the *Experimentum Crucis* (which is that which I depend on) can have nothing to do with a cloudy day, then is it to no purpose to talk of a cloudy day in the first Experiment, which does but lead on to that. But if this satisfie not, let the *Tranfactions* N. 83. *p.* 4060, be confulted : For. there I tell you, how *by* applying a *Lens* to the Prifm, the ftreight edges of the oblong Image became diftincter than they would have been *without* the *Lens :* A circumftance which cannot happen in Mr. *Linus's* cafe of a bright Cloud.

For the *Pofition of the Prifm* ; I tell you *N.*8o. *p.*3076, that it was placed *at the Sun's entrance* into the Chamber, and in *p.*3085. I bad to make a hole in the fhut, and *there* place the Prifm, and in the next page I fay again, that the Prifm ABC is to be fet *clofe* by the hole F of the window EG ; and accordingly reprefent it clofe in the Figure. Alfo in *pag.* 3077 I tell you, that the diftance of the *Image* from the *hole* or *prifm* was 22 foot ; which is as much as to fay, that the Prifm (fuppofe that fide of it next the hole) was as far from the Image as the hole it felf was , and confequently that the Prifm and Hole were contiguous. Alfo in *p.*3078, where inftead of the Window fhut I made ufe of a hole in a loofe board , I tell you exprefly, that I placed the board *clofe* behind the Prifm. All thefe paffages are in my very firft Letter about Colours ; and who therefore would imagine, that any one that had read that Letter fhould fo much as fufpect, that I placed the Prifm, I fay not at fo great a diftance as Mr. *Linus* fuppofes, but at any diftance worth confidering ?

Laftly, for the *Pofition of the Image* , it is reprefented tranfvers to the axis of the Prifm in the figures *N.*8o. *p.*3086. *N.*83. *p.*4061, and *N.*85. *p.*5016. And in *N.*88. *p.*5093, where I made ufe of two crofs Prifms, I tell you exprefly , that the Image was crofs to both of them at an angle of 45 degrees. The calcu'ations alfo *N.* 8o. *p.* 3077. are not to be underftood without fuppofing the Image crofs. Nor are my notions about different Refrangibility otherwife intelligible : For in Mr. *Linus's* fuppofition , the rays that go to the two ends of the Image, are equally refracted. So for colours, the *red*, according to my defcription, falls at one end of the Image, and the *blew* at the other ; which cannot happen but in a tranfvers Image. The fame pofition is alfo demonftrable from what I faid in *N.* 8o. *p.* 3076, about turning the long Image into a round one , by the

Dddd

contrary

(560)

contrary refraction of a fecond Prifm, further explained in *Num.*
83. *p.* 4061. For this is not to be done in Mr. *Linus* furmife of a
parallel Image, and therefore had Mr. *Linus* confidered it, he could
never have run into that furmife.

This I fuppofe is enough to manifeft the three particulars; any
one of which being evidenced, is fufficient to take away the fcruple.
And therefore Mr. *Linus* Friends need not fear but that the further
directions I fent them lately for trying the Experiment are the fame
with thofe I have follow'd from the beginning; nor trouble themfelves about any thing but to try the Experiment right. But yet,
becaufe Mr. *Gafcoin* has been pleafed to infinuate his fufpicion that
I do differ from himfelf in thofe directions, I fhall not fcruple here
to reduce them into particulars, and fhew where each particular
is to be found.

1. Then, he is to get a Prifm with an angle about 60 or 65 degrees,
N. 80. *p.* 3077, and *p.* 3086. If the angle be about 63 degrees,
as that was which I made ufe of *N.* 80. *p.* 3077, he will find all
things fucceed exactly as I defcribed them there. But if it be bigger
or lefs, as 30, 40, 50, or 70 degrees, the Refraction will be accordingly bigger or lefs, and confequently the Image longer or fhorter.
If his Prifm be pretty nearly equilateral (fuch as I fuppofe are ufually fold in other places as well as in *England*) he may make ufe of
the biggeft angle. But he mnft be fure to place the Prifm fo, that
the Refraction be made by the two planes which comprehend this
angle. I could almoft fufpect, by confidering fome circumftances
in Mr. *Linus*'s Letter, that his error was in this point, he expecting
the Image fhould become as long by a little refraction as by a great
one; which yet being too grofs an error to be fufpected of any O-
ptician, I fay nothing of it, but only hint this to Mr. *Gafcoin*, that
he may examine all things.

2. Having fuch a Prifm, he muft place it fo, that its Axis be perpendicular to the rays *N.* 84, *p.* 4091, *lin.* 18, 19. A little error
in this point makes no fenfible variation of the effect.

3. The Prifm muft be fo placed, that the Refractions on both fides
be equal *N.* 80, *p.* 3077: which how it was to be readily done by
turning it about its Axis, and ftaying it when you fee the Image
reft between too contrary motions, as I explained in my late Defcriptions, fo I hinted before *N.* 80. *p.* 3077, *lin.* 34, 35, 36. If there
fhould be a little error in this point alfo, it can do no hurt.

4. The

(561)

4. The Diameter of the hole I put $\frac{1}{4}$ of an inch *N.* 80, *p.* 3077, and placed the Prifm clofe to it, even fo clofe as to be contiguous, *N.* 80, *p.* 3077, *lin.* 4, 5. But yet there needs no curiofity in thefe circumſtances. The hole may be of any other bignefs, and the Prifm at a diſtance from the hole, , provided things be fo ordered, that the light appear of a round form, if intercepted perpendicularly at its coming out of the Prifm. Nor needs there any curiofity in the *day.* The clearer it is the better ; but if it be a little cloudy, that cannot much prejudice the Experiment, fo the Sun do but fhine diſtinctly through the cloud.

Thefe things being thus ordered, if the refracted light fall perpendicularly on a wall or paper at 20 foot or more from the Prifm, it will appear in an oblong form, crofs to the axis of the Prifm, *red* at one end, and *violet* at the other; the length five times the breadth (more or lefs according to the quantity of the refraction,) the fides, ſtreight lines, parallel to one another, and the ends confufed, but yet feeming femi-circular.

I hope therefore, Mr. *Linus*'s Friends will not entertain themfelves any further about incongruous *furmifes*, but try the Experiment as Mr. *Gafcoin* has promifed. And then, fince Mr. *Gafcoin* tells you, That *the Experiment being of it felf extraordinary and furprizing, and befides ufhering in new Principles into Opticks, quite contrary to the common and received, it will be hard to perfwade it as a truth, till it be made fo vifible to all as it were a fhame to deny it:* if he efteem it fo extraordinary, he may have the priviledg of making it fo vifible to all, that it will be a fhame to deny it. For, I dare fay, after his teſtimony no body elfe will fcruple it. And I make no queſtion but he will hit of it, it being fo plain and eafy, that I am very much at a lofs to imagine what way Mr. *Linus* took to mifs. Dat. *Cambridge Feb.* 29. 167$\frac{5}{6}$.

(692)

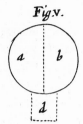

Fig.V.

a b

d

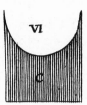

VI

c

A Letter from Liege *concerning* Mr. Newton's *Experiment of the coloured* Spectrum ; *together with some Exceptions against his Theory of* Light *and* Colours.

Hon.rd Sir,

MR *Gascoigne* having received your obliging Letter of *Jan.*18, with fresh directions from Mr. *Newton*; but wanting convenience to make the Experiment according to the said instructions, he has requested me to supply his want. In compliance with his request I have made many Trials; the issue whereof I here acquaint you with : next, with some exceptions, grounded on Experiments, against Mr. *Newton's* new Theory of *Light* and *Colours.*

The vertical angle of my Prism was 60 *deg*;the distance of the Wall, whereon the coloured *Spectrum* appeared,from the Window,about 18 foot : The diameter of the Hole in the Window-shuts in length the line *a,*which upon occasions I contracted to half the said diameter; but still with equal success as to the main of the Experiment.The refractions on both sides the Prism, were as near as I could make them, equal,

(693)

equal, and consequently about 48 *deg.*40', the refractive power of Glass being computed according to the *Ratio* of the *Sines* 2 to 3. The distance of the Prism from the hole in the Shuts was about 2 inches: The Room darkned to that degree as to equal the darkest night, while the hole in the Shuts was covered.

Now as to the issue of my Trials; I constantly found the length of the coloured image (transverse to the axis of the Prism) considerably greater than its breadth, as often as the Experiment was made on a clear day; but if a bright Cloud were near the Sun, I found it sometimes exactly as Mr. *Line* wrote you, namely broader than long, especially while the Prism was placed at a great distance from the hole. Which Experiment will not, I conceive, be questioned by Mr. *Newton*, it being so agreeable to the received laws of Refractions. And indeed the Observations of these two Learned persons, as to this particular, are easily reconcileable to each other, and both to truth; Mr *Newton* (as appears by his Letter of *Nov.* last, wherein more fully he delivers his mind) contending only for the length of the Image (transverse to the axis of the Prism) in a very clear day; whereas Mr. *Line* only maintain'd the excess of breadth, parallel to the same axis, while the Sun is in a bright cloud. Though as to what is further delivered by Mr. *Newton* (*Phil.Transact*. *N.* 80. *p.* 3077; and opposed by Mr. *Line*, *N.* 129. *p* 501.) namely that the length of the coloured Image was five times the diameter of its breadth; I never yet have found the excess above thrice the diameter, or at most 3½, while the refractions on both sides the Prism were equal. So much as to the matter of fact.

Now as to Mr. *Newton*'s Theory of *Light* and *Colours*, I confess, his neat Sett of very ingenious and natural inferences, was to me upon the first perusal a strong conjecture in favour of his new doctrine; I having formerly observ'd the like chain of Inferences upon search into Natural truths. But since several experiments of Refractions remain still untouch'd by him, I conceived, a further search into them would be very proper in order to a further discovery of the truth of his Assertion. For, accordingly as they are found either agreeing with, or disagreeing from, his new Theory, they must needs much strengthen

(694)

then, or wholly overthrow the fame. The Experiments I pitched upon for this purpofe, are as follow:

1. Having frequently obferved, that the form of Objects viewed in the Microfcope (or rather of the Microfcope it felf) confifts almoft in an indivifible point, I concluded, two very fmall pieces of Silk, the one fcarlet, the other violet colour, placed near together, fhould, according to Mr. *Newton*'s Theory, appear in the Microfcope in a very different degree of clarity, in regard their unequal refrangibility muft caufe the fcarlet rays or fpecies to over-reach the *Retina*, while placed in the due focus of the violet ones, and confequently muft occafion a fenfible confufion in the vifion of the former, one and the fame point of the Scarlet object affecting feveral nerves in the *Retina*. Yet upon frequent trials I have not been able to perceive any inequality in this point.

2. The fecond Experiment I made in Water. I took a brafs Ruler, and faftening thereunto feveral pieces of Silk, red, yellow, green, blew and violet, I placed it at the bottom of a fquare veffel of Water: then I retired from the Veffel fo far as not to be able to fee the aforefaid Ruler and coloured Silks otherwife than by help of the refracted Ray. Now, did Mr. *Newton*'s doctrine hold, I conceiv'd, I fhould not fee all the mentioned Colours in a ftreight line with the Ruler, in regard the unequal refrangibility of different Rays muft needs difplace fome more than others. Yet in effect, upon many Trials, I conftantly found them in as ftreight a line as the bare Ruler had appeared in.

3. To advance this Experiment, I adjoyned a fecond refraction to the former of the Water, by placing my Prifm fo as to receive *perpendicularly* the refracted *fpecies* of the Silk and Ruler; whereby only the emergent *fpecies* fuffered a fecond refraction. But ftill with equal fuccefs, as to their appearing in a ftraight line, to the eye placed behind the Prifm.

4. To thefe two Refractions I further added a third, by receiving the coloured fpecies *obliquely* upon the Prifm; whereby both incident and emergent *fpecies* fuffered their refpective refractions. But ftill with the fame fuccefs as formerly, as to the ftreight line they appeared in.

For

(695)

For further affurance in this Experiment, left prepoffeffi-on, occafioned from previous knowledge of the Silks fcitua-tion in a ftreight line, might poffibly prejudice the judgment of the eye (as fometimes I have obferved to happen to the judgment the Eye paffeth upon the diftance of Objects) I cal-led into the room fome unconcerned perfons, wholly ignorant what the Experiment aimed at; and demanding whether they faw not the coloured Silks and Ruler in a crooked line? they anfwered in the negative.

5. The next Experiment I made in uncompounded Co-lours (as Mr. *Newton* terms them, *Prop.* 5 & 13) as follows. Having caft two coloured Images upon the Wall, fo as the Scarlet colour of the one did fall in a ftreight line (parallel to the Horizon) with the Violet of the other: I then looked up-on both through another Prifm, and found them ftill appear in a ftreight line parallel to the Horizon, as they had formerly done to the naked eye. Now according to Mr. *Newton*'s Af-fertion of different refrangibility in different Rays, I con-ceive the Violet rays fhould fuffer a greater refraction in the Prifm at the eye, than the Scarlet ones, and confequently both colours fhould not appear in a ftreight line parallel to the Ho-rizon.

6. Another Experiment I made in order to fome further difcovery of that furprizing *Phænomenon* of the coloured Image, which occafioned Mr. *Newtons* ingenious Theory of *Light* and *Colours*, as alfo his excellent invention of the re-flecting *Telefcope* and *Microfcope*. Having then fometimes fuf-pected, that not only the direct Sun-beams, but alfo other ex-traneous light might poffibly influence the coloured *Spectrum*, I hoped to difcover the truth of this fufpicion by means of the Sun-fpots, made to appear in the coloured Image by placing a Telefcope behind the Prifm. But my endeavours proving ineffectual herein by reafon of fome intervening difficulties, I thought at length of a more feafible method in order to the defigned difcovery, as in the following Experiment.

I faftened a very white Paper-circle (about an inch in dia-meter) upon my Window-fhuts; and beholding it through my Prifm, I found a Coloured image painted thereby upon my *Retina*, anfwerable in almoft all refpects to the former of the

Yyyy

Sun

(696)

Sun-beams upon the Wall, efpecially when the Paper-circle was indifferently well illuminated. This Image indeed appeared contrary to the former as to the fcituation of Colours, that is, the Scarlet appearing above, the Violet below, though but faint. But this I was not furprized at, having obferv'd upon diffecting the eye, that objects are painted on the *Retina* after a contrary pofture to what they appear to Sight. Having thus rendred the Coloured image much more tractable than formerly it was, I conceived good hopes of fome further difcovery in the point mentioned.

In purfuance then of my former fufpicion, having fixed my Prifm in a fteady pofture, I caufed the paper *C* to be applied clofe up to the Paper-circle *a b d*: whereupon the former Violet *d*, and Scarlet colour of *C* vanifhed into whitenefs. Next, I removed the mentioned Circle from the Shuts, and placed it in the open window, fupported only by the edge *d*: whereupon, to my aftonifhment, all the former Colours exchanged poftures in the *Retina*, the Scarlet now appearing below, the Violet above; the intermediate Colours fcarce difcernible. And here, on the by, 'tis very remarkable, that, during this Obfervation, I clearly perceived both Blew- and Scarlet-light to be tranfparent, I being able to difcern feveral objects through both, namely Steeples oppofit to my window. Whence it follows, that thefe Colours do in great part arife from the neighbouring light. Laftly, I placed the Paper-circle anew, fo as the one half *b* was faftened to the Shuts, the other femicircle *a* being expofed to the open Air. Whereupon the femicircle *a* became bordered with Violet above, Scarlet below; but the other femicircle *b* quite contrary. Hence I make the following Inferences.

Firft, That not only the Light reflected from the Paper-circle, but alfo from the ambient Air, hath great influence upon the Coloured image, efpecially as to the Violet and Scarlet colours. Whence perchance it will not hereafter feem ftrange, that the coloured *Spectrum* on the Wall is fo long, but only that the breadth is not greater. *Secondly*, Were there a more luminous body behind the Sun, we fhould in all likelyhood have the colours of the *Spectrum* in a contrary fcituation to what they appear in at prefent: Whence (*thirdly*) it feems to follow, that the

(margin note: V. Tab.II. Fig.5 & 6.)

(697)

the prefent fcituation and order of Colours, arifeth not from any intrinfecal property of refrangibility (as maintained by Mr. *Newton*) but from contingent and extrinfecal circumftances of neighbouring objeds. For accordingly as the body behind the Paper-circle was more or lefs illuminated than the Circle it felf, all the feveral Colours changed their fcituation.

8. The next Experiment was made in order to Mr. *Newtons* doctrine of primary Colours, as *Prop.*5. Having covered the Hole in the Window-fhuts with a thin flice of *Ivory*, the tranfmitted light appeared yellow ; but upon adding three, four, and more flices, it became red. Whence it feems to follow, that Yellownefs of light is not a primary colour, but a compound of Red,&c.

9. The laft Experiment was made in reference to Mr. *Newton*'s 12 *Prop.*where from his own principles he renders a very plaufible Reafon of a furprizing *Phænomenon*, related by Mr. *Hooke*; namely of two liquors, the one Blew, the other Red, both feverally tranfparent, yet both, if placed together, became opake. The reafon whereof, faith Mr. *Newton*, is, becaufe if one liquor tranfmitted only Red, the other only Blew, no rays could pafs through both.

In reference then to this point , I filled two fmall Glaffes with flat polifhed bottoms, the one with *Aqua fortis*, deeply died Blew ; the other with Oyl of *Turpentine*, died Red ; both to that degree, as to reprefent all objeds through them refpedively Blew or Red. Then placing the one upon the other , I was able to difcern feveral bodies through both : whereas according to Mr. *Newtons* Theory, no objed fhould appear through both Liquors ; becaufe if one tranfmit only Red, the other only Blew, no rays can pafs through both.

Thefe Experimental Exceptions will not, I hope, be unwelcome to Mr. *Newton*, his only aim being the improvement of Natural knowledge,as it is alfo of,

Sir,
Your humble Servant,
Anthony Lucas.

(698)

Poſtſcript.

Juſt upon the cloſe of the adjoyned Letter, I received from Mr. Gaſcoine, yours of May the fourth ; wherein you are pleaſed to favour us with an exact account of the famous Experiment of the coloured Spectrum, lately exhibited before the Royal Society. I was much rejoyced to ſee the Trials of that Illuſtrious Company, agree ſo exactly with ours here, though in ſomewhat ours diſagree from Mr. Newton, as you will underſtand by the incloſed impartial account from,

Sir, &c.

Mr. Newton's Anſwer to the precedent Letter, ſent to the Publiſher.

Sir,

THe things oppoſed by Mr. Line being upon Trials found true and granted me ; I begin with the new queſtion about the proportion of the length of the Image to its breadth. This I call a new one ; for, though Mr. Line in his laſt Letter ſpake againſt ſo great a length as I aſſign, yet, as it ſeems to me, it was not to grant any tranſverſe length ſhorter than that aſſigned by me, (for in his firſt Letter he abſolutely denied that there would be any ſuch length ;) but to lay the greater emphaſis upon his diſcourſe whilſt in defence of common Optiques he was diſputing in general againſt a tranſverſe Image : And therefore in my Anſwer I did not preſcribe the juſt quantity of the refracting Angle with which I would have the Experiment repeated : which would have been a neceſſary circumſtance, had the diſpute been about the *In my firſt Letter juſt proportion of the length to the breadth. in Phil. Tranſ. N. Yet I added * this Note, that the bigger the 121. p.500. angle of the Priſm is, the greater will be the length in proportion to the breadth: not imagining but that when he had found in any Priſm the length of the Image tranſverſe to the axis, he would eaſily thence conclude, that a Priſm with a greater angle would make the Image longer, and conſequently that by uſing an angle great enough he might bring it to equal or exceed the length aſſigned by me ; as indeed he might : for, by taking an Angle of 70 or 75 degrees, or a little

greater,

(699)

greater, he might have made the length not only five, but ſix or eight times the breadth and more. No wonder therefore, that Mr. *Lucas* found the Image ſhorter than I did, ſeeing he tried the Experiment with a leſs Angle.

The Angle indeed which I uſed was but about 63 degrees 12 minutes, and his is ſet down 60 degrees : the difference of which from mine, being but 3 degrees 12 minutes, is too little to reconcile us, but yet it will bring us conſiderably nearer together. And if his Angle was not exactly meaſured, but the round number of 60 degrees ſet down by gueſs or by a leſs accurate meaſure (as I ſuſpect by the conjectural meaſure of the refraction of his Priſm by the *ratio* of the ſigns 2 to 3, ſet down at the ſame time, inſtead of an Experimental one,) then might it be two or three degrees leſs than 60, if not ſtill leſs : and all this, if it ſhould be ſo, would take away the greateſt part of the difference between us.

But however it be, I am well aſſured, my own obſervation was exact enough. For I have repeated it divers times ſince the receipt of Mr. *Lucas*'s Letter, and that without any conſiderable difference of my Obſervations either from one another, or from what I wrote before. And that it might appear experimentally, how the increaſe of the Angle increaſes the length of the Image, and alſo that no body who has a mind to try the Experiment exactly, might be troubled to procure a Priſm which has an angle juſt of the bigneſs aſſigned by me; I tried the Experiment with divers Angles, and have ſet down my Trials in the following Table; where the firſt column expreſſes the ſix Angles of two Priſms which I uſed, which were meaſured as exactly as I could by applying them to the angle of a Sector ; and the ſecond column expreſſes in inches the length of the Image made by each of thoſe Angles; its breadth being two inches, its diſtance from the Priſm 18 feet and four inches, and the breadth of the hole in the Window-ſhut ¼ of an inch.

The Angles of degr. min.		The Lengths of the Image.
The firſt Priſm	56 10	7¾
	60 24	9½
	63 26	10⅓

The

(700)

The Angles of degr. min.		The Lengths of the Image.
the second Prifm.	54 0	$7\frac{1}{3}$
	62 12	$10\frac{1}{8}$
	63 48	$10\frac{3}{4}$

You may perceive, that the length of the Images in refpect of the angles that made them, are fomething greater in the fecond Prifm than in the firft; but that was becaufe the glafs, of which the fecond Prifm was made, had the greater refractive power.

The days in which I made thefe Trials were pretty clear, but not fo clear as I defired, and therefore afterwards meeting with a day as clear as I defired, I repeated the Experiment with the fecond Prifm, and found the lengths of the Image made by its feveral angles to be about $\frac{1}{4}$ of an inch greater than before, the meafures being thofe fet down in this Table.

The Angles of degr. min.		The Lengths of the Image.
the fecond Prifm	54 0	$7\frac{2}{3}$
	62 12	$10\frac{1}{2}$
	63 48	11

The reafon of this difference I apprehend was, that in the cleareft days the light of the white skies, which dilutes and renders invifible the fainteft Colours at the ends of the Image, is a little diminifhed in a clear day, and fo gives leave to the Colours to appear to a greater length; the Suns light at the fame time becoming brisker, and fo ftrengthning the Colours and making the faint ones at the two ends more confpicuous. For I have obferved, that in days fomething cloudy, whilft the Prifm has ftood unmoved at the window, the Image would grow a little longer or a little fhorter, accordingly as the Sun was more or lefs obfcured by thin Clouds which paffed over it; the Image being fhorteft when the Cloud was brighteft and the Suns light fainteft. Whence it is eafie to apprehend, that, if the light of the Clouds could be quite taken away, fo that the
Sun

(701)

Sun might appear furrounded with darknefs, or if the Suns light were much ftronger than it is, the colours would ftill appear to a greater length.

In all thefe Obfervations the breadth of the Image was juft two inches. But obferving, that the fides of the two Prifms, I ufed, were not exactly plain, but a little convex, (the convexity being about fo much as that of a double Convex-glafs of a fixteen or eighteen foot *Telefcope*) I took a third Prifm, whofe fides were as much concave as thofe of the other were convex; and this made the breadth of the Image to be two inches and a third part of an inch; the angles of this Prifm, and the lengths of the Image made by each of thofe Angles being thofe expreft in this Table.

The Angles of the Prifm. degr.	The Lengths of the Image in inches.
58	$8\frac{1}{2}$
$59\frac{1}{2}$	9
$62\frac{1}{2}$	$10\frac{1}{3}$

In this cafe you fee, the concave figure of the fides of the Prifm by making the rays diverge a little, caufes the breadth of the Image to be greater in proportion to its length than it would be otherwife. And this I thought fit to give you notice of, that Mr. *Lucas* may examine, whether his Prifm have not this fault. If a Prifm may be had with fides exactly plain, it may do well to try the Experiment with that; but its better, if the fides be about fo much convex as thofe of mine are, becaufe the Image will thereby become much better defined. For this convexity of the fides does the fame effect, as if you fhould ufe a Prifm with fides exactly plain, and between it and the hole in the Window-fhut, place an Object-glafs of an 18 foot *Telefcope*, to make the round Image of the Sun appear diftinctly defined on the wall when the Prifm is taken away, and confequently the long Image made by the Prifm to be much more diftinctly defined (efpecially at its ftreight fides) than it would be otherwife.

One thing more I fhall add: That the utmoft length of the Image from the fainteft Red at one end to the fainteft Blew at
the

(702)

the other, muft be meafured. For in my firft Letter about Colours, where I fet down the length to be five times the breadth, I called that length the utmoft length of the image ; and I meafured the utmoft length , becaufe I account all that length to be caufed by the immediate light of the Sun, feeing the Colours (as I noted above) become vifible to the greateft length in the cleareft days, that is, when the light of the Sun tranfcends moft the light of the Clouds. Sometimes there will happen to fhoot out from both ends of the Image a glaring light a good way beyond thefe colours, but this is not to be regarded, as not appertaining to the Image. If the meafures be taken right, the whole length will exceed the length of the ftreight fides by about the breadth of the Image.

By thefe things fet down thus circumftantially, I prefume Mr. *Lucas* will be enabled to accord his tryals of the Experiment with mine ; fo nearly, at leaft, that there fhall not remain any very confiderable difference between us. For, if fome little difference fhould ftill remain , that need not trouble us any further, feeing there may be many various circumftances which may conduce to it ; fuch as are not only the different figures of prifms, but alfo the different refractive power of Glaffes, the different diameters of the Sun at divers times of the year, and the little errors that may happen in meafuring lines and angles, or in placing the prifm at the window ; though, for my part, I took care to do thefe things as exactly as I could. However Mr. *Lucas* may make fure to find the Image as long or longer than I have fet down, if he take a prifm whofe fides are not hollow ground, but plain, or (which is better) a very little convex, and whofe refracting angle is as much greater than that I ufed, as that he has hitherto tryed it with, is lefs ; that is, whofe angle is about 66 or 67 degrees, or (if he will) a little greater.

Concerning Mr. *Lucas*'s other Experiments, I am much obliged to him that he would take thefe things fo far into confideration, and be at fo much pains for examining them ; and I thank him fo much the more, becaufe he is the firft that has fent me an experimental examination of them. By this I may prefume he really defires to know what truth there is in thefe matters. But yet it will conduce to his more fpeedy and full

fatif-

(703)

fatisfaction if he a little change the method which he has propounded, and inftead of a multitude of things try only the *Experimentum Cancis*. For it is not number of Experiments, but weight to be regarded ; and where one will do, what need many ?

Had I thought more requifite, I could have added more : For before I wrote my firft Letter to you about Colours, I had taken much pains in trying Experiments about them, and written a Tractate on that fubject , wherin I had fet down at large the principal of the Experiments I had tried ; amongft which there happened to be the principal of thofe Experiments which Mr. *Lucas* has now fent me. And as for the Experiments fet down in my firft Letter to you, they were only fuch as I thought convenient to felect out of that Tractate.

But fuppofe thofe had been my whole ftore, yet Mr. *Lucas* fhould not have grounded his difcourfe upon a fuppofition of my want of Experiments, till he had examined thofe few. For if any of thofe be demonftrative, they will need no affiftants, nor leave room for further difputing about what they demonftrate.

The main thing he goes about to examine is, *the different refrangibility* of Light. And this I demonftrated by the *Experimentum Crucis*. Now if this demonftration be good , there needs no further examination of the thing; if not good , the fault of it is to be fhewn : for the only way to examine a demonftrated propofition is, to examine the demonftration. Let that Experiment therefore be examined in the firft place, and that which it proves be acknowledged, and then if Mr. *Lucas* want my affiftance to unfold the difficulties which he fancies to be in the Experiments he has propounded, he fhall freely have it ; for then I fuppofe a few words may make them plain to him : whereas, fhould I be drawn from demonftrative Experiment to begin with thofe, it might create us both the trouble of a long difpute, and by the multitude of words, cloud rather than clear up the truth. For if it has already coft us fo much trouble to agree upon the matter of fact in the firft and plaineft Experiment , and yet we are not fully agreed; what an endlefs trouble might it create us, if we fhould give our felves up to difpute upon every Argument that occurs, and what would become of Truth in fuch a tedious difpute ?

Zzzz   The

(704)

The way therefore that I propound, being the shorteſt and cleareſt (not to ſay, the only proper way,) I queſtion not but Mr. *Lucas* will be glad that I have recommended it, ſeeing he profeſſes, that it is the knowledge of *truth* that he ſeeks after. And therefore at preſent I ſhall ſay nothing in anſwer to his Experimental diſcourſe, but this in general; that it has pro- ceeded partly from ſome miſunderſtanding of what he writes againſt, and partly from want of due caution in trying Expe- riments; and that amongſt his Experiments there is one, which when duly tried, is, next to the *Experimentum Crucis*, the moſt conſpicuous Experiment, I know, for proving the different re- frangibility of Light, which he brings it to prove againſt.

By the *Poſt-ſcript* of Mr. *Lucas*'s Letter, one not acquainted with what has paſſed, might think, that he quotes the Obſerva- tion of the *R. Society* againſt me; whereas the relation of their Obſervation, which you ſent to *Liege*, contained nothing at all about the juſt proportion of the Length of the Image to its Breath according to the angle of the Priſm, nor any thing more (ſo far as I can perceive by your laſt) than what was pertinent to the things then in diſpute, *viz.* that they found them ſucceed as I had affirmed. And therefore ſince Mr. *Lucas* has found the ſame ſucceſs, I ſuppoſe, that when he expreſſed, that *he much rejoyced to ſee the Trials of the* R. Society *agree ſo exactly with his,* he meant only ſo far as his agreed with mine.

And becauſe I am again upon this firſt Experiment, I ſhall deſire, that Mr. *Lucas* will repeat it with all the exactneſs and caution that may be, regard being had to the information about it, ſet down in this Letter; and then I deſire to have the *length* and *breadth* of the Image with its *diſtance* from the Priſm, ſet down exactly in feet and inches, and parts of an inch, that I may have an opportunity to conſider what relation its length and breadth have to the Suns diameter. For I know, that Mr. *Lucas*Obſervation cannot hold where the refracting angle of the Priſm is full 60 degrees, and the day is clear, and the full length of theColours is meaſured, and the breadth of the Image anſwers to the Sun's diameter: And ſeeing I am well aſſured of the truth and exactneſs of my own Obſervations, I ſhall be unwilling to be diverted by any other Experiments, from having a fair end made of this in the firſt place. *Sir, I am, &c.*

Poſt-

(705)

Poſtſcript.

I Had like to have forgotten to adviſe, that the Experimentum Crucis, and ſuch others as ſhall be made for knowing the nature of Colours, be made with Priſms which refract ſo much, as to make the length of the Image five times its breadth, and rather more than leſs; for, otherwiſe Experiments will not ſucceed ſo plainly with others as they have done with me.

December 9. There was produced a manuscript of Mr. Newton, touching his theory of light and colours, containing partly an hypothesis to explain the properties of light discoursed of by him in his former papers, partly the principal phænomena of the various colours exhibited by thin plates or bubbles, esteemed by him to be of a more difficult consideration; yet to depend also on the said properties of light.

Of the hypothesis only the first part was read, giving an account of refraction, reflection, transparency, and opacity; the second part explaining colours being referred to the next meeting.

The first was as follows [h]:

"Sir,
"I have sent you the papers I mentioned, by John Stiles. Upon reviewing
"them, I find some things so obscure, as might have deserved a further explication
"by schemes; and some other things, I guess, will not be new to you, though al-
"most all was new to me when I wrote them. But as they are, I hope you will accept
"of them, though not worth the ample thanks you sent. I remember, in some
"discourse with Mr. Hooke, I happened to say, that I thought light was re-
"flected, not by the parts of glass, water, air, or other sensible bodies; but by
"the same confine or superficies of the æthereal mediums, which refracts it, the
"rays finding some difficulty to get through it in passing out of the denser into
"the rarer medium, and a greater difficulty in passing out of the rarer into the
"denser; and so being either refracted or reflected by that superficies, as the
"circumstances they happened to be in at their incidence make them able or
"unable to get through it. And, for confirmation of this, I said further, that
"I thought the reflection of light, at its tending out of glass into air, would not
"be diminished or weakened by drawing away the air in an air-pump, as it ought
"to be, if they were the parts of air that reflected: and added, that I had not
"tried this experiment, but thought he was not unacquainted with notions of
"this kind. To which he replied, that the notion was new, and he would the
"first opportunity try the experiment I propounded. But upon reviewing the
"papers I send you, I found it there set down for tried; which makes me recol-
"lect, that about the time I was writing these papers, I had occasionally observed
"in an air-pump here at Christ's College, that I could not perceive the reflection
"of the inside of the glass diminished in drawing out the air. This I thought
"fit to mention, least my former forgetfulness, through having long laid aside
"my thoughts on these things, should make me seem to have set down for cer-
"tain what I never tried.

[h] Register, vol. v. p. 65.

"Sir,

" Sir, I had formerly purpofed never to write any hypothefis of light and
" colours, fearing it might be a means to engage me in vain difputes : but I hope
" a declared refolution to anfwer nothing, that looks like a controverfy, unlefs
" poffibly at my own time upon fome by-occafion, may defend me from that
" fear.   And therefore confidering, that fuch an hypothefis would much illuftrate
" the papers I promifed to fend you; and having a little time this laft week to
" fpare, I have not fcrupled to defcribe one, fo far as I could on a fudden recol-
" lect my thoughts about it; not concerning myfelf, whether it fhall be thought
" probable or improbable, fo it do but render the papers I fend you, and others
" fent formerly, more intelligible.   You may fee, by the fcratching and inter-
" lining, it was done in hafte; and I have not had time to get it tranfcribed,
" which makes me fay I referve a liberty of adding it; and defire, that you would
" return thofe and the other papers when you have done with them.   I doubt
" there is too much to be read at one time, but you will foon know how to
" order that.   At the end of the hypothefis you will fee a paragraph to be in-
" ferted as is there directed : I fhould have added another or two, but I had not
" time, but fuch as it is, I hope you will accept it.   Sir, I am, &c.

Is. NEWTON.

" An Hypothefis explaining the Properties of Light, difcourfed of in my fe-
" veral Papers.

" Sir,
" In my anfwer to Mr. HOOKE, you may remember, I had occafion to fay
" fomething of hypothefes, where I gave a reafon, why all allowable hypothefes
" in their genuine conftitution fhould be conformable to my theories; and faid
" of Mr. HOOKE's hypothefis, that I took the moft free and natural application
" of it to phænomena to be this [i] : that the agitated parts of bodies, according
" to their feveral fizes, figure, and motions, do excite vibrations in the æther of
" various depths or bigneffes, which being promifcuoufly propagated through that
" medium to our eyes, effect in us a fenfation of light of a white colour ; but,
" if by any means thofe of unequal bigneffes be feparated from one another, the
" largeft beget a fenfation of a red colour ; the leaft, or fhorteft, of a deep
" violet ; and the intermediate ones, of intermediate colours : much after the
" manner that bodies, according to their feveral fizes, fhapes, and motions, ex-
" cite vibrations in the air of various bigneffes, which, according to thofe big-
" neffes, make feveral tones in found, &c.   I was glad to underftand, as I ap-
" prehend, from Mr. HOOKE's difcoufe at my laft being at one of your affem-
" blies, that he had changed his former notion of all colours being compounded
" of only two original ones, made by the two fides of an oblique pulfe ; and
" accommodated his hypothefis to this my fuggeftion of colours, like founds,
" being various, according to the various bignefs of the pulfes.   For this I take
" to be a more plaufible hypothefis than any other defcribed by former authors,
" becaufe I fee not how the colours of thin tranfparent plates or fkins can be
" handfomely explained, without having recourfe to æthereal pulfes : but yet I

<hr>

[i] Tranfact. n° 88. p. 5088.

" Ili-

" like another hypothefis better, which I had occafion to hint fomething of in the
" fame letter in thefe words [k] :

" *The hypothefis of light's being a body, had I propounded it, has a much greater*
" *affinity with the objector's own hypothefis, than he feems to be aware of ; the vibra-*
" *tions of the æther being as ufeful and neceffary in this as in his. For, affuming the*
" *rays of light to be fmall bodies emitted every way from fhining fubftances, thofe,*
" *when they impinge on any refracting or reflecting fuperficies, muft as neceffarily ex-*
" *cite vibrations in the æther, as ftones do in water when thrown into it. And, fup-*
" *pofing thefe vibrations to be of feveral depths or thickneffes, accordingly as they are*
" *excited by the faid corpufcular rays of various fizes and velocities ; of what ufe*
" *they will be for explicating the manner of reflexion and refraction ; the production of*
" *heat by the fun-beams ; the emiffion of light from burning, putrifying, or other fub-*
" *ftances, whofe parts are vehemently agitated ; the phænomena of thin tranfparent*
" *plates, and bubbles, and of all natural bodies ; the manner of vifion, and the dif-*
" *ference of colours ; as alfo their harmony and difcord ; I fhall leave to their confi-*
" *deration, who may think it worth their endeavour to apply this hypothefis to the*
" *folution of phænomena.*

" Were I to affume an hypothefis, it fhould be this, if propounded more ge-
" nerally, fo as not to determine what light is, farther than that it is fomething
" or other capable of exciting vibrations in the æther : for thus it will become
" fo general and comprehenfive of other hypothefes, as to leave little room for
" new ones to be invented. And therefore, becaufe I have obferved the heads
" of fome great virtuofos to run much upon hypothefes, as if my difcourfes want-
" ed an hypothefis to explain them by, and found, that fome, when I could not
" make them take my meaning, when I fpake of the nature of light and colours
" abftractedly, have readily apprehended it, when I illuftrated my difcourfe by
" an hypothefis ; for this reafon I have here thought fit to fend you a defcrip-
" tion of the circumftances of this hypothefis as much tending to the illuftration
" of the papers I herewith fend you. And though I fhall not affume either this or
" any other hypothefis, not thinking it neceffary to concern myfelf, whether the
" properties of light, difcovered by me, be explained by this, or Mr. HOOKE's,
" or any other hypothefis capable of explaining them ; yet while I am defcrib-
" ing this, I fhall fometimes, to avoid circumlocution, and to reprefent it more
" conveniently, fpeak of it, as if I affumed it, and propounded it to be believed.
" This I thought fit to exprefs, that no man may confound this with my other
" difcourfes, or meafure the certainty of one by the other, or think me obliged
" to anfwer objections againft this fcript : for I defire to decline being involved
" in fuch troublefome and infignificant difputes.

" But to proceed to the hypothefis : Firft, it is to be fuppofed therein, that
" there is an æthereal medium much of the fame conftitution with air, but far
" rarer, fubtler, and more ftrongly elaftic. Of the exiftence of this medium
" the motion of a pendulum in a glafs exhaufted of air almoft as quickly as in

[k] Tranfact. n° 88. p. 5087.

" the open air, is no inconfiderable argument. But it is not to be fuppofed,
" that this medium is one uniform matter, but compounded, partly of the main
" phlegmatic body of æther, partly of other various æthereal fpirits, much after
" the manner, that air is compounded of the phlegmatic body of air intermixed
" with various vapours and exhalations : for the electric and magnetic effluvia,
" and gravitating principle, feem to argue fuch variety. Perhaps the whole
" frame of nature may be nothing but various contextures of fome certain æthe-
" real fpirits, or vapours, condenfed as it were by precipitation, much after the
" manner, that vapours are condenfed into water, or exhalations into groffer fub-
" ftances, though not fo eafily condenfible ; and after condenfation wrought into
" various forms ; at firft by the immediate hand of the Creator ; and ever fince
" by the power of nature ; which, by virtue of the command, increafe and
" multiply, became a complete imitator of the copies fet her by the protoplaft.
" Thus perhaps may all things be originated from æther.

" At leaft, the elaftic effluvia feem to inftruct us, that there is fomething of
" an æthereal nature condenfed in bodies. I have fometimes laid upon a table
" a round piece of glafs about two inches broad fet in a brafs ring, fo that the
" glafs might be about one eighth or one fixth of an inch from the table, and
" the air between them inclofed on all fides by the ring, after the manner as if
" I had whelmed a little fieve upon the table ; and then rubbing a pretty while
" the glafs brifkly with fome rough and raking ftuff, till fome very little fragments
" of very thin paper, laid on the table under the glafs, began to be attracted and
" move nimbly to and fro ; after I had done rubbing the glafs, the papers would
" continue a pretty while in various motions ; fometimes leaping up to the glafs
" and refting there a while; then leaping down and refting there ; then leaping
" up, and perhaps down and up again, and this fometimes in lines feeming per-
" pendicular to the table; fometimes in oblique ones ; fometimes alfo they would
" leap up in one arch and down in another, divers times together, without
" fenfibly refting between ; fometimes fkip in a bow from one part of the glafs
" to another without touching the table, and fometimes hang by a corner, and
" turn often about very nimbly, as if they had been carried about in the midft
" of a whirlwind, and be otherwife varioufly moved, every paper with a diverfe
" motion. And upon fliding my finger on the upper fide of the glafs, though
" neither the glafs, nor inclofed air below, were moved thereby, yet would the
" papers, as they hung under the glafs, receive fome new motion, inclining this
" way or that way, accordingly as I moved my finger. Now, whence all thefe
" irregular motions fhould fpring, I cannot imagine, unlefs from fome kind of
" fubtil matter lying condenfed in the glafs, and rarefied by rubbing, as water is
" rarefied into vapour by heat, and in that rarefaction diffufed through the fpace
" round the glafs to a great diftance, and made to move and circulate varioufly,
" and accordingly to actuate the papers till it return into the glafs again, and be
" recondenfed there. And as this condenfed matter by rarefaction into an æthe-
" real wind (for by its eafy penetrating and circulating through glafs I efteem it
" æthereal) may caufe thefe odd motions, and by condenfing again may caufe
" electrical attraction with its returning to the glafs to fucceed in the place of
" what is there continually recondenfed ; fo may the gravitating attraction of the
" earth

" earth be caufed by the continual condenfation of fome other fuch like æthereal
" fpirit, not of the main body of phlegmatic æther, but of fomething very
" thinly and fubtilly diffufed through it, perhaps of an unctuous or gummy,
" tenacious, and fpringy nature, and bearing much the fame relation to æther,
" which the vital aereal fpirit, requifite for the confervation of flame and vital
" motions, does to air. For, if fuch an æthereal fpirit may be condenfed in
" fermenting or burning bodies, or otherwife coagulated in the pores of the earth
" and water into fome kind of humid active matter, for the continual ufes of
" nature, adhering to the fides of thofe pores, after the manner that vapours
" condenfe on the fides of a veffel ; the vaft body of the earth, which may be
" every where to the very center in perpetual working, may continually condenfe
" fo much of this fpirit, as to caufe it from above to defcend with great celerity
" for a fupply ; in which defcent it may bear down with it the bodies it pervades
" with force proportional to the fuperficies of all their parts it acts upon ; nature
" making a circulation by the flow afcent of as much matter out of the bowels
" of the earth in an aereal form, which, for a time, conftitutes the atmofphere ;
" but being continually buoyed up by the new air; exhalations and vapours rifing
" underneath, at length (fome part of the vapours, which return in rain, excepted)
" vanifhes again into the æthereal fpaces, and there perhaps in time relents, and is
" attenuated into its firft principle : for nature is a perpetual worker, generating
" fluids out of folids, and folids out of fluids, fixed things out of volatile, and
" volatile out of fixed, fubtil out of grofs and grofs out of fubtil ; fome things
" to afcend, and make the upper terreftrial juices, rivers, and the atmofphere ; and
" by confequence, others to defcend for a requital to the former. And, as the
" earth, fo perhaps may the fun imbibe this fpirit copioufly, to conferve his fhin-
" ing, and keep the planets from receding further from him. And they, that
" will, may alfo fuppofe, that this fpirit affords or carries with it thither the folary
" fewel and material principle of light : and that the vaft æthereal fpaces between
" us and the ftars are for a fufficient repofitory for this food of the fun and
" planets. But this of the conftitution of æthereal natures by the by.

" In the *fecond* place, it is to be fuppofed, that the æther is a vibrating medium
" like air, only the vibrations far more fwift and minute ; thofe of air, made by
" a man's ordinary voice, fucceeding one another at more than half a foot or a
" foot diftance ; but thofe of æther at a lefs diftance than the hundred thoufandth
" part of an inch. And, as in air the vibrations are fome larger than others,
" but yet all equally fwift (for in a ring of bells the found of every tone is heard
" at two or three miles diftance, in the fame order that the bells are ftruck ;) fo,
" I fuppofe, the æthereal vibrations differ in bignefs, but not in fwiftnefs. Now,
" thefe vibrations, befide their ufe in reflexion and refraction, may be fuppofed
" the chief means, by which the parts of fermenting or putrifying fubftances,
" fluid liquors, or melted, burning, or other hot bodies, continue in motion, are
" fhaken afunder like a fhip by waves, and diffipated into vapours, exhalations,
" or fmoke, and light loofed or excited in thofe bodies, and confequently by
" which a body becomes a burning coal, and fmoke, flame; and, I fuppofe,
" flame is nothing but the particles of fmoke turned by the accefs of light and
" heat to burning coals, little and innumerable.

K k 2   " *Thirdly*,

" *Third'y*, as the air can pervade the bores of fmall glafs pipes, but yet not fo
" eafily as if they were wider ; and therefore ftands at a greater degree of rarity
" than in the free aereal fpaces, and at fo much a greater degree of rarity as the
" pipe is fmaller, as is known by the rifing of water in fuch pipes to a much
" greater hight than the furface of the ftagnating water, into which they are
" dipped ; fo I fuppofe æther, though it pervades the pores of cryftal, glafs,
" water, and other natural bodies, yet it ftands at a greater degree of rarity in
" thofe pores, than in the free æthereal fpaces, and at fo much a greater degree of
" rarity, as the pores of the body are fmaller. Whence it may be, that the fpirit
" of wine, for inftance, though a lighter body, yet having fubtiler parts, and
" confequently fmaller pores, than water, is the more ftrongly refracting liquor.
" This alfo may be the principal caufe of the cohefion of the parts of folids and
" fluids, of the fpringinefs of glafs, and bodies, whofe parts flide not one upon
" another in bending, and of the ftanding of the mercury in the Torricellian
" experiment, fometimes to the top of the glafs, though a much greater hight
" than twenty-nine inches. For the denfer æther, which furrounds thefe bodies,
" muft croud and prefs their parts together, much after the manner that air
" furrounding two marbles preffes them together, if there be little or no air be-
" tween them. Yea, and that puzzling problem ; *By what means the mufcles are*
" *contracted and dilated to caufe animal motion, may receive greater light from hence*
" *than from any means men have hitherto been thinking on.* For, if there be any
" power in man to condenfe and dilate at will the æther, that pervades the
" mufcle, that condenfation or dilation muft vary the compreffion of the mufcle,
" made by the ambient æther, and caufe it to fwell or fhrink accordingly. For
" though common water will fcarce fhrink by compreffion, and fwell by relax-
" ation, yet (fo far as my obfervation reaches) fpirit of wine and oil will ; and
" Mr. BOYLE's experiment of a tadpole fhrinking very much by hard compref-
" fing the water, in which it fwam, is an argument, that animal juices do the
" fame. And as for their various preffion by the ambient æther, it is plain,
" that that muft be more or lefs accordingly as there is more or lefs æther with-
" in, to fuftain and counterpoife the preffure of that without. If both æthers
" were equally denfe, the mufcle would be at liberty, as if preffed by neither :
" if there were no æther within, the ambient would comprefs it with the whole
" force of its fpring. If the æther within were twice as much dilated as that
" without, fo as to have but half as much fpringinefs, the ambient would have
" half the force of its fpringinefs counterpoifed thereby, and exercife but the
" other half upon the mufcle ; and fo in all other cafes the ambient compreffes
" the mufcle by the excefs of the force of its fpringinefs above that of the fpring-
" inefs of the included. To vary the compreffion of the mufcle therefore, and
" fo to fwell and fhrink it, there needs nothing but to change the confiftence
" of the included æther ; and a very little change may fuffice, if the fpring of
" æther be fuppofed very ftrong, as I take it to be many degrees ftronger
" than that of air.

" Now for the changing the confiftence of the æther ; fome may be ready to
" grant, that the foul may have an immediate power over the whole æther in
" any part of the body, to fwell or fhrink it at will : but then how depends the
" mufcular

" mufcular motion on the nerves ?   Others therefore may be more apt to think
" it done by fome certain æthereal fpirit included within the *dura mater*, which
" the foul may have power to contract or dilate at will in any mufcle, and fo
" caufe it to flow thither through the nerves.   But ftill there is a difficulty, why
" this force of the foul upon it does not take off the power of its fpringinefs,
" whereby it fhould fuftain, more or lefs, the force of the outward æther.   A
" third fuppofition may be, that the foul has a power to infpire any mufcle with
" this fpirit, by impelling it thither through the nerves.   But this too has its
" difficulties, for it requires a forcible intending the fpring of the æther in the
" mufcles, by preffure exerted from the parts of the brain : and it is hard to
" conceive, how fo great force can be exercifed amidft fo tender matter as the
" brain is.   And befides, why does not this æthereal fpirit, being fubtil enough,
" and urged with fo great force, go away through the dura mater and fkins of
" the mufcle ; or at leaft fo much of the other æther go out to make way for
" this, which is crouded in ?   To take away thefe difficulties is a digreffion ; but
" feeing the fubject is a deferving one, I fhall not ftick to tell you how I think
" it may be done.

    " Firft then, I fuppofe, there is fuch a fpirit ; that is, that the animal fpirits
" are neither like the liquor, vapour, or gas of fpirit of wine ; but of an æthereal
" nature, fubtil enough to pervade the animal juices, as freely as the electric, or
" perhaps magnetic, effluvia do glafs.   And to know, how the coats of the
" brain, nerves, and mufcles, may become a convenient veffel to hold fo fubtil
" a fpirit, you may confider, how liquors and fpirits are difpofed to pervade or
" not pervade things on other accounts than their fubtilty.   Water and oil per-
" vade wood and ftone, which quickfilver does not ; and quickfilver metals,
" which water and oil do not : water and acid fpirits pervade falts, which oil
" and fpirit of wine do not ; and oil and fpirit of wine pervade fulphur, which
" water and acid fpirits do not.   So fome fluids, as oil and water, though their
" parts are in freedom enough to mix with one another, yet by fome fecret
" principle of unfociablenefs they keep afunder ; and fome, that are fociable, may
" become unfociable, by adding a third thing to one of them, as water to fpirit
" of wine, by diffolving falt of tartar in it.   The like unfociablenefs may be in
" æthereal natures, as perhaps between the æthers in the vortices of the fun and
" planets ; and the reafon, why air ftands rarer in the boxes of fmall glafs-pipes,
" and æther in the pores of bodies, than elfewhere, may be, not want of fub-
" tilty, but fociablenefs.   And on this ground, if the æthereal vital fpirit in a
" man be very fociable to the marrow and juices, and unfociable to the coats of
" the brain, nerves, and mufcles, or to any thing lodged in the pores of thofe
" coats, it may be contained thereby, notwithftanding its fubtilty ; efpecially if
" we fuppofe no great violence done to it to fqueeze it out ; and that it may not
" be altogether fo fubtil as the main body of æther, though fubtil enough to
" pervade readily the animal juices, and that, as any of it is fpent, it is continu-
" ally fupplied by new fpirit from the heart.

    " In the next place, for knowing how this fpirit may be ufed for animal mo-
" tion, you may confider, how fome things unfociable are made fociable by the
                                                              " mediation

" mediation of a third. Water, which will not diffolve copper, will do it, if
" the copper be melted with fulphur : aqua fortis, which will not pervade gold,
" will do it by addition of a little fal armoniac, or fpirit of falt : lead will not
" mix in melting with copper, but if a little tin or antimony be added, they mix
" readily, and part again of their own accord, if the antimony be wafted by
" throwing faltpeter or otherwife : and fo lead melted with filver quickly per-
" vades and liquefies the filver in a much lefs heat than is requifite to melt the
" filver alone; but, if they be kept in the teft till that little fubftance, that re-
" conciled them, be wafted or altered, they part again of their own accord. And,
" in like manner, the æthereal animal fpirit in a man may be a mediator between
" the common æther and the mufcular juices, to make them mix more freely;
" and fo, by fending a little of this fpirit into any mufcle, though fo little as to
" caufe no fenfible tenfion of the mufcle by its own force; yet, by rendering the
" juices more fociable to the common external æther, it may caufe that æther to
" pervade the mufcle of its own accord in a moment more freely and copioufly
" than it would otherwife do, and to recede again as freely, fo foon as this medi-
" ator of fociablenefs is retracted. Whence, according to what I faid above,
" will proceed the fwelling or fhrinking of the mufcle, and confequently the ani-
" mal motion depending thereon.

" Thus may therefore the foul, by determining this æthereal animal fpirit or
" wind into this or that nerve, perhaps with as much eafe as air is moved in cpen
" fpaces, caufe all the motions we fee in animals : for the making which motions
" ftrong, it is not neceffary, that we fhould fuppofe the æther within the mufcle
" very much condenfed or rarified by this means, but only that its fpring is fo
" very great, that a little alteration of its denfity fhall caufe a great alteration in
" the preffure. And what is faid of mufcular motion, may be applied to the mo-
" tion of the heart, only with this difference, that the fpirit is not fent thither,
" as into other mufcles, but continually generated there by the fermentation of
" the juices, with which its flefh is replenifhed, and as it is generated, let out by
" ftarts into the brain through fome convenient ductus to perform thofe motions
" in other mufcles by impreffion, which it did in the heart by its generation.
" For I fee not, why the ferment in the heart may not raife as fubtil a fpirit out
" of its juices, to caufe thefe motions, as rubbing does out of a glafs, to caufe
" electric attraction, or burning out of fewel, to penetrate glafs, as Mr. BOYLE
" has fhewn, and calcine by corrofion metals melted therein.

" Hitherto I have been contemplating the nature of æther and æthereal fub-
" ftances by their effects and ufes; and now I come to join therewith the confi-
" deration of light.

" In the fourth place therefore, I fuppofe light is neither æther, nor its vibrating
" motion, but fomething of a different kind propagated from lucid bodies. They,
" that will, may fuppofe it an aggregate of various peripatetic qualities. Others
" may fuppofe it multitudes of unimaginable fmall and fwift corpufcles of various
" fizes, fpringing from fhining bodies at great diftances one after another; but
" yet without any fenfible interval of time, and continually urged forward by a
" principle

7

" principle of motion, which in the beginning accelerates them, till the refiftence
" of the æthereal medium equal the force of that principle, much after the
" manner that bodies let fall in water are accelerated till the refiftance of the wa-
" ter equals the force of gravity. God, who gave animals felf-motion beyond
" our underftanding, is, without doubt, able to implant other principles of mo-
" tion in bodies, which we may underftand as little. Some would readily grant
" this may be a fpiritual one; yet a mechanical one might be fhewn, did not I
" think it better to pafs it by. But they, that like not this, may fuppofe light
" any other corporeal emanation, or any impulfe or motion of any other medium
" or æthereal fpirit diffufed through the main body of æther, or what elfe they
" can imagine proper for this purpofe. To avoid difpute, and make this hypo-
" thefis general, let every man here take his fancy: only, whatever light be, I
" fuppofe, it confifts of rays differing from one another in contingent circum-
" ftances, as bignefs, form, or vigour; like as the fands on the fhore, the waves
" of the fea, the faces of men, and all other natural things of the fame kind
" differ; it being almoft impoffible for any fort of things to be found without
" fome contingent variety. And further, I would fuppofe it diverfe, from the
" vibrations of the æther, becaufe (befides, that were it thefe vibrations, it
" ought always to verge copioufly in crooked lines into the dark or quiefcent
" medium, deftroying all fhadows; and to comply readily with any crooked pores
" or paffages, as founds do,) I fee not how any fuperficies (as the fide of a glafs
" prifm, on which the rays within are incident at an angle of above forty de-
" grees) can be totally opake. For the vibrations beating againft the refract-
" ing confine of the rarer and denfer æther muft needs make that pliant fuper-
" ficies undulate, and thofe undulations will ftir up and propagate vibrations on
" the other fide. And further, how light, incident on very thin fkins or plates
" of any tranfparent body, fhould, for many fucceffive thicknefles of the plate,
" in arithmetical progreffion, be alternately reflected and tranfmitted, as I find
" it is, puzzles me as much. For, though the arithmetical progreffion of thofe
" thicknefles, which reflect and tranfmit the rays alternately, argues, that it de-
" pends upon the number of vibrations between the two fuperficies of the plate,
" whether the ray fhall be reflected or tranfmitted: yet I cannot fee, how the
" number fhould vary the cafe, be it greater or lefs, whole or broken, unlefs
" light be fuppofed fomething elfe than thefe vibrations. Something indeed
" I could fancy towards helping the two laft difficulties, but nothing which I fee
" not infufficient.

" Fifthly, it is to be fuppofed, that light and æther mutually act upon one
" another, æther in refracting light, and light in warming æther; and that the
" denfeft æther acts moft ftrongly. When a ray therefore moves through æther
" of uneven denfity, I fuppofe it moft preffed, urged, or acted upon by the me-
" dium on that fide towards the denfer æther, and receives a continual impulfe or
" ply from that fide to recede towards the rarer, and fo is accelerated, if it move
" that way, or retarded, if the contrary. On this ground, if a ray move
" obliquely through fuch an unevenly denfe medium (that is, obliquely to thofe
" imaginary fuperficies, which run through the equally denfe parts of the me-
" dium, and may be called the refracting fuperficies) it muft be incurved, as it

" is

" is found to be, by obfervation in water ¹, whofe lower parts were made gradu-
" ally more falt, and fo more denfe than the upper.   And this may be the ground
" of all refraction and reflexion : for as the rarer air within a fmall glafs-pipe,
" and the denfer without, are not diftinguifhed by a meer mathematical fuper-
" ficies, but have air between them, at the orifice of the pipe, running through
" all intermediate degrees of denfity : fo I fuppofe the refracting fuperficies of
" æther, between unequally denfe mediums, to be not a mathematical one ; but
" of fome breadth, the æther therein, at the orifices of the pores of the folid body,
" being of all intermediate degrees of denfity between the rarer and denfer æthe-
" real mediums ; and the refraction I conceive to proceed from the continual
" incurvation of the ray all the while it is paffing the phyfical fuperficies.   Now,
" if the motion of the ray be fuppofed in this paffage to be increafed or dimi-
" nifhed in a certain proportion, according to the difference of the denfities of the
" æthereal mediums, and the addition or detraction of the motion be reckoned
" in the perpendicular from the refracting fuperficies, as it ought to be, the fines
" of incidence and refraction will be proportional according to what Des Cartes
" has demonftrated.

" The ray therefore, in paffing out of the rarer medium into the denfer,
" inclines continually more and more towards parallelifm with the refracting fu-
" perficies ; and if the differing denfities of the mediums be not fo great, nor the
" incidence of the ray fo oblique, as to make it parallel to that fuperficies before
" it gets through, then it goes through and is refracted ; but if, through the afore-
" faid caufes, the ray become parallel to that fuperficies before it can get through,
" then it muft turn back and be reflected.   Thus, for inftance, may be obferved
" in a triangular glafs-prifm O E F, that the rays A n,
" that fend out of the glafs into air, do, by inclining
" them more and more to the refracting fuperficies, emerge
" more and more obliquely till they be infinitely oblique ;
" that is, in a manner parallel to the fuperficies, which hap-
" pens when the angle of incidence is about forty degrees ;
" and then, if they be a little more inclined are all reflected,
" as at A V λ, becoming, I fuppofe, parallel to the fuperficies before they can get
" through it.   Let A B D C reprefent the rarer medium ; E F H G the denfer,
" C D F E the fpace between them, or re-
" fracting phyfical fuperficies, in which the
" æther is of all. intermediate degrees of
" denfity, from the rareft æther at C D,
" to the denfeft, at E F ; A m n L a ray,
" A m its incident part, m n its incurvation
" by the refracting fuperficies, and n L its
" emergent part.   Now, if the ray A m be
" fo much incurved as to become at its
" emergence n, as nearly as may be, paral-
" lel to C D, it is plain, that if that ray
" had been incident a little more obliquely,

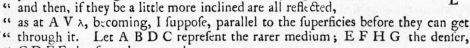

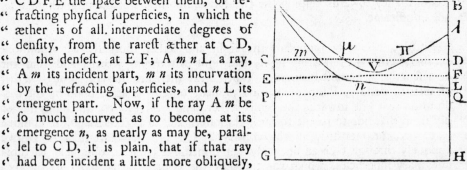

¹ See Mr. Hooke's Micrographia, where he fpeaks of the inflexion of rays.

" it

' it muft have become parallel to C D, before it had arrived at E F, the further
' fide of the refracting fuperficies; and fo could have got no nearer to E F, but
' muft have turned back by further incurvation, and been reflected, as it is re-
' prefented at A μ V λ. And the like would have happened, if the denfity
' of the æther had further increafed from E F to P Q; fo that P Q H G might
' be a denfer medium than E F H G was fuppofed; for then the ray, in paff-
' ing from m to n, being fo much incurved, as at n to become parallel to C D
' or P Q, it is impoffible it fhould ever get nearer to P Q, but muft at n be-
' gin by further incurvation to turn back, and fo be reflected. And becaufe, if
' a refracted ray, as n L, be made incident, the incident, A m, fhall become the
' refracted; and therefore, if the ray A μ V, after it is arrived at V, where I
' fuppofe it parallel to the refracting fuperficies, fhould be reflected perpendicu-
' larly back, it would return back in the line of incidence V μ A. Therefore
' going forward, it muft go forward in fuch another line, V π λ, both cafes be-
' ing alike, and fo be reflected at an angle, equal to that of incidence.

" This may be the caufe and manner of reflection, when light tends from the
' rarer towards the denfer æther: but to know, how it fhould be reflected,
' when it ftands from the denfer towards the rarer, you are further to confider,
' how fluids near their fuperficies are lefs pliant and yielding than in their more
' inward parts; and, if formed into thin plates, or fhells, they become much
' more ftiff and tenacious than otherwife. Thus, things, which readily fall in
' water, if let fall upon a bubble of water, they do not eafily break through it,
' but are apt to flide down by the fides of it, if they be not too big and heavy.
' So, if two well polifhed convex glaffes, ground on very large fpheres, be laid
' one upon another, the air between them eafily recedes, till they almoft touch;
' but then begins to refift fo much, that the weight of the upper glafs is too
' little to bring them together fo as to make the black, mentioned in the other
' papers I fend you, appear in the midft of the rings of colours: and, if the
' glaffes be plain, though no broader than a two-pence, a man with his whole
' ftrength is not able to prefs all the air out from between them, fo as to make
' them fully touch. You may obferve alfo, that infects will walk upon water
' without wetting their feet, and the water bearing them up; alfo motes fal-
' ling upon water will often lie long upon it without being wetted: and fo,
' I fuppofe, æther in the confine of two mediums is lefs pliant and yielding
' than in other places, and fo much the lefs pliant by how much the mediums
' differ in denfity: fo that in paffing out of denfer æther into rarer, when there
' remains but a very little of the denfer æther to be paft through, a ray finds
' more than ordinary difficulty to get through; and fo great difficulty, where the
' mediums are of very differing denfity, as to be reflected by incurvation, after
' the manner defcribed above; the parts of æther on that fide, where they are
' lefs pliant and yielding, acting upon the ray much after the manner that they
' would do were they denfer there than on the other fide: for the refiftance of
' the medium ought to have the fame effect on the ray, from what caufe foever
' it arifes. And this, I fuppofe, may be the caufe of the reflection of quick-
' filver, and other metalline bodies. It muft alfo concur to increafe the reflective
' virtue of the fuperficies, when rays tend out of the rarer medium into the

" denfer : and, in that cafe therefore, the reflection having a double caufe, ought
" to be ftronger than in the æther, as it is apparently. But in refraction, this ri-
" gid tenacity or unpliablenefs of the fuperficies need not be confidered, becaufe
" fo much as the ray is thereby bent in paffing to the moft tenacious and rigid
" part of the fuperficies, fo much it is thereby unbent again in paffing on from
" thence through the next parts gradually lefs tenacious.

" Thus may rays be refracted by fome fuperficies, and reflected by others, be
" the medium they tend into, denfer or rarer. But it remains further to be ex-
" plained, how rays alike incident on the fame fuperficies (fuppofe of cryftal, glafs,
" or water) may be at the fame time fome refracted, others reflected. And for ex-
" plaining this, I fuppofe, that the rays, when they impinge on the rigid refift-
" ing æthereal fuperficies, as they are acted upon by it, fo they react upon it and
" caufe vibrations in it, as ftones thrown into water do in its furface ; and that
" thefe vibrat ons are propagated every way into both the rarer and denfer me-
" diums ; as the vibrations of air, which caufe found, are from a ftroke, but yet
" continue ftrongeft where they began, and alternately contract and dilate the æther
" in that phyfical fuperficies. For it is plain by the heat, which light produces in
" bodies, that it is able to put their parts in motion, and much more to heat and
" put in motion the more tender æther ; and it is more probable, that it com-
" municates motion to the grofs parts of bodies by the mediation of æther than
" immediately ; as for inftance, in the inward parts of quickfilver, tin, filver,
" and other very opake bodies, by geneiating vibrations, that run through them,
" than by ftriking the outward parts only, without entering the body. The fhock
" of every fingle ray may generate many thoufand vibrations, and by fending
" them all over the body, move all the parts, and that perhaps with more mo-
" tion than it could move one fingle part by an immediate ftroke ; for the vi-
" brations, by fhaking each particle backward and forward, may every time
" increafe its motion, as a ringer does a bell by often pulling it, and fo at length
" move the particles to a very great degree of agitation, which neither the fimple
" fhock of a ray, nor any other motion in the æther, befides a vibrating-one could
" do. Thus in air fhut up in a veffel, the motion of its parts caufed by heat,
" how violent foever, is unable to move the bodies hung in it, with either a trem-
" bling or progreffive motion : but if air be put into a vibrating motion by beat-
" ing a drum or two, it fhakes glafs-windows, the whole body of a man, and
" other maffy things, efpecially thofe of a congruous tone : yea I have obferved it
" manifeftly fhake under my feet a cellared free-ftone floor of a large hall, fo as,
" I believe, the immediate ftroke of five hundred drumfticks could not have done,
" unlefs perhaps quickly fucceeding one another at equal intervals of time. Æthe-
" real vibrations are therefore the beft means by which fuch a fubtile agent as
" light can fhake the grofs particles of folid bodies to heat them : and fo fup-
" pofing that light, impinging on a refracting or reflecting æthereal fuperficies, puts
" it into a vibrating motion, that phyfical fuperficies being by the perpetual ap-
" pulfe of rays always kept in a vibrating motion, and the æther therein conti-
" nually expanded and compreffed by turns ; if a ray of light impinge upon it,
" while it is much compreffed, I fuppofe it is then too denfe and ftiff to let the ray

" pafs

" pafs through, and fo reflects it ; but the rays, that impinge on it at other times,
" when it is either expanded by the interval of two vibrations, or not too much
" compreffed and condenfed, go through and are refracted.

" Thefe may be the caufes of refractions and reflections in all cafes ; but, for
" underftanding how they come to be fo regular, it is further to be confidered,
" that in a heap of fand, although the furface be rugged, yet if water be poured
" on it to fill its pores, the water, fo foon as its pores are filled, will evenly over-
" fpread the furface, and fo much the more evenly, as the fand is finer : fo, al-
" though the furface of all bodies, even the moft polifhed, be rugged, as I con-
" ceive, yet where that ruggednefs is not too grofs and coarfe, the refracting æthe-
" real fuperficies may evenly overfpread it.   In polifhing glafs or metal, it is not
" to be imagined, that fand, putty, or other fretting powders, fhould wear the
" furface fo regularly, as to make the front of every particle exactly plain, and
" all thofe plains look the fame way, as they ought to do in well polifhed bodies,
" were reflection performed by their parts : but that thofe fretting powders fhould
" wear the bodies firft to a coarfe ruggednefs, fuch as is fenfible, and then to a finer
" and finer ruggednefs, till it be fo fine that the æthereal fuperficies evenly over-
" fpreads it, and fo makes the body put on the appearance of a polifh, is a very na-
" tural and intelligible fuppofition.   So in fluids, it is not well to be conceived, that
" the furfaces of their parts fhould be all plain, and the plains of the fuperficial parts
" always kept looking all the fame way, notwithftanding that they are in perpetual
" motion.   And yet without thefe two fuppofitions, the fuperficies of fluids could
" not be fo regularly reflexive as they are, were the reflexion done by the parts them-
" felves, and not by an æthereal fuperficies evenly overfpreading the fluid.

" Further, concerning the regular motion of light, it might be fufpected, whe-
" ther the various vibrations of the fluid, through which it paffes, may not much
" difturb it : but that fufpicion, I fuppofe, will vanifh, by confidering, that
" if at any time the foremoft part of an oblique wave begin to turn it awry,
" the hindermoft part, by a contrary action, muft foon fet it ftraight again.

" Laftly, becaufe without doubt there are, in every tranfparent body, pores of
" various fizes, and I faid, that æther ftands at the greateft rarity in the fmalleft
" pores ; hence the æther in every pore fhould be of a differing rarity, and fo
" light be refracted in its paffage out of every pore into the next, which would
" caufe a great confufion, and fpoil the body's tranfparency.   But confidering that
" the æther, in all denfe bodies, is agitated by continual vibrations, and thefe vi-
" brations cannot be performed without forcing the parts of æther forward and
" backward, from one pore to another, by a kind of tremor, fo that the æther,
" which one moment is in a greater pore, is the next moment forced into a lefs ;
" and on the contrary, this muft evenly fpread the æther into all the pores not
" exceeding fome certain bignefs, fuppofe the breadth of a vibration, and fo make
" it of an even denfity throughout the tranfparent body, agreeable to the middle
" fort of pores.   But where the pores exceed a certain bignefs, I fuppofe
" the æther fuits its denfity to the bignefs of the pore, or to the medium within
" it ; and fo being of a diverfe denfity from the æther that furrounds it, refracts

260   **THE HISTORY OF THE**   [1675.

" or reflects light in its fuperficies, and fo make the body, where many fuch in-
" terftices are, appear opake."

Some of the members taking particular notice, among other things, of an
experiment mentioned in this hypothefis, defired, that it might be tried ; viz.
that having laid upon a table a round piece of glafs, about two inches broad, in a
brafs ring ; fo that the glafs might be one third part of an inch from the table ;
and then rubbing the glafs brifkly, till fome little fragments of paper laid on the
table under the glafs began to be attracted, and move nimbly to and fro ; after
he had done rubbing the glafs, the papers would continue a pretty while in various motions, fometimes leaping up to the glafs, and refting there a while, then
leaping down, and refting there, and then leaping up and down again, and this
fometimes in lines feeming perpendicular to the table, fometimes in oblique
ones ; fometimes alfo leaping up in one arch, and leaping down in another divers
times together, without fenfibly refting between ; fometimes fkipping in a bow
from one part of the glafs to another, without touching the table, and fometimes
hanging by a corner, and turning often about very nimbly, as if they had been
carried about in the middle of a whirlwind ; and being otherwife varioufly moved,
every paper with a different motion.   And upon fliding his finger upon the upper fide of the glafs, though neither the glafs nor the inclofed air below were moved
thereby, yet would the papers, as they hung under the glafs, receive fome new
motion, inclining this or that way, according as he moved his finger.

This experiment Mr. NEWTON propofed to be varied with a larger glafs placed
farther from the table, and to make ufe of bits of leaf gold inftead of papers ;
thinking, that this would fucceed much better, fo as perhaps to make the leaf gold
rife and fall in fpiral lines, or whirl for a time in the air, without touching either
the table or glafs.

It was ordered, that this experiment fhould be tried at the next meeting ; and
Mr. HOOKE promifed to prepare it for that meeting.

Mr. OLDENBURG was defired to enquire by letter of Mr. NEWTON, whether
he would confent, that a copy might be taken of his papers, for the better confideration of their contents.

Mr. OLDENBURG prefented from Mr. MARTYN, the printer to the Society,
Mr. WILLUGHBY's *Ornithologia*, printed at London, 1676, in fol.

December 16.   Mr. NEWTON's experiment of glafs rubbed to caufe various motions in bits of paper underneath, was tried, but did not fucceed in thofe circumftances, with which it was tried.   This trial was made upon the reading of a letter
of his to Mr. OLDENBURG, dated at Cambridge, 14th December, 1675 [m], in
which he gives fome more particular directions about that experiment.

The letter was as follows :

* Letter-book, vol. vii. p. 280.

The

" The notice you gave me of the Royal Society's intending to fee the experi-
" ment of glafs rubbed, to caufe various motions in bits of paper underneath,
" put me upon recollecting myfelf a little further about it ; and then remembring,
" that, if one edge of the brafs hoop was laid downward, the glafs was as near
" again to the table as it was when the other edge was laid downward, and that
" the papers played beft when the glafs was neareft to the table ; I began to fuf-
" pect, that I had fet down a greater diftance of the glafs from the table than I
" fhould have done ; for in fetting down that experiment, I trufted to the idea I
" had of the bignefs of the hoop, in which I might eafily be miftaken, having
" not feen it of a long time. And this fufpicion was increafed by trying the ex-
" periment with an object glafs of a telefcope, placed about the third part of an
" inch from the table ; for I could not fee the papers play any thing near fo well
" as I had feen them formerly. Whereupon I looked for the old hoop with its
" glafs, and at length found the hoop, the glafs being gone ; but by the hoop I
" perceived, that, when one edge was turned down, the glafs was almoft the
" third part of an inch from the table, and when the other edge was down,
" which made the papers play fo well, the glafs was fcarce the eighth part of an
" inch from the table. This I thought fit to fignify to you, that, if the expe-
" riment fucceed not well at the diftance I fet down, it may be tried at a lefs
" diftance, and that you may alter my paper, and write in it the eighth part of an
" inch inftead of $\frac{1}{4}$ or $\frac{1}{3}$ of an inch. The bits of paper ought to be very little,
" and of thin paper ; perhaps little bits of the wings of a fly, or other light fub-
" ftances, may do better than paper. Some of the motions, as that of hanging
" by a corner and twirling about, and that of leaping from one part of the glafs
" to another, without touching the table, happen but feldom ; but it made me take
" the more notice of them.

" Pray prefent my humble fervice to Mr. BOYLE, when you fee him, and thanks
" for the favour of the converfe I had with him at Spring. My conceit of tre-
" paning the common æther, as he was pleafed to exprefs it, makes me begin
" to have the better thoughts on that he was pleafed to entertain it with a fmile.
" I am apt to think, that when he has a fet of experiments to try in his air-pump,
" he will make that one, to fee how the compreffion or relaxation of a mufcle will
" fhrink or fwell, foften or harden, lengthen or fhorten it.

" As for regiftring the two difcourfes, you may do it ; only I defire you would
" fufpend till my next letter, in which I intend to fet down fomething to be al-
" tered, and fomething to be added in the hypothefis."

It was ordered, that Mr. OLDENBURG fhould again write to Mr. NEWTON, and
acquaint him with the want of fuccefs of his experiment, and defire him to fend
his own apparatus, with which he had made it: as alfo to enquire, whether he
had fecured the papers being moved from the air, that might fomewhere fteal in.

Hereupon the fequel of his hypothefis, the firft part of which was read at the
preceding meetings, was read to the end.

2

" Thus

" Thus much of refraction, reflection, tranfparency, and opacity; and now to
" explain colours; I fuppofe, that as bodies of various fizes, denfities, or fenfa-
" tions, do by percuffion or other action excite founds of various tones, and
" confequently vibrations in the air of various bignefs; fo when the rays of
" light, by impinging on the ftiff refracting fuperficies, excite vibrations in the
" æther, thofe rays, whatever they be, as they happen to differ in magnitude,
" ftrength or vigour, excite vibrations of various bignefs; the biggeft, ftrongeft,
" or moft potent rays, the largeft vibrations; and others fhorter, according to
" their bignefs, ftrength, or power: and therefore the ends of the capillamenta of
" the optic nerve, which pave or face the retina, being fuch refracting fuperfi-
" cies, when the rays impinge upon them, they muft there excite thefe vibra-
" tions, which vibrations (like thofe of found in a trunk or trumpet) will run
" along the aqueous pores or cryftalline pith of the capillamenta through the
" optic nerves into the fenforum (which light itfelf cannot do) and there, I fup-
" pofe, affect the fenfe with various colours, according to their bignefs and mix-
" ture; the biggeft with the ftrongeft colours, reds and yellows; the leaft with
" the weakeft, blues and violets; the middle with green, and a confufion of
" all with white, much after the manner, that in the fenfe of hearing, nature
" makes ufe of aereal vibrations of feveral bigneffes to generate founds of divers
" tones; for the analogy of nature is to be obferved. And further, as the
" harmony and difcord of founds proceed from the proportions of the aereal vi-
" brations, fo may the harmony of fome colours, as of golden and blue, and the
" difcord of others, as of red and blue, proceed from the proportions of the æthe-
" real. And poffibly colour may be diftinguifhed into its principal degrees, red,
" orange, yellow, green, blue, indigo, and deep violet, on the fame ground,
" that found within an eighth is graduated into tones. For, fome years paft, the
" prifmatic colours being in a well darkened room caft perpendicularly upon
" a paper about two and twenty foot diftant from the prifm, I defired a friend
" to draw with a pencil lines crofs the image, or pillar of colours, where every
" one of the feven aforenamed colours was moft full and brifk, and alfo where he
" judged the trueft confines of them to be, whilft I held the paper fo, that the faid
" image might fall within a certain compafs marked on it. And this I did, partly
" becaufe my own eyes are not very critical in diftinguifhing colours, partly be-
" caufe another, to whom I had not communicated my thoughts about this mat-
" ter, could have nothing but his eyes to determine his fancy in making thofe
" marks. This obfervation we repeated divers times, both in the fame and di-
" vers days, to fee how the marks on feveral papers would agree; and comparing
" the obfervations, though the juft confines of the colours are hard to be affigned,
" becaufe they pafs into one another by infenfible gradation; yet the *differences*
" of the obfervations were but little, efpecially towards the red end, and taking
" means between thofe differences, that were, the length of the image (reckoned
" not by the diftance of the verges of the femicircular ends, but by the diftance of
" the centres of thofe femicircles, or length of the ftrait fides as it ought to be)
" was divided in about the fame proportion that a ftring is, between the end and
" the middle, to found the tones in the eighth. You will underftand me beft
" by viewing the annexed figure, in which A B and C D reprefent the ftrait
" fides, about ten inches long, A B C and B T D the femicircular ends, X and

" Y

" Y the centres of thofe femicircles, X Z the length of a mufical ftring double to

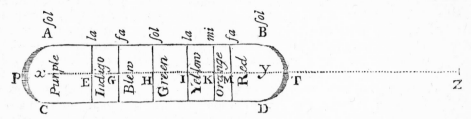

" X Y, and divided between X and Y, fo as to found the tones expreffed at the
" fide (that is X H the half, X G and G I the third part, Y K the fifth part,
" Y M the eighth part, and G E the ninth part of X Y) and the intervals between
" thefe divifions exprefs the fpaces which the colours written there took up, every
" colour being moft brifkly fpecific in the middle of thofe fpaces.

" Now for the caufe of thefe and fuch like colours made by refraction, the
" biggeft or ftrongeft rays muft penetrate the refracting fuperficies more freely
" and eafily than the weaker, and fo be lefs turned awry by it, that is, lefs re-
" fracted; which is as much as to fay, the rays, which make red, are leaft refran-
" gible, thofe, which make blue and violet, moft refrangible, and others otherwife
" refrangible according to their colour : whence, if the rays, which come promif-
" cuoufly from the fun, be refracted by a prifm, as in the aforefaid experiment,
" thefe of feveral forts being varioufly refracted, muft go to feveral places on an
" oppofite paper or wall, and fo parted, exhibit every one their own colours,
" which they could not do while blended together. And, becaufe refraction only
" fevers them, and changes not the bignefs or ftrength of the ray, thence it is,
" that after they are once well fevered, refraction cannot make any further changes
" in their colour.

" On this ground may all the phænomena of refractions be underftood : but to
" explain the colours made by reflections, I muft further fuppofe, that, though
" light be unimaginably fwift, yet the æthereal vibrations, excited by a ray, move
" fafter than the ray itfelf, and fo overtake and outrun it one after another. And
" this, I fuppofe, they will think an allowable fuppofition, who have been in-
" clined to fufpect, that thefe vibrations themfelves might be light. But to make
" it the more allowable, it is poffible light itfelf may not be fo fwift, as fome are
" apt to think; for, notwithftanding any argument, that I know yet to the con-
" trary, it may be an hour or two, if not more, in moving from the fun to us.
" This celerity of the vibrations therefore fuppofed, if light be incident on a thin
" fkin or plate of any tranfparent body, the waves, excited by its paffage through
" the firft fuperficies, overtaking it one after another, till it arrive at the fecond
" fuperficies, will caufe it to be there reflected or refracted accordingly as the con-
" denfed or expanded part of the wave overtakes it there. If the plate be of fuch
" a thicknefs, that the condenfed part of the firft wave overtake the ray at the fe
" cond fuperficies, it muft be reflected there ; if double that thicknefs, that the
" following rarified part of the wave, that is, the fpace between that and the next
" wave,

" wave, overtake it, there it muſt be tranſmitted ; if triple the thickneſs, that the
" condenſed part of the ſecond wave overtake it, there it muſt be reflected, and
" ſo where the plate is five, ſeven, or nine times that thickneſs, it muſt be *reflected*
" by reaſon of the third, fourth, or fifth wave, overtaking it at the ſecond ſuper-
" ficies; but when it is four, ſix, or eight times that thickneſs, ſo that the ray
" may be overtaken there by the dilated interval of thoſe waves, it ſhall be *tranſ-*
" *mitted,* and ſo on ; the ſecond ſuperficies being made able or unable to reflect
" accordingly as it is condenſed or expanded by the waves. For inſtance, let
" A H Q repreſent the ſuperficies of a ſpherically convex glaſs laid upon a plain
" glaſs A I R, and A I R Q H the thin plane-concave plate of air between them,
" and B C, D E, F G, H I, &c. thickneſſes of that plate, or diſtances of the
" glaſſes in the arithmetical progreſſion of the numbers 1. 2. 3. 4. &c. whereof

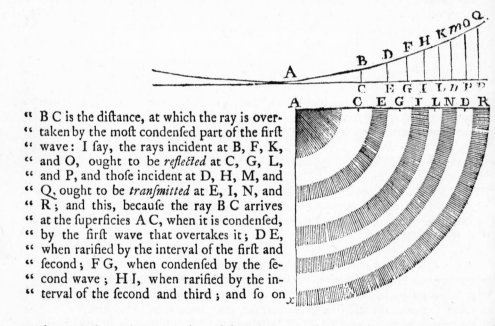

" B C is the diſtance, at which the ray is over-
" taken by the moſt condenſed part of the firſt
" wave : I ſay, the rays incident at B, F, K,
" and O, ought to be *reflected* at C, G, L,
" and P, and thoſe incident at D, H, M, and
" Q, ought to be *tranſmitted* at E, I, N, and
" R ; and this, becauſe the ray B C arrives
" at the ſuperficies A C, when it is condenſed,
" by the firſt wave that overtakes it ; D E,
" when rarified by the interval of the firſt and
" ſecond ; F G, when condenſed by the ſe-
" cond wave ; H I, when rarified by the in-
" terval of the ſecond and third ; and ſo on

" for an indeterminate number of ſucceſſions ; and at A, the center or contact of
" the glaſſes, the light muſt be *tranſmitted,* becauſe there the æthereal mediums
" in both glaſſes are continued as if but one uniform medium. Whence, if the
" glaſſes in this poſture be looked upon, there ought to appear at A, the contact
" of the glaſſes, a black ſpot, and about that many concentric circles of light and
" darkneſs, the ſquares of whoſe ſemidiameters are to ſenſe and arithmetical pro-
" greſſion. Yet all the rays, without exception, ought not to be thus reflected or
" tranſmitted : for ſometimes a ray may be overtaken at the ſecond ſuperficies,
" by the vibrations raiſed by another collateral or immediately ſucceeding ray ;
" which vibration, being as ſtrong or ſtronger than its own, may cauſe it to be
" reflected or tranſmitted when its own vibration alone would do the contrary.
" And hence ſome little light will be reflected from the black rings, which makes
" them

" them rather black than totally dark ; and fome tranfmitted at the lucid rings,
" which makes the black rings, appearing on the other fide of the glaffes, not fo
" black as they would otherwife be. And fo at the central black fpot, where the
" glaffes do not abfolutely touch, a little light will be reflected, which makes the
" fpot darkeft in the middle, and only black at the verges. For thus I have ob-
" ferved it to be, by tying very hard together two glafs prifms, which were ac-
" cidentally (one of them at leaft) a very little convex, and viewing by divers
" lights this black fpot at their contact. If a white paper was placed at a little
" diftance behind a candle, and the candle and paper viewed alternately by re-
" flection from the fpot, the verges of the fpot, which looked by the light of the
" paper as black as the middle part, appeared by the ftronger light of the candle
" lucid enough, fo as to make the fpot feem lefs than before ; but the middle part
" continued as abfolutely black in one cafe as in the other, fome fpecks and ftreaks
" in it only excepted, where I fuppofe the glaffes, through fome unevennefs in
" the polifh, did not fully touch. The fame I have obferved by viewing the fpot
" by the like reflection of the fun and clouds alternately.

" But to return to the lucid and black rings, thofe rings ought always to ap-
" pear after the manner defcribed, were light uniform. And after that manner,
" when the two contiguous glaffes A Q and A R have been illuftrated, in a dark
" room, by light of any uniform colour made by a prifm, I have feen the lucid
" circles appear to about twenty in number, with many dark ones between them,
" the colour of the lucid ones being that of the light, with which the glaffes were
" illuftrated. And if the glaffes were held between the eye and prifmatic colours,
" caft on a fheet of white-paper, or if any prifmatic colour was directly trajected
" through the glaffes to a fheet of paper placed a little way behind, there would
" appear fuch other rings of colour and darknefs (in the firft cafe between the
" glaffes, in the fecond, on the paper) oppofitely correfponding to thofe, which
" appeared by reflection : I mean, that, whereas by reflected light there appeared
" a black fpot in the middle, and then a coloured circle ; on the contrary, by tranf-
" mitted light there appeared a coloured fpot in the middle, and then a black circle,
" and fo on ; the diameters of the coloured circles, made by tranfmiffion, equall-
" ing the diameters of the black ones made by reflection.

" Thus, I fay, the rings do and ought to appear when made by uniform light ;
" but in compound light it is otherwife. For the rays, which exhibit red and
" yellow, exciting, as I faid, larger pulfes in the æther than thofe, which make
" blue and violet, and confequently making bigger circles in a certain propor-
" tion, as I have manifeftly found they do, by illuminating the glaffes fucceffively
" by the aforefaid colours of prifm in a well darkened room, without changing
" the pofition of my eye or of the glaffes ; hence the circles, made by illuftrating
" the glaffes with white light, ought not to appear black and white by turns, as
" the circles made by illuftrating the glaffes ; for inftance, with red light, appear
" red and black ; but the colours, which compound the white light, muft difplay
" themfelves by being reflected, the blue and violet nearer to the center than the
" red and yellow, whereby every lucid circle muft become violet in the inward
" verge, red in the outward, and of intermediate colours in the intermediate

" parts, and be made broader than before, fpreading the colours both ways into
" thofe fpaces, which I call the black rings, and which would here appear black,
" were the red, yellow, blue, and violet, which make the verge of the rings, taken
" out of the incident white light, which illuftrates the glaffes, and the green only
" left to make the lucid rings. Suppofe C B, G D, L F, P M, R N, S X, re-
" prefent quadrants of the circles made in a dark room by the very deepeft prif-

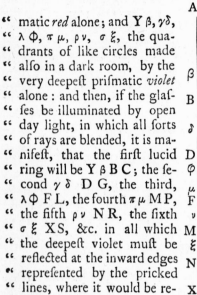

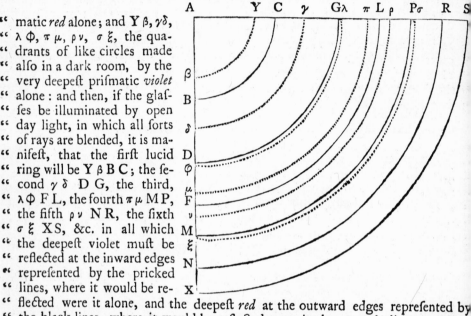

" matic *red* alone; and Y β, γ δ,
" λ φ, π μ, ρ ν, σ ξ, the qua-
" drants of like circles made
" alfo in a dark room, by the
" very deepeft prifmatic *violet*
" alone : and then, if the glaf-
" fes be illuminated by open
" day light, in which all forts
" of rays are blended, it is ma-
" nifeft, that the firft lucid
" ring will be Y β B C; the fe-
" cond γ δ D G, the third,
" λ φ F L, the fourth π μ M P,
" the fifth ρ ν N R, the fixth
" σ ξ X S, &c. in all which
" the deepeft violet muft be
" reflected at the inward edges
" reprefented by the pricked
" lines, where it would be re-
" flected were it alone, and the deepeft *red* at the outward edges reprefented by
" the black lines, where it would be reflected, were it alone ; and all intermediate
" colours at thofe places, in order, between thefe edges, at which they would be re-
" flected were they alone ; each of them in a dark room, parted from all other
" colours by the refraction of a prifm. And becaufe the fquares of the femidia-
" meters of the outward verges A C, A G, A L, &c. as alfo of A Y, A γ, A λ,
" &c. the femidiameters of the inward are in arithmetical progreffion of the num-
" bers 1, 3, 5, 7, 9, 11, &c. and the fquares of the inward are to the fquares
" of the outward (A Y⁹ to A C⁹, A γ⁹ to A G⁹, A λ⁹ to A L⁹, &c.) as 9 to 14;
" (as I have found by meafuring them carefully and often, and comparing the
" obfervations :) therefore the outward *red* verge of the fecond ring, and inward
" *violet* one of the third, fhall border upon one another (as you may know by com-
" putation, and fee them reprefented in the figure) and the like edges of the third
" and fourth rings fhall interfere, and thofe of the fourth and fifth interfere more,
" and fo on. Yea, the colours of every ring muft fpread themfelves fomething
" more both ways than is here reprefented, becaufe the quadrantal arcs here de-
" fcribed reprefent not the verges, but the middle of the rings made in a dark
" room by the extreme violet and red ; the *violet* falling on both fides the pricked
" arches, and *red* on both fides the black line arches. And hence it is, that
" thefe rings or circuits of colours fucceed one another continually, without any

" inter-

" intervening black, and that the colours are pure only in the three or four firſt
" rings, and then intervening and mixing more and more, dilute one another ſo
" much, that after eight or nine rings they are no more to be diſtinguiſhed, but
" ſeem to conſtitute an even whiteneſs; whereas, when they were made in a dark
" room by one of the priſmatic colours alone, I have, as I ſaid, ſeen above twenty
" of them, and without doubt could have ſeen them to a greater number, had I
" taken the pains to make the priſmatic colour more uncompounded. For by
" unfolding theſe rings from one another, by certain refractions expreſſed in the
" other ⁵ papers I ſend you, 1 have, even in day-light, diſcovered them to above
" an hundred; and perhaps they would have appeared innumerable, had the light
" or colour illuſtrating the glaſſes been abſolutely uncompounded, and the pupil
" of my eye but a mathematical point; ſo that all the rays, which came from
" the ſame point of the glaſs might have gone into my eye at the ſame obliquity
" to the glaſs.

" What has been hitherto ſaid of the rings, is to be underſtood of their appear-
' ance to an unmoved eye : but if you vary the poſition of the eye, the more
" obliquely you look on the glaſs, the larger the rings appear. And of this the
" reaſon may be, partly that an oblique ray is longer in paſſing through the
" firſt ſuperficies, and ſo there is more time between the waving forward and back-
" ward of that ſuperficies, and conſequently a larger wave generated, and partly,
" that the wave in creeping along between the two ſuperficies may be impeded and
" retarded by the rigidneſs of thoſe ſuperficies, bounding it at either end, and ſo
" not overtake the ray ſo ſoon as a wave, that moves perpendicularly croſs.

" The bigneſs of the circles made by every colour, and at all obliquities of the
" eye to the glaſſes, and the thickneſs of the air, or intervals of the glaſſes,
" where each circle is made, you will find expreſſed in the other papers I ſend
" you; where alſo I have more at large deſcribed, how much theſe rings inter-
' fere, or ſpread into one another; what colours appear in every ring, where
" they are moſt lively, where and how much diluted by mixing with the colours of
' other rings; and how the contrary colours appear on the back ſide of the glaſſes
" by the tranſmitted light, the glaſſes tranſmitting light of one colour at the ſame
' place, where they reflect that of another. Nor need I add any thing further of
' the colours of other thinly plated mediums, as of water between the aforeſaid
' glaſſes, or formed into bubbles, and ſo encompaſſed with air, or of glaſs blown
' into very thin bubbles at a lamp furnace, &c. the caſe being the ſame in all theſe,
' excepting that, where the thickneſs of the plate is not regular, the rings will not
" be ſo; that in plates of denſer tranſparent bodies, the rings are made at a leſs
" thickneſs of the plate (the vibrations, I ſuppoſe, being ſhorter in rarer æther than
' in denſer) and that in a denſer plate, ſurrounded with a rarer body, the colours
" are more vivid than in the rarer ſurrounded with the denſer; as, for inſtance,
" more vivid in a plate of glaſs ſurrounded with air, than in a plate of air ſur-
' rounded with glaſs; of which the reaſon is, that the reflection of the ſecond ſu-
' perficies, which cauſes the colours, is, as was ſaid above, ſtronger in the for-

⁵ Obſ. 24.

M m 2   " mer

" mer cafe than in the latter : for which reafon alfo the colours are moft vivid,
" when the difference of the denfity of the medium is greateft.

" Of the colours of natural bodies alfo I have faid enough in thofe papers, fhew-
" ing how the various fizes of the tranfparent particles, of which they confift, is
" fufficient to produce them all, thofe particles reflecting or tranfmitting this or
" that fort of rays, according to their thicknefs, like the aforefaid plates, as if they
" were fragments thereof. For, I fuppofe, if a plate of an even thicknefs, and
" confequently of an uniform colour, were broken into fragments of the fame thick-
" nefs with the plate, a heap of thofe fragments would be a powder much of the
" fame colour with the plates. And fo, if the parts be of the thicknefs of the
" water in the black fpot at the top of a bubble defcribed in the feventeenth of
" the obfervations I fend you, I fuppofe the body muft be black. In the pro-
" duction of which blacknefs, I fuppofe, that the particles of that fize being dif-
" pofed to reflect almoft no light outward, but to refract it continually in its paf-
" fage from every part to the next ; by this multitude of refractions, the rays
" are kept fo long ftraggling to and fro within the body, till at laft almoft all
" impinge on the folid parts of the body, and fo are ftopped and ftifled ; thofe
" parts having no fufficient elafticity, or other difpofition to return nimbly enough
" the fmart fhock of the ray back upon it.

" I fhould here conclude, but that there is another ftrange phænomenon of
" colours, which may deferve to be taken notice of. Mr. HOOKE, you may re-
" member, was fpeaking of an odd ftraying of light, caufed in its paffage near the
" edge of a razor, knife, or other opake body in a dark room ; the rays, which
" pafs very near the edge, being thereby made to ftray at all angles into the
" fhadow of the knife.

" To this Sir WILLIAM PETTY, then prefident, returned a very pertinent query,
" Whether that ftraying was in curve lines ? and that made me, having heard
" Mr. HOOKE fome days before compare it to the ftraying of found into the qui-
" efcent medium, fay, that I took it to be only a new kind of refraction, caufed
" perhaps by the external æther's beginning to grow rarer a little before it
" came at the opake body, than it was in free fpaces ; the denfer æther without
" the body, and the rarer within it, being terminated not in a mathematical
" fuperficies, but paffing into one another through all intermediate degrees of
" denfity : whence the rays, that pafs fo near the body, as to come within that
" compafs, where the outward æther begins to grow rarer, muft be refracted by
" the uneven denfenefs thereof, and blended inwards toward the rarer medium of
" the body. To this Mr. HOOKE was then pleafed to anfwer, that though it
" fhould be but a new kind of refraction, yet it was a new one. What to make
" of this unexpected reply, I knew not ; having no other thoughts, but that a
" new kind of refraction might be as noble an invention as any thing elfe about
" light ; but it made me afterwards, I know not upon what occafion, happen to
" fay, among fome that were prefent to what paffed before, that I thought I had
" feen the experiment before in fome Italian author. And the author is HONO-
" RATUS FABER, in his dialogue De Lumine, who had it from GRIMALDO;
                                                                " whom

' whom I mention, becaufe I am to defcribe fomething further out of him, which
' you will apprehend by this figure : fuppofe the fun fhine through the little hole
' H K into a dark room upon the paper P Q, and with a wedge M N O intercept
' all but a little of that beam, and you will fee
' upon the paper fix rows of colours, R, S, T,
' V, X, Y, and beyond them a very faint light
' fpreading either way, fuch as rays broken, like
' H N Z, muft make. The author defcribes it
' more largely in divers fchemes. I have time
' only to hint the fum of what he fays.

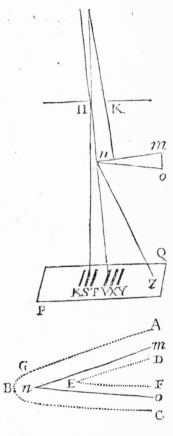

" Now for the breaking of the ray H N Z, fup-
' pofe, in the next figure M N O be the folid
' wedge, A B C the inward bound of the uniform
' rarer æther within, between which bounds the
' æther runs through all the intermediate degrees ;
' and it is manifeft, that, if a ray come between
' B and N, it muft in its paffage there bend from
' the denfer medium towards C, and that fo much
' the more, by how much it comes nearer N. Fur-
' ther, for the three rows of colours V X Y, thofe
' may perhaps proceed from the number of vibra-
' tions (whether one, two, or three) which over-
' take the ray in its paffage from G, till it be about
' the mid-way between G and H ; that is, at its
' neareft diftance to N, fo as to touch the circle
' defcribed about N, with that diftance ; by the
' laft of which vibrations, expanding or con-
' tracting the medium there, the ray is licenfed
' to recede again from N, and go on to make the
' colours ; or further bent about N, till the inter-
' val of the next wave overtake it, and give it li-
' berty to go from N, very nearly in the line it is
' then moving, fuppofe toward Z, to caufe the faint light fpoken of above, you
' will underftand me a little better, by comparing this with what was faid of the
' colours of thin tranfparent plates, comparing the greateft diftance that the ray
' goes from G B H towards N, to the thicknefs of one of thofe plates. Some-
' thing too there is in Des Cartes's explication of the rainbow's colours, which
' would give further light in this. But I have no time left to infift further upon
' particulars ; nor do I propound this without diffidence, having not made fuffici-
' ent obfervation about it."

After reading this difcourfe, Mr. Hooke faid, that the main of it was contained
in his *Micrographia*, which Mr. Newton had only carried farther in fome parti-
ulars.

The Society adjourned till December 30.

December 30.   There was read a letter to Mr. OLDENBURG from Mr. NEW-
TON, dated at Cambridge 21ſt December, 1675 ᵗ, in anſwer to what had been
written to him by Mr. OLDENBURG concerning the want of ſucceſs of his experiment made with a glaſs rubbed, &c.   This letter was as follows :

" Upon your letter I took another glaſs four inches broad, and one fourth of
" an inch thick, of ſuch glaſs as teleſcopes are made of, and placed it a one ſixth
" part of an inch from the table.   It was ſet in ſuch a piece of wood, as the ob-
" ject-glaſſes of teleſcopes uſe to be ſet in : and the experiment ſucceeded well.
" After the rubbing was ſtill, and all was ſtill, the motion of the papers would
" continue ſometimes while I counted a hundred, every paper leaping up about
" twenty times more or leſs, and down as often. I tried it alſo with two other glaſſes
" that belong to a teleſcope, and it ſucceeded with both ; and I make no queſtion
" but any glaſs will do that, if it be excited to electric virtue, as I think any may.
" If you have a mind to any of theſe glaſſes, you may have them ; but I ſup-
" poſe, if you cannot make it do in other glaſs, you will fail in any I can ſend
" you.   I am apt to ſuſpect the failure was in the manner of rubbing ; for I have
" obſerved, that the rubbing variouſly, or with various things, alters the caſe.   At
" one time I rubbed the aforeſaid great glaſs with a napkin, twice as much as I
" uſed to do with my gown, and nothing would ſtir ; and yet preſently rubbing
" it with ſomething elſe, the motions ſoon began.   After the glaſs has been
" much rubbed too, the motions are not ſo laſting ; and the next day I found the
" motions fainter and difficulter to excite than the firſt.   If the Society have a
" mind to attempt it any more, I can give no better advice than this : to take a
" new glaſs not yet rubbed (perhaps one of the old ones may do well enough after
" it has lain ſtill a while) and let this be rubbed, not with linen, nor ſoft nappy
" woolen, but with ſtuff, whoſe threads may rake the ſurface of the glaſs, ſup-
" poſe tamerine, or the like, doubled up in the hand, and this with a briſk mo-
" tion as may be, till an hundred or an hundred and fifty may be counted, the
" glaſs lying all the while over the papers.   Then, if nothing ſtir, rub the glaſs
" with the finger ends half a ſcore of times to and fro, or knock your finger-
" ends as often upon the glaſs ; for this rubbing or knocking with your fingers,
" after the former rubbing, conduces moſt to excite the papers.   If nothing ſtir
" yet, rub again with the cloth till ſixty or eighty may be counted, and then
" rub or knock again with your fingers, and repeat this till the electric virtue of
" the glaſs be ſo far excited as to take up the papers, and then a very little rubb-
" ing or knocking now and then will revive the motions.   In doing all this, let
" the rubbing be always done as nimbly as may be ; and if the motion be circu-
" lars, like that of glaſs-grinding, it may do better.   But if you cannot make it
" yet ſucceed, it muſt be let alone till I have ſome opportunity of trying it be-
" fore you.   As for the ſuſpicion of the papers being moved by the air, I am ſe-
" cure from that ; yet in the other, of drawing leaf-gold to above a foot diſtance,
" which I never went about to try myſelf till the laſt week, I ſuſpect the air might
" raiſe the gold, and then a ſmall attraction might determine it towards the glaſs ;
" for I could not make it ſucceed."

ᵗ Letter-book, vol. vii. p. 284.

I

1675⅚.]   R O Y A L   S O C I E T Y   O F   L O N D O N.   271

It was ordered, that Mr. NEWTON's directions in this letter fhould be obferved in the experiment to be made at the next meeting of the Society.

Mr. OLDENBURG read a letter to himfelf from Mr. JOHN GASCOIGNE, dated at Liege, 15th December, 1675 [u], acquainting him with the death of Mr. LINUS of the epidemical difeafe, which then raged through fo many countries, and with the refolution of Mr. LINUS's difciples, to try Mr. NEWTON's experiment concerning light and colours more clearly and carefully, and before more witnefses, according to the directions given them by Mr. NEWTON's laft letter : intimating withal, that if the faid experiment be made before the Royal Society, and be attefted by them to fucceed, as Mr. NEWTON affirmed, they would reft fatisfied.

It was ordered, that when the fun fhould ferve, the experiment fhould be made before the Society.

Mr. AUBREY prefented the Society with his obfervations made in Wiltfhire, which being read, he was defired to endeavour to procure fome of the iron-ore of Sein in that county, faid to be fo rich, that the fmith could melt it in his forge : as alfo to procure from Eafton-Peires in Malmefbury hundred, fome of the blue clay, free from fand, and almoft of the colour of ultramarine ; which clay Mr. DOIGHT fuppofed to be very fit for porcelane.

The Society adjourned till the 13th of January following.

January 13. Captain HENRY SHEERES, JOHN MAPLETOFT, M. D. [x], and Signor FRANCISCO TRAVAGINI were propofed candidates, the firft in the name of Sir JOSEPH WILLIAMSON, the fecond by Mr. HOOKE, and the third by Mr. OLDENBURG.

Mr. NEWTON's experiment of glafs rubbed, to caufe various motions in bits of paper underneath, being made according to his more particular directions, fucceeded very well.   The rubbing was made both with a fcrubbing brufh, made of fhort hog's briftles, with a knife, the haft of the knife made of whalebone, and with the nail of one's finger.   It appeared, that touching many parts at once with a hard and rough body, produced the effect expected.

It was ordered, that Mr. NEWTON fhould have the thanks of the Society, for giving himfelf the trouble of imparting to them fuch full inftructions for making the experiment.

Mr. OLDENBURG produced and read a Latin letter of Mr. FLAMSTEAD to Sir JONAS MOORE, dated at Greenwich, 24th December, 1675 [y], containing an account of his obfervations made of the late eclipfe of the moon on the 21ft December, *p. m.*

---

[u] Letter-book, vol. vii. p. 282.   [y] It is printed in the Philofoph. Tranfact. vol. x. n°
[x] Profeffor of phyfic at Grefham College.   121. p. 495.

It

It was ordered, that Mr. OLDENBURG fhould be defired, according to the motion made by Mr. FLAMSTEAD, to impart thefe obfervations to Signor CASSINI at Paris, and to defire him to communicate to the Society his obfervations on the fame eclipfe.

Mr. OLDENBURG produced likewife fome papers of Mr. AUBREY, containing his obfervations of the county of Surry. But the time being elapfed, thefe papers were referred to the next meeting.

January 20.   Mr. AUBREY's papers of obfervations on Surrey were read.

There was alfo read the beginning of Mr. NEWTON's difcourfe, containing fuch obfervations, as conduce to further difcoveries for completing his theory of light and colours, efpecially as to the conftitution of natural bodies, on which their colours or tranfparency depend : in which he defcribes firft the principal of his obfervations, and then confiders and makes ufe of them.

At this time there were read the firft fifteen of thofe obfervations as follow [z] :

" I fuppofe you underftand, that all tranfparent fubftances (as glafs, water,
" air, &c.) when made very thin by being blown into bubbles, or otherwife
" formed into plates, do exhibit various colours, according to their various thin-
" nefs, although at a greater thicknefs they appear very clear and colourlefs. In
" my former difcourfe about the conftitution of light, I omitted thefe colours,
" becaufe they feemed of a more difficult confideration, and were not neceffary for
" the eftablifhing of the doctrine, which I propounded ; but becaufe they may con-
" duce to further difcoveries for compleating that theory, efpecially as to the
" conftitution of the parts of natural bodies, on which their colours or tranfpa-
" rency depend, I have now fent you an account of them. To render this dif-
" courfe fhort and diftinct, I have firft defcribed the principal of my obfervations,
" and then confidered and made ufe of them. The obfervations are thefe :

" Obf. 1.   Compreffing two prifms hard together, that their fides (which by
" chance were a very little convex) might fomewhere touch one another, I found
" the place, in which they touched, to become [a] abfolutely tranfparent, as if they
" had been there one continued piece of glafs ; for when the light fell fo ob-
" liquely on the air, which in other places was between them, as to be all re-
" flected, in that place of contact it feemed wholly tranfmitted ; infomuch that
" when looked upon, it appeared like a black or dark fpot, by reafon of no fen-
" fible light was reflected from thence, as from other places ; and when looked
" through, it feemed, as it were, a hole in that air, that was formed into a thin

[z] Regifter, vol. v. p. 89.
[a] " Note, that there is fome light reflected from
" thofe parts of this black fpot, where the glaffes,
" by reafon of their convexity, and fome little un-
" evennefs of their furfaces, do not come to abfo-
" lute contact. For by viewing the fun, by re-

" flection from this fpot, not only the verges of
" it became lucid, but divers lucid veins, as fpecks,
" appeared in the midft of the blacknefs : but yet
" fome parts of the fpot feemed ftill as black as
" before, which parts I take to be thofe, where
" the glaffes touched.

" plate by being compreſſed between the glaſſes ; and through this hole objects,
" that were beyond, might be ſeen diſtinctly, which could not at all be ſeen through
" other parts of the glaſſes, where the air was interjacent.   Although the glaſſes
" were a little convex, yet this tranſparent ſpot was of a conſiderable breadth,
" which breadth ſeemed principally to proceed from the yielding inwards of the
" parts of the glaſſes by reaſon of their mutual preſſure ; for by preſſing them very
" hard together, it would become much broader than otherwiſe.

" Obſ. 2.   When the plate of air, by turning the priſms about their common
" axis, became ſo little inclined to the incident rays, that ſome of them began to
" be tranſmitted, there aroſe in it many ſlen-
" der arcs of colours, which at firſt were   Fig. I.
" ſhaped almoſt like the conchoid, as you ſee
" them here delineated.   And by continuing
" the motion of the priſms, theſe arcs in-
" creaſed and bended more and more about
" the ſaid tranſparent ſpot, till they were

" compleated into circles or rings incompaſſing it, and afterwards continually
" grew more and more contracted.

" Theſe arcs, at their firſt appearance, were of a violet and blue colour, and
" between them were white arcs of circles, which preſently became a little tinged
" in their inward limbs with red and yellow, and to their outward limbs the blue
" was adjacent; ſo that the order of theſe colours from the central dark ſpot,
" was at that time white, blue, violet, black, red, orange, yellow, white, blue,
" violet, &c. but the yellow and red were much fainter than the blue and vio-
" let.
" The motion of the priſms about their axis being continued, theſe colours
" contracted more and more, ſhrinking towards the whiteneſs on either ſide of
" it, until they totally vaniſhed into it ; and then the circles in thoſe parts ap-
" peared black, and white, without any other colours intermixed ; but by fur-
" ther moving the priſms about, the colours again emerged out of the whiteneſs,
" the violet and blue at its inward limb, and at its outward limb the red and yel-
" low; ſo that now their order from the central ſpot was white, yellow, red,
" black, violet, blue, white, yellow, red, &c. contrary to what it was before.

" Obſ. 3.   When the rings or ſome parts appeared only black and white, they
" were very diſtinct and well defined, and the blackneſs ſeemed as intenſe as that
" of the central ſpot ; alſo, in the borders of theſe rings, where the colours began
" to emerge out of the whiteneſs, they were pretty diſtinct, which made them vi-
" ſible to a very great multitude.   I have ſometimes numbered above thirty ſuc-
" ceſſions (reckoning every black and white ring for one ſucceſſion) and ſeen more
" of them, which by reaſon of their ſmallneſs I could not number.   But in other
" poſitions of the priſms, at which the rings appeared of many colours, I could
" not diſtinguiſh above eight or nine of them, and the exterior of thoſe too
" were confuſed and dilute.

" In thefe two obfervations, to fee the rings diftinct, and without any other colour
" but black and white, I found it neceffary that I held my eye at a good diftance
" from them. For by approaching nearer, although in the fame inclination of
" my eye, yet there emerged a bluifh colour out of the white, which by dilating
" itfelf more and more into the black, rendered the circles lefs diftinct, and left
" the white a little tinged with red and yellow. I found alfo, that by looking
" through a flit or oblong hole, which was narrower than the pupil of my eye,
" and held clofe to it parallel to the prifms, I could fee the circles much diftincter
" and vifible to a far greater number than otherwife.

" Obf. 4. To obferve more nicely the order of the colours, which arofe out of
" the white circles, as the rays became lefs and lefs inclined to the plate of air ; I
" took two object-glaffes, the one a plane-convex for a fourteen foot telefcope,
" and the other a large double convex for one of fifty foot ; and upon this lay-
" ing the other with its plane fide downwards, I preffed them flowly together,
" to make the colours fucceffively emerge in the middle of the circles, and then
" flowly lifted the upper glafs from the lower, to make them fucceffively vanifh
" again in the fame place, where being of a confiderable breadth, I could more
" eafily difcern them. And by this means I obferved their fucceffion and quan-
" tity to be as followeth.

" Next to the pellucid central fpot made by the contact of the glaffes, fuc-
" ceeded violet, blue, white, yellow, and red. The violet and blue were fo very
" little in quantity, that I could not difcern them in the circles made by the
" prifms ; but the yellow and red were pretty copious, and feemed about as much
" in extent as the white, and four or five times more than the blue and violet.
" The next circuit or order of colours immediately encompaffing thefe was vio-
" let, blue, green, yellow, and red. And thefe were all of them copious and
" vivid, excepting the green, which was very little in quantity, and feemed much
" more faint and dilute than the other colours. Of the other four the violet
" was leaft, and the blue lefs than the yellow or red. The third circuit or order
" was alfo purple, blue, green, yellow, and red, in which the purple feemed more
" reddifh than the violet in the former circuit, and the green was much more
" confpicuous, being as brifk and copious as any of the other colours except the
" yellow; but the red began to be a little faded, inclining very much to purple.
" After thefe fucceeded green and red: the green was very copious and lively, in-
" clining on the one fide to blue, and the other to yellow. But in this fourth
" circuit there was neither violet, blue, nor yellow, and the red was very imper-
" fect and dirty. Alfo the fucceeding colours became more and more imperfect
" and dilute, till after three or four more revolutions they ended in perfect white-
" nefs.

" Obf. 5. To determine the interval of the glaffes, or thicknefs of the interja-
" cent air, by which each colour was produced ; I meafured the diameter of the
" firft fix rings at the moft lucid part of their orbits, and fquaring them I found
" their fquares to be in arithmetical progreffion of the odd numbers, 1. 3. 5. 7.
" 9. 11. And fince one of the glaffes was plane and the other fpherical, their

" intervals

" intervals at those rings muſt be in the ſame progreſſion. I meaſured alſo the
" diameters of the dark or faint rings between the more lucid colours, and found
" their ſquares to be in arithmetical progreſſion, of the even numbers 2, 4, 6,
" 8, 10, 12; and it being very nice and difficult to take theſe meaſures exactly,
" I repeated them divers times, at divers parts of the glaſſes, that by their agree-
" ment I might be confirmed in them; and the ſame method I uſed in deter-
" mining ſome others of the following obſervations.

" Obſ. 6. The diameter of the firſt ring, at the moſt lucid part of its orbit,
" was $\frac{58}{100}$ parts of an inch, and the diameter of the ſphere, on which the double
" convex object-glaſs was ground, was an hundred and two foot, as I found by
" meaſuring it; and conſequently the thickneſs of the air, or aereal interval of the
" glaſſes at that ring, was $\frac{1}{14554}$ of an inch. For as the diameter of the ſaid ſphere
" (an hundred and two foot, or twelve hundred and twenty-four inches) is to
" the ſemidiameter of the ring $\frac{29}{100}$, ſo very nearly is that ſemidiameter to $\frac{1}{14554}$,
" the ſaid diſtance of the glaſſes. Now, by the precedent obſervations, the
" eleventh part of this diſtance ($\frac{1}{160094}$) is the thickneſs of the air at that part
" of the firſt ring, where the yellow would be moſt vivid, were it not mixed
" with other colours in the white; and this doubled gives the difference of its
" thickneſs at the yellow in all the other rings, viz. $\frac{1}{80047}$, or, to uſe a round
" number, the eighty thouſand part of an inch.

" Obſ. 7. Theſe dimenſions were taken, when my eye was placed perpendicu-
" larly over the glaſſes, in or near the axis of the rings; but when I viewed
" them obliquely, they became bigger, continually ſwelling as I removed my eye
" farther from their axis; and partly by meaſuring the diameter of the ſame
" circle at ſeveral obliquities of my eye, partly by other means; as alſo by mak-
" ing uſe of the two priſms for very great obliquities, I found its diameter, and
" conſequently the thickneſs of the air at its perimeter in all thoſe obliquities, to
" be very nearly in the proportions expreſſed in this table.

Incidence on the air.		Refraction into the air.		Diameter of the ring.	Thickneſs of the air.
gr.	min.	gr.	min.		
00	00	00	00	. 10	. 10
6	26	10	00	. $10\frac{1}{13}$	. $10\frac{2}{16}$
12	45	20	00	. $10\frac{1}{3}$	. $10\frac{2}{3}$
18	49	30	00	. $10\frac{3}{4}$	. $11\frac{1}{2}$
24	30	40	00	. $11\frac{2}{5}$	. 13
29	37	50	00	. $12\frac{1}{2}$	. $15\frac{1}{2}$
33	58	60	00	. 14	. 20
35	47	65	00	. $15\frac{1}{4}$	. $23\frac{1}{5}$
37	19	70	00	. $16\frac{4}{5}$	. $28\frac{1}{2}$
38	33	75	00	. $19\frac{1}{4}$	. 37
39	27	80	00	. $22\frac{6}{7}$	. $52\frac{1}{4}$
40	00	85	00	. 29	. 84
40	11	90	00	. 35	. $122\frac{1}{2}$

In

" In the two firſt columns are expreſſed the obliquities of the rays to the plate
" of air; that is, their angles of incidence and refraction. In the third column,
" the diameter of any coloured ring of thoſe obliquities is expreſſed in parts, of
" which ten conſtitute that diameter, when the rays are perpendicular. And [in
" the fourth column the thickneſs of the air at the circumference of that ring is
" expreſſed in parts, of which alſo ten conſtitute that thickneſs, when the rays
" are perpendicular.

" Obſ. 8. The dark ſpot in the middle of the rings increaſed alſo by that
" obliquation of the eye, although almoſt inſenſibly. But, if inſtead of the
" object-glaſſes, the priſms were made uſe of, its increaſe was more manifeſt, when
" viewed ſo obliquely, that no colours appeared about it. It was leaſt, when the
" rays were incident moſt obliquely on the interjacent air, and increaſed more and
" more, until the coloured rings appeared, and then decreaſed again, but not ſo
" much as it increaſed before. And hence it is evident, that the tranſparency
" was not only at the abſolute contact of the glaſſes, but alſo where they had ſome
" little interval. I have ſometimes obſerved the diameter of that ſpot to be be-
" tween half and two fifth parts of the diameter of the exterior circumference of
" the red in the firſt circuit or revolution of colours, when viewed almoſt per-
" pendicularly; whereas, when viewed obliquely, it hath wholly vaniſhed, and
" become opake and white, like the other parts of the glaſs. Whence it may
" be collected, that the glaſſes did then ſcarcely, or not at all, touch one ano-
" ther; and that their interval of the perimeter of that ſpot, when viewed per-
" pendicularly, was about a fifth or ſixth part of their interval at the circum-
" ference of the ſaid red.

" Obſ. 9. By looking through the two contiguous object-glaſſes, I found, that
" the interjacent air exhibited rings of colours, as well by tranſmitting light as
" by reflecting it. The central ſpot was now white, and from it the order of
" the colours were yellowiſh, red, black, violet, blue, white, yellow, red;
" violet, blue, green, yellow, red, &c. but theſe colours were very faint and
" dilute, unleſs when the light was trajected very obliquely through the glaſſes;
" for by that means they became pretty vivid, only the firſt yellowiſh red, like
" the blue in the fourth obſervation, was ſo little and faint as ſcarcely to be diſ-
" cerned. Comparing the coloured rings made by reflection with theſe made by
" tranſmiſſion of the light, I found, that white was oppoſite to black, red to blue,
" yellow to violet, and green to a compound of red and violet; that is, thoſe
" parts of the glaſs were black when, looked through, which when looked upon
" appeared white, and on the contrary; and ſo thoſe, which in one caſe exhibited
" blue, did in the other caſe exhibit red; and the like of the other colours.

" Obſ. 10. Wetting the object-glaſs a little at their edges, the water crept in
" ſlowly between them, and the circles thereby became leſs, and the colours
" more faint; inſomuch that, as the water crept along, one half of them, at which
" it firſt arrived, would appear broken off from the other half, and contracted
" into a leſs room. By meaſuring them I found the proportion of their diameters
" to the diameters of the like circles made by air, to be about ſeven to eight;
" and

" and confequently the intervals of the glaffes at like circles, caufed by thefe two
" mediums, water and air, are as about three to four.   Perhaps it may be a general
" rule, that if any other medium, more or lefs denfe than water, be compreffed
" between the glaffes, their interval at the rings, caufed thereby, will be to their
" interval, caufed by interjacent air, as the fines are, which meafure the refrac-
" tion made out of that medium into air.

" Obf. 11.   When the water was between the glaffes, if I preffed the upper
" glafs varioufly at its edges to make the rings move nimbly from one place to
" another, a little bright fpot would immediately follow the center of them,
" which, upon creeping in of the ambient water into that place, would prefently
" vanifh.   Its appearance was fuch, as interjacent air would have caufed, and it
" exhibited the fame colours ; but it was not air, for where any aereal bubbles
" were in the water they would not vanifh.   The reflection muft rather have been
" caufed by a fubtiler medium, which could recede through the glafs at the
" creeping in of the water.

" Obf. 12.   Thefe obfervations were made in the open air.   But further, to
" examine the effects of coloured light falling on the glaffes, I darkened the
" room, and viewed them by reflection of the colours of a prifm caft on a fheet
" of white paper ; and by this means the rings became diftincter, and vifible to
" a far greater number than in the open air.

" I have feen more than twenty of them, whereas in the open air I could not
" difcern above eight or nine.

" Obf. 13.   Appointing an affiftant to move the prifm to and fro about its
" axis, that all its colours might fucceffively fall on the fame place of the paper,
" and be reflected from the circles to my eye whilft I held it immoveable ; I
" found the circles, which the red light made, to be manifeftly bigger than
" thofe, which were made by the blue and violet ; and it was very pleafant to fee
" them gradually fwell or contract, accordingly as the colour of the light was
" changed.   The interval of the glafs at any of the rings, when they were made
" by the utmoft red light, was to their interval at the fame ring, when made
" by the utmoft violet, greater than three to two, and lefs than thirteen to eight.
" By the moft of my obfervations it was as nine to fourteen.   And this pro-
" portion feemed very nearly the fame in all obliquities of my eye, unlefs when
" two prifms were made ufe of inftead of the object-glaffes : for then, at a
" certain great obliquity, the rings made by the feveral colours feemed equal ;
" and, at a greater obliquity, thofe made by the violet would be greater than the
" fame rings made by the red.

" Obf. 14.   While the prifm was turned about uniformly, the contraction or
" dilatation of a ring made by all the feveral colours of the prifm fucceffively
" reflected from the object-glaffes, was fwifteft in the red, floweft in the violet,
" and in intermediate colours it had intermediate degrees of celerity.   Comparing
the extent, which each colour obtained by this contraction or dila⸳⸳⸳   I found,
" that

" that the blue was fenfibly more extended than the violet, the yellow than the
" blue, and the red than the yellow. And, to make a jufter eftimation of their
" proportions, I obferved, that the extent of the red was almoft double to that
" of the violet, and that the light was of a middle colour between yellow and
" green at that interval of the glaffes, which was an arithmetical mean between
" the two extremes; contrary to what happens in the colours made by the re-
" fraction of a prifm, where the red is moft contracted, the violet moft expanded,
" and in the midft of them is the confine of green and blue.

   " Obf. 15. Thefe rings were not of various colours, like thofe in the open
" air, but appeared all over of that prifmatic colour only, with which they were
" illuminated : and, by projecting the prifmatic colours immediately upon the
" glaffes, I found, that the light, which fell on the dark fpaces, which were be-
" tween the coloured rings, was tranfmitted through the glaffes without any va-
" riation of colour. For, on a white paper placed behind, it would paint rings
" of the fame colour with thofe, which were reflected, and of the bignefs of their
" intermediate fpaces. And from hence the origin of thefe rings is manifeft,
" namely, that the aereal interval of the glaffes, according to its various thick-
" nefs, is difpofed in fome places to reflect, and in others to tranfmit, the light
" of any colour; and, in the fame place to reflect one colour, where it tranfmits
" another.

Thefe obfervations fo well pleafed the Society, that they ordered Mr. OLDEN-
BURG to defire Mr. NEWTON to permit them to be publifhed, together with the
reft ; which, they prefumed, did correfpond with thofe, that had been now read
to them.

Befides, there was read a paffage of Mr. NEWTON's letter to Mr. OLDENBURG,
of 21 December, 1675, ftating the difference between his hypothefis and that of
Mr. HOOKE. Which paffage was as follows :

   " As for Mr. HOOKE's infinuation, that the fum of the hypothefis I fent you
" had been delivered by him in his Micrography, I need not be much concerned
" at the liberty he takes in that kind : yet, becaufe you think it may do well,
" if I ftate the difference I take to be between them, I fhall do it as briefly as I
" can, and that the rather, that I may avoid the favour of having done any
" thing unjuftifiable or unhandfome towards Mr. HOOKE. But, for this end, I
" muft firft (to fee what is his) caft out what he has borrowed from DES CAR-
" TES, or others, viz. that there is an æthereal medium ; that light is the action
" of this medium; that this medium is lefs implicated in the parts of folid
" bodies, and fo moves more freely in them, and tranfmits light more readily
" through them, and that after fuch a manner, as to accelerate the rays in a cer-
" tain proportion; that refraction arifes from this acceleration, and has fines
" proportional; that light is at firft uniform ; that its colours are fome diftur-
" bance or new modification of its rays by refraction or reflection ; that the co-
" lours of a prifm are made by means of the quiefcent medium, accelerating
" fome motion of the rays on one fide, where red appears, and retarding it on
                     " the

" the other fide, where blue appears ; and, that there are but thefe two original
" colours, or colour-making modifications of light, which by their various de-
" grees, or, as Mr. HOOKE calls it, dilutings, produce all intermediate ones.
" This rejected, the remainder of his hypothefis is, that he has changed DES
" CARTES's preffing or progreffive motion of the medium to a vibrating one, the
" rotation of the globuli to the obligation of pulfes, and the accelerating their
" rotation on the one hand, and retarding it on the other, by the quiefcent me-
" dium, to produce colours, to the like action of the medium on the two ends of
" his pulfes for the fame end. And having thus far modified his by the Carte-
" fian hypothefis, he has extended it further, to explicate the phænomena of thin
" plates, and added another explication of the colours of natural bodies, fluid
" and folid.

" This, I think, is in fhort the fum of his hypothefis ; and in all this I have
" nothing common with him, but the fuppofition, that æther is a fufcep-
" tible medium of vibrations, of which fuppofition I make a very different ufe ;
" he fuppofing it a light itfelf, which I fuppofe it is not. This is as great a dif-
" ference as is between him and DES CARTES. But befides this, the manner of
" refraction and reflection, and the nature and production of colours in all cafes
" (which takes up the body of my difcourfe) I explain very differently from
" him ; and even in the colours of thin tranfparent fubftances, I explain every
" thing after a way fo differing from him, that the experiments I ground my
" difcourfe on, deftroy all he has faid about them ; and the two main experi-
" ments, without which the manner of the production of thofe colours is not to
" be found out, were not only unknown to him, when he wrote his Micrlogra-
" phy, but even laft fpring, as I underftood, in mentioning them to him. This
" therefore is the fum of what is common to us, that æther may vibrate ; and
" fo, if he thinks fit to ufe that notion of colours, arifing from the various big-
" nefs of pulfes (without which his hypothefis will do nothing) his will borrow
" as much from my anfwer to his objections, as that I fend you does from his
" Micrography.

" But, it may be, he means, that I have made ufe of his obfervations, and of
" fome I did ; as, that of the inflection of rays, for which I quoted him ; that
" of opacity, arifing from the interftices of the parts of bodies, which I infift
" not on ; and that of plated bodies exhibiting colours, a phænomenon, for the
" notice of which I thank him. But he left me to find out and make fuch ex-
" periments about it, as might inform me of the manner of the production of thofe
" colours, to ground an hypothefis on ; he having given no further infight to it
" than this, that the colour depended on fome certain thicknefs of the plate ;
" though what that thicknefs was at every colour, he confeffes in his Micrlogra-
" phy, he had attempted in vain to learn ; and therefore, feeing I was left to
" meafure it myfelf, I fuppofe he will allow me to make ufe of what I took
" the pains to find out. And this I hope may vindicate me from what Mr.
" HOOKE has been pleafed to charge me with."

The reading of the reft of Mr. NEWTON's difcourfe was referred to the next
meeting.

January

January 27. Mr. OLDENBURG produced from his highnefs prince RUPERT a piece of marble, having feveral pictures of boys and trees painted upon it in fuch a manner, that all the out-lines of the pictures were exactly defined without any flowing of the colours abroad, and the colours fixed by the fire, and afterwards fo polifhed, that they would be permanent, and laft as long as the marble.

This was acknowledged by the members to be a very great improvement of what had been done at Oxford by a certain ftone-cutter there ; and that all, that had been performed before in this art, was not comparable to this degree of improvement.

Mr. HOOKE remarked, that he conceived, that there were but two colours in this piece ; and that he had a method of doing it with moft colours, and to paint with them upon marble almoft as curioufly as with a pencil.

Mr. NEWTON's letter of January 25, 167⅚ [c], in which he acknowledged the favour of the Society in their kind acceptance of his late papers ; and declared, that he knew not how to deny any thing, which they defired fhould be done : but he requefted, that the printing of his obfervations about colours might be fufpended for a time, becaufe he had fome thoughts of writing fuch another fet of obfervations for determining the manner of the production of colours by the prifm : which obfervations, he faid, ought to precede thofe now in the Society's poffeffion, and would be moft proper to be joined with them.

There was alfo read a letter of Mr. PASCALL of Somerfetfhire to Mr. AUBREY, dated 18 January, 167⅚, containing fome natural obfervations of that county, viz. concerning the nature of the lead-mines in Mendip-Hills ; a well refembling the fulphur-well near the Spaw in Yorkfhire ; a fpring petrifying far more than the dropping-well at Knarefborough in the north ; the motion of fome underground waters in the parifhes of ZOLANDE, formerly recovered from the fea, &c.

It was ordered, that the reading of Mr. NEWTON's obfervations about colours be continued at the next meeting.

February 3. There was prefented from Dr. WALLIS his edition of ARCHIMEDES's *Arenarius*, with a new tranflation of his and notes, printed at Oxford, in 1676.

The reading of Mr. NEWTON's obfervations on colours was continued, viz. hat part, wherein he explains by the fimpleft of colours the moft recompounded ; as follows :

" Obf. 16. The fquares of the diameters of thefe rings, made by prifmatic
" colour, were in arithmetical progreffion, as in the fifth obfervation. And the
" diameter of the fixth circle, when made by the yellow, and viewed almoft
perpendicularly, was obout $\frac{58}{100}$ parts of an inch, agreeable to the fixth obfer-
" vation.

[c] There are no letters entered from the beginning of the year 167⅚ till July 1677.

" perpen-

" The precedent obfervations were made with a rarer thin medium terminated
" by a denfer, fuch as was air or water compreffed betwixt two glaffes.   In
" thofe, that follow, are fet down the appearances of a denfer medium thinned
" within a rarer; fuch as are plates of Mufcovy-glafs, bubbles of water, and
" fome others thin fuftances terminated on all fides with air.

" Obf. 17.   If a bubble be blown with water, firft made tenacious by diffolv-
" ing a little foap in it, it is a common obfervation, that after a while it will
" appear tinged with a great variety of colours.   To defend thefe bubbles from
" being agitated by the external air (whereby their colours are irregularly moved
" one among another, fo that no accurate obfervation can be made of them) as
" foon as I had blown any of them, I covered it with a clear glafs, and by that
" means its colours emerged in a very regular order, like fo many concentric
" rings incompaffing the top of the bubble.   And as the bubble grew thinner
" by the continual fubfiding of the water, thefe rings dilated flowly, and over-
" fpread the whole bubble, defcending in order to the bottom of it, where they
" vanifhed fucceffively.   In the mean while, after all the colours were emerged
" at the top, there grew in the center of the rings a fmall, round, black fpot,
" like that in the firft obfervation, which continually dilated itfelf, till it became
" fometimes more than one half or three fourths of an inch in breadth, before the
" bubble broke.   At firft I thought there had been no light reflected from the water
" in that place; but obferving it more curioufly, I faw within it feveral fmaller,
" round fpots, which appeared much blacker and darker than the reft, whereby
" I knew, that there was fome reflection at the other places, which were not fo
" dark as thofe fpots.   And by further trial I found, that I could fee the images
" (as of a candle or the fun) very faintly reflected, not only from the great black
" fpot, but alfo from the little darker fpots, which were within it.

" Befides the aforefaid coloured rings, there would often appear fmall fpots of
" colours afcending and defcending up and down the fide of the bubble, by rea-
" fon of fome inequalities in the fubfiding of the water; and fometimes fmall black
" fpots generated at the fides, would afcend up to the larger black fpot at the
" top of the bubble, and unite with it.

" Obf. 18.   Becaufe the colours of thefe bubbles were more extended and
" lively than thofe of air thinned between two glaffes, and fo more eafy to be
" diftinguifhed, I fhall here give you a further defcription of their order, as they
" were obferved in viewing them by reflection of the fkies, when of a white
" colour, whilft a black fubftance was placed behind the bubble: and they were
" thefe; red, blue, red, blue; red, blue; red, green; red, yellow; green, blue,
" purple; red, yellow, green, blue, violet; red, yellow, white, blue, black.

" The three firft fucceffions of red and blue were very dilute and dirty, efpe-
" cially the firft, where the red feemed in a manner to be white.   Amongft thefe
" there was fcarcely any other colour fenfible, only the blues (and principally the
" fecond blue) inclined a little to green.

VOL. III.   O o   " The

" The fourth red was alſo dilute and dirty, but not ſo much as the former
" three : after that ſucceeded little or no yellow, but a copious green, which at
" firſt was inclined a little to yellow, and then became a pretty briſk and good
" willow green, and afterwards changed to a blueiſh colour; but there ſucceded
" neither blue nor violet.

" The fifth red at firſt was very much inclined to purple, and afterwards be-
" came more bright and briſk, but yet not very pure. This was ſucceeded with
" a very bright and intenſe yellow, which was but little in quantity, and ſoon
" changed to green; but that green was copious, and ſomething more pure,
" deep, and lively, than the former green. After that followed an excellent blue
" of a bright ſky colour ; and then a purple, which was leſs in quantity than the
" blue, and much inclined to red.

" The ſixth red was at firſt of a very fair and lively ſcarlet, and ſoon after
" of a brighter colour, being very pure and briſk, and the beſt of all the reds.
" Then, after a lively orange, fol owed an intenſe, bright, and copious yellow,
" which was alſo the beſt of all the yellows; and this changed, firſt to a greeniſh
" yellow, and then to a greeniſh blue; but the green between the yellow and
" blue was very little and dilute, ſeeming rather a greeniſh white than a green.
" The blue, which ſucceeded, became very good, and of a fair, bright, ſky-colour;
" but yet ſomething inferior to the former blue : and the violet was intenſe and
" deep, with little or no redneſs in it, and leſs in quantity than the blue.

" In the laſt red appeared a tincture of ſcarlet next the violet, which ſoon
" changed to a brighter colour, inclining to an orange : and the yellow, which
" followed, was at firſt pretty good and lively, but afterwards it grew more and
" more dilute, until by degrees it ended in perfect whiteneſs : and this whiteneſs,
" if the water was very tenacious and well tempered, would ſlowly ſpread and
" dilate itſelf over the greateſt part of the bubble, continually growing paler at
" the top, where at length it would crack, and thoſe cracks, as they dilated,
" would appear of a pretty good, but yet obſcure and dark, ſky-colour ; the
" white between the blue ſpots diminiſhing, until it reſembled the threads of an
" irregular net-work, and ſoon after vaniſhed and left all the upper part of the
" bubble of the ſaid dark blue colour ; and this colour, after the aforeſaid man-
" ner, dilated itſelf downwards, until ſometimes it hath overſpread the whole
" bubble. In the mean while, at the top, which was of a darker blue than the
" bottom, and appeared alſo of many round blue ſpots, ſomething darker than
" the reſt, there would emerge one or more very black ſpots, and within thoſe,
" other ſpots of an intenſer blackneſs, which I mentioned in the former obſerva-
" tion; and thoſe continually dilated themſelves until the bubble broke.

" If the water was not very tenacious, the black ſpots would break furth in
" the white, without any ſenſible intervention of the blue : and ſometimes they
" would break forth within the precedent yellow, or red, or perhaps within
" the blue of the ſecond order, before the intermediate colours had time to diſ-
" play themſelves.

" By

167$\frac{5}{6}$.]   ROYAL SOCIETY OF LONDON.   283

" By this defcription you may perceive, how great an affinity thefe colours
" have with thofe of air, defcribed in the fourth obfervation, although fet down
" in a contrary order, by reafon that they begin to appear, when the bubble is
" thickeft, and are moft conveniently reckoned from the loweft and thickeft part
" of the bubble upwards.

" Obf. 19. Viewing, at feveral oblique pofitions of my eye, the rings of
" colours emerging on the top of the bubble, I found, that they were fenfibly
" dilated by increafing the obliquity, but yet not fo much by far, as thofe made
" by thinned air in the feventh obfervation. For there they diftended fo much,
" as, when viewed moft obliquely, to arrive at a part of the plate more than
" twelve lines thicker than that where they appeared, when viewed perpendicu-
" larly; whereas in this cafe the thicknefs of the water, at which they arrived
" when viewed moft obliquely, was, to that thicknefs, which exhibited them by
" perpendicular rays, fomething lefs than eight to five. By the beft of my ob-
" fervations, it was between fifteen and fifteen and a half to ten, an increafe
" about twenty-four times lefs than in the other cafe.

" Sometimes the bubble would become of an uniform thicknefs all over, ex-
" cept at the top of it near the black fpot, as I knew, becaufe it would exhibit
" the fame appearance of colours in all pofitions of the eye; and then the co-
" lours, which were feen at its apparent circumference by the obliqueft rays,
" would be different from thofe, that were feen in other places by rays lefs
" oblique to it. And divers fpectators might fee the fame part of it of differing
" colours, by viewing it at very differing obliquities. Now, obferving how
" much the colours at the fame place of the bubble, or at divers places of equal
" thicknefs, were varied by the feveral obliquities of the rays, by affiftance of
" the fourth, fourteenth, fixteenth, and eighteenth obfervations, as they are
" hereafter explained, I collected the thicknefs of the water, requifite to exhibit
" any one the fame colour at feveral obliquities, to be very nearly in the propor-
" portion expreffed in this table.

Incidence on the water.		Refraction into the water.		Thicknefs of the water.
degr.	min.	degr.	min.	
00	00	00	00	10
15	00	11	11	10$\frac{1}{4}$
30	00	22	1	10$\frac{4}{5}$
45	00	32	2	11$\frac{4}{5}$
60	00	40	30	13
75	00	46	25	14$\frac{1}{5}$
90	00	48	35	15$\frac{1}{5}$

" In the two firft columns are expreffed the obliquities of the rays to the
" fuperficies of the water; that is, their angles of incidence and refraction;
" where, I fuppofe, that the lines, which meafure them, are in round numbers,
" as three to four, though probably the diffolution of foap in the water may a
" little alter its refractive virtue. In the third column the thicknefs of the bubble,

O o 2   " at

" at which any one colour is exhibited in thofe feveral obliquities, is expreft· in
" parts, of which ten conftitute that thicknefs, when the rays are perpendicular.

" I have fometimes obferved of the colours, which arife on polifhed fteel by
" heating it, or on bell metal and fome other metalline fubftances, when melted
" and poured on the ground, where it may cool in the open air, that they have,
" like thofe of water-bubbles, been a little changed by viewing them at divers
" obliquities; and particularly, that a deep blue or violet, when viewed very
" obliquely, hath been changed to a deep red. But the changes of thefe colours
" are not fo fenfible as of thofe made by water; for the fcoria, or vitrified part
" of the metal, which moft metals, when heated or melted, continually protrude
" to their furface, where, by covering them in form of a thin glaffy fkin, it
" caufes thefe colours, is much denfer than water, and I find, that the change
" made by the obliquation of the eye, is leaft in colours of the denfeft thin fub-
" ftances.

" Obf. 20. As in the ninth obfervation, fo here, the bubble, by tranfmitted
" light appeared of a contrary colour to that, which it exhibited by refledion.
" Thus, when the bubbles, being looked on by the light of the clouds refleded
" from it, feemed red at its apparent circumference, if the clouds at the fame
" time, or very fuddenly, were viewed through it, the colour at its circumfe-
" rence would be blue. And, on the contrary, when by refleded light it ap-
" peared blue, it would appear red by tranfmitted light.

" Obf. 21. By wetting plates of Mufcovy-glafs, whofe thinnefs made the like
" colours appear, the colours became more faint, efpecially by wetting the plates
" on that fide oppofite the eye; but I could not perceive any variation of their
" fpecies. So that the thicknefs of a plate requifite to produce any colour, de-
" pends only on the denfity of the plate, and not of the ambient medium.
" And hence, by the tenth and fixteenth obfervations, may be known the thick-
" nefs of bubbles of water or plates of Mufcovy-glafs, or of any other fubftan-
" ces, which they have at any colour produced by them.

" Obf. 22. A thin tranfparent body, which is denfer than its ambient me-
" dium, exhibits more brifk and vivid colours than that, which is fo much
" rarer; as I have particularly obferved in air and glafs: for, blowing glafs
" very thin at a lamp furnace, thofe plates encompaffed with air did exhibit co-
" lours much more vivid than thofe of air made thin between two glaffes.

" Obf. 23. Comparing the quantity of light refleded from the feveral rings,
" I found it was moft copious from the firft or inmoft, and in the exterior rings be-
" came gradually lefs and lefs. Alfo the whitenefs of the firft ring was ftronger than
" that refleded from thofe parts of the thinned medium, which were without the
" rings, as I could manifeftly perceive by viewing at diftance the rings made by
" the two objed glaffes; or by comparing two bubbles of water blown at diftant
" times, in the firft of which the whitenefs appeared, which fucceeded the colours,
" and the whitenefs, which preceded them, in the other.

6

" Obf.

" Obf. 24.   When the two objeét-glaffes were laid upon one another, fo as to
" make the rings of colours appear, though with my naked eye I could not
" difcern above eight or nine of thofe rings, yet, by viewing them through a
" prifm, I have feen a far greater multitude, infomuch, that I could number
" more than forty, befides many others, that were fo very fmall and clofe toge-
" ther, that I could not keep my eye fo fteady on them feverally as to number
" them : but by their extent I have fometimes eftimated them to be more than
" a hundred.   And, I believe, the experiment may be improved to the difcovery
" of far greater numbers; for they feem to be really unlimited, though vifible
" only fo far as they can be feparated by the refraétion, as I fhall hereafter
" explain.

" But it was but one fide of thefe rings, namely, that, towards which the re-
" fraétion was made, which by that refraétion was rendered diftinét; and the
" other fide became more confufed than to the naked eye, infomuch that there I
" could not difcern above one or two, and fometimes none of thofe rings, of
" which I could difcern eight or nine with my naked eye.   And their fegments,
" or arcs, which on the other fide appeared fo numerous, for the moft part ex-
" ceeded not the third part of a circle.   If the refraétion was very great, or the
" prifms very diftant from the objeét-glaffes, the middle part of thofe arcs be-
" came alfo confufed, fo as to difappear and conftitute an even whitenefs, whilft
" on either fide their ends, as alfo the whole arcs fartheft
" from the center, became diftinéter than before, appearing
" in the form you fee them here defigned.

Fig. II.

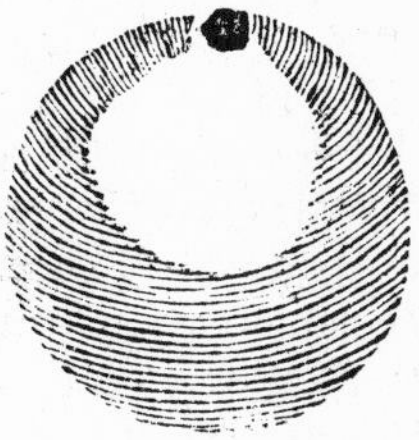

" The arcs, where they feemed diftinéteft, were only white
" and black fucceffively, without any other colours in-
" termixed.   But in other places there appeared colours
" whofe order was inverted by the refraétion, in fuch man-
" ner, that, if I firft held the prifm very near the objeét-
" glaffes, and then gradually removed it farther off towards
" my eye, the colours of the fecond, third, fourth, and following rings fhrunk
" towards the white, that emerged between them, until they wholly vanifhed into
" it at the middle of the arcs, and afterwards emerged again in a contrary or-
" der : but at the end of the arcs they retained their order unchanged.

" I have fometimes fo laid one objeét-glafs upon the other, that, to the naked
" eye, they have all over feemed uniformly white, without the leaft appearance
" of any of the coloured rings ; and yet, by viewing them through a prifm, great
" multitudes of thofe rings have difcovered themfelves.   And, in like manner,
" plates of Mufcovy glafs, and bubbles of glafs blown at a lamp furnace,
" which were not fo thin, as to exhibit any colours to the naked eye, have
" through the prifm exhibited a great variety of them, ranged irregularly up
" and down, in the form of waves.   And fo bubbles of water, before they be-
" gan to exhibit their colours to the naked eye of a by-ftander, have appeared,
" through a prifm, girded about with many parallel and horizontal rings ; to pro-
" duce which effeét, it was neceffary to hold the prifm parallel, or very nearly paral-
" lel, to the horizon, and to difpofe it fo, that the rays might be refraéted upwards.
" Having

" Having given my obfervations of thefe colours, before I make ufe of them " to unfold the caufes of the colours of natural bodies, it is convenient, that, by " the fimpleft of them, I firft explain the more compounded; fuch as are the " fecond, third, fourth, ninth, twelfth, eighteenth, twentieth, and twenty-fourth.

" And firft, to fhow how the colours in the fourth and eighteenth obfervations " are produced, let there be taken in any " right line the lengths Y Z, Y A, and " Y H, in proportion as four, nine, and " fourteen; and between Z A and Z H " eleven mean proportionals, of which let " Z B be the fecond, Z C the third, Z D " the fifth, Z E the feventh, Z F the ninth, " and Z G the tenth. And at the points " A, B, C, D, E, F, G, H, let perpendi- " diculars A α, B β, &c. be erected, by " whofe intervals, the extent of the feveral " colours fet underneath againft them, is to " be reprefented. Then divide the line A α " in fuch proportion as the numbers 1, 2, 3; " 5, 6, 7; 9, 10, 11, &c. fet at the point " of divifion denote. And through thofe " divifions from Y draw lines 1 I, 2 K, 3 L; " 5 m, 6 n, 7 o, &c.

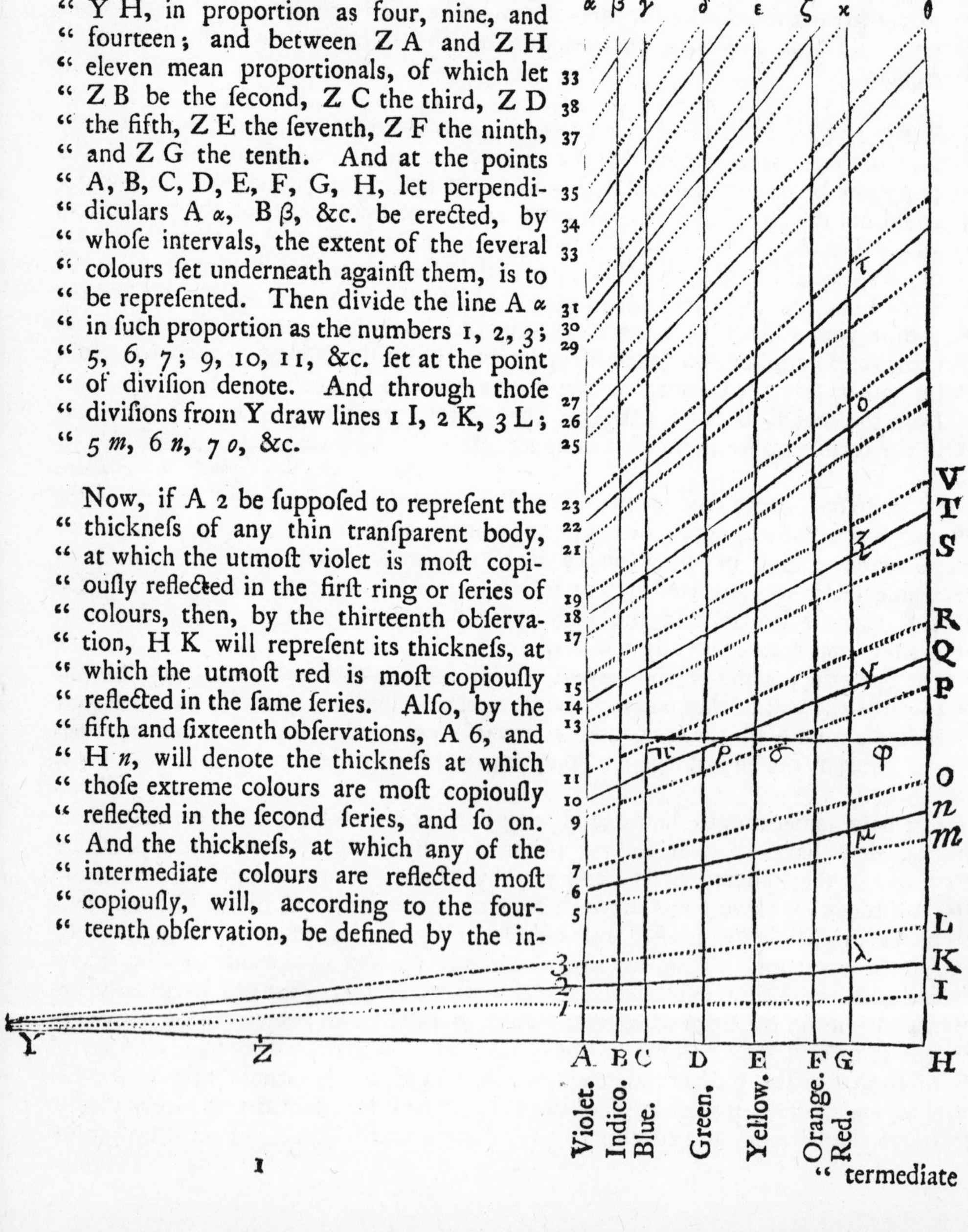

Now, if A 2 be fuppofed to reprefent the " thicknefs of any thin tranfparent body, " at which the utmoft violet is moft copi- " oufly reflected in the firft ring or feries of " colours, then, by the thirteenth obferva- " tion, H K will reprefent its thicknefs, at " which the utmoft red is moft copioufly " reflected in the fame feries. Alfo, by the " fifth and fixteenth obfervations, A 6, and " H n, will denote the thicknefs at which " thofe extreme colours are moft copioufly " reflected in the fecond feries, and fo on. " And the thicknefs, at which any of the " intermediate colours are reflected moft " copioufly, will, according to the four- " teenth obfervation, be defined by the in-

Fig. III.

Violet. Indico. Blue. Green. Yellow. Orange. Red.

" termediate

1

" termediate parts of the lines 2 K, 6 *n*, &c. againſt which the names of thoſe
" colours are written below.

" But farther, to define the latitude of theſe colours in each ring or ſeries, let
" A 1 deſign the leaſt thickneſs, and A 3 the greateſt thickneſs, at which the
" extreme violet in the firſt ſeries is reflected ; and let H I and H L deſign the
" like limit for the extreme red, and the intermediate colours be limited by the
" intermediate parts of the lines, 1 I and 3 L ; againſt which the names of thoſe
" colours are written.   And in the ſecond ſeries, let thoſe limits be the lines
" 5 M and 7 O ; and ſo on : but yet with this caution, that the reflections be
" ſuppoſed ſtrongeſt at the intermediate ſpaces, 2 K, 6 N, 10 R, &c. and to
" decreaſe gradually towards theſe limits, 1 I, 3 L ; 5 M, 7 O, &c. on either
" ſide, where you muſt not conceive them to be preciſely limited, but to decay
" indefinitely.   And whereas I have deſigned the ſame latitude to every ſeries, I
" did it, becauſe, although the colours in the firſt ſeries ſeem to be a little broader
" than the reſt, by reaſon of a ſtronger reflection there ; yet that inequality is ſo
" inſenſible as ſcarcely to be determined by obſervation.

" Now, according to this deſcription, conceiving, that the rays, in which ſeve-
" ral colours in here, are by turns reflected at the ſpace 1 K, 3 L, 5 M, O 7,
" 9 P, R 11, &c. and tranſmitted at the ſpaces A H I 1, 3 L, M 5, 7 O,
" P 9, &c. it is eaſy to know what colour in the open air muſt be exhibited
" at any thickneſs of a tranſparent thin body.   For, if a ruler be applied paral-
" lel to A H, at that diſtance from it by which the thickneſs of the body is
" repreſented, the alternate ſpaces 1 I, L 3, 5 M, O 7, &c. which it croſſeth,
" will denote the reflected original colours, of which the colour exhibited in the
" open air is compounded.   Thus, if the conſtitution of the green in the third
" ſeries of colours be deſired ; apply the ruler, as you ſee, at $\pi \rho \sigma \varphi$, and by its
" paſſing through ſome of the blue at π, and yellow at σ, as well as through the
" green ρ, you may conclude, that green, exhibited at that thickneſs of the
" body, is principally conſtituted of original green, but not without a mixture
" of ſome blue and yellow.   By this means you may know, how the colours
" from the center of the rings outwards ought to ſucceed in order, as they were
" deſcribed in the fourth and eighteenth obſervations : for, if you move the ruler
" gradually from A H through all diſtances, having paſt over the firſt ſpace,
" which denotes little or no reflection to be made by thinneſt ſubſtances, it will firſt
" arrive at 1, the violet, and then very quickly at the blue and green, which, to-
" gether with that violet compounded blue, and then at the yellow and red, by
" whoſe further addition, that blue is converted into whiteneſs, which white-
" neſs continues during the tranſit from I to 3 ; and after that, by the ſucceſſive
" deficience of its component colours, turns firſt to compound yellow, and then
" to red, and laſt of all the red ceaſeth at L   Then begin the colours of the ſecond
" ſeries, which ſucceed in order between 5 and O, and are more lively than be-
" fore, becauſe more expanded and ſevered.   And, for the ſame reaſon, inſtead of
" the former white, there intercedes between the blue and yellow a mixture of
" orange, yellow, green, blue and indico, all which together ought to exhibit
" a dilute an imperfect green.   So the colours of the third ſeries all ſucceed in
                                                                        " order

" order; firſt the violet, which a little interferes with the red of the ſecond or-
" der, and is thereby inclined to a rediſh purple; then the blue and green, which
" are leſs mixed with other colours, and conſequently more lively than before,
" eſpecially the green. Then follows the yellow, ſome of which towards the
" green is diſtinct and good; but that part of it towards the ſucceeding red, as
" alſo that red, is mixed with the violet and blue of the fourth ſeries, whereby va-
" rious degrees of red, very much inclining to purple, are compounded. The
" violet and blue, which ſhould ſucceed this red, being mixed with, and hidden
" in it, there ſucceeds a green; and this at firſt is much inclined to blue, but
" ſoon becomes a good green; the only unmixed and lively colour in this fourth
" ſeries: for as it verges towards the yellow, it begins to interfere with the
" colours of the fifth ſeries, by whoſe mixture the ſucceeding yellow and red are
" very much diluted, and made dirty, eſpecially the yellow, which being the
" weaker colour, is ſcarce able to ſhew itſelf. After this the ſeveral ſeries inter-
" fere more and more, and their colours become more and more intermixed, till
" after three or four revolutions (in which the red and blue predominate by
" turns) all ſorts of colours are in all places pretty equally blended, and com-
" pound one even whiteneſs.

" And ſince, by the fifteenth obſervation, the rays indued with one colour are
" tranſmitted, where thoſe of another colour are reflected, the reaſon of the co-
" lours made by the tranſmitted light, in the ninth and twentieth obſervations, is
" alſo from hence evident.

" If not only the order and ſpecies of theſe colours, but alſo the preciſe thick-
" neſs of the plate, or thin body, at which they are exhibited, be deſired in parts
" of an inch, that may be alſo performed by aſſiſtance of the ſixth or ſixteenth
" obſervation. For, according to thoſe obſervations, the thickneſs of the thinned
" air, which, between two glaſſes, exhibited the orange or bright red of the
" ſixth order, was $\frac{1}{14154}$ parts of an inch. Now, ſuppoſe this thickneſs be
" repreſented by G τ, and the eleventh part of it, G λ, will be about $\frac{1}{160000}$ of
" an inch. And ſo G μ, G V, G ξ, G o, will be $\frac{3}{160000}$, $\frac{5}{160000}$, $\frac{7}{160000}$,
" and $\frac{9}{160000}$. And this being known, it is eaſy to determine what thickneſs
" of air is repreſented by G φ, or any other diſtance of the ruler from A H.

" But further, ſince, by the tenth obſervation, the thickneſs of air was to the
" thickneſs of water, which between the ſame glaſſes exhibited the ſame colour,
" as four to three; and, by the twenty-firſt obſervation, the colours of thin
" bodies are not varied by varying the ambient medium; the thickneſs of a
" bubble of water exhibiting any colour will be three fourths of the thickneſs of
" air producing the ſame colour. And ſo, according to the ſame tenth and twenty-
" firſt obſervations, the thickneſs of a plate of glaſs, whoſe refraction is meaſured
" by the proportion of the ſines thirty-one to twenty, may be $\frac{20}{31}$ of the thickneſs
" of air producing the ſame colours: and the like of other mediums. On theſe
" grounds I have compoſed the following table; wherein the thickneſs of air,
" water, and glaſs, at which each colour is moſt intenſe and ſpecific, is expreſſed
" in parts of an inch divided into ten hundred thouſand equal parts.

" The

1675/6.] ROYAL SOCIETY OF LONDON.

		The thickneſs of		
		Air	Water	Glaſs
The colours of the firſt order	Black	2	$1\frac{1}{2}$	$1\frac{1}{4}$ or leſs.
	Blue	$2\frac{2}{3}$	2	$1\frac{3}{4}$
	White	$5\frac{1}{3}$	4	$3\frac{1}{2}$
	Yellow	8	6	$5\frac{1}{4}$
	Orange	9	$6\frac{3}{4}$	$5\frac{4}{5}$
	Red	10	$7\frac{1}{2}$	$6\frac{1}{2}$
Of the ſecond order	Violet	12	9	$7\frac{3}{4}$
	Indico	$13\frac{1}{4}$	$9\frac{11}{12}$	$8\frac{1}{2}$
	Blue	$14\frac{3}{4}$	11	$9\frac{1}{2}$
	Green	16	12	$10\frac{1}{3}$
	Yellow	$17\frac{1}{2}$	$13\frac{1}{8}$	$11\frac{1}{3}$
	Orange	$19\frac{1}{4}$	$14\frac{1}{2}$	$12\frac{2}{5}$
	Bright red	20	15	13
	Scarlet	$21\frac{1}{4}$	16	$13\frac{2}{3}$
Of the third order	Purple	23	$17^{\frac{}{4}}$	$14\frac{4}{5}$
	Indico	24	18	$15\frac{1}{2}$
	Blue	$25\frac{1}{5}$	19	$16\frac{1}{4}$
	Green	$27\frac{1}{5}$	$20\frac{2}{5}$	$17\frac{1}{2}$
	Yellow	$29\frac{1}{2}$	22	19
	Red	31	$23\frac{1}{4}$	20
	Bluiſh red	$33\frac{1}{2}$	25	$21\frac{2}{5}$
Fourth order	Bluiſh	36	27	$23\frac{1}{4}$
	Green	$37\frac{2}{3}$	$28\frac{1}{4}$	$24\frac{1}{3}$
	Yellowiſh green	$39\frac{1}{3}$	$29\frac{1}{2}$	$25\frac{1}{3}$
	Red	44	33	$28\frac{1}{3}$
Fifth order	Greeniſh blue	$50\frac{2}{3}$	38	$32\frac{2}{3}$
	Red	$57\frac{1}{3}$	43	37
Sixth order	Greeniſh blue	64	48	$41\frac{1}{3}$
	Red	$70\frac{2}{3}$	53	$45\frac{2}{3}$
Seventh order	Greeniſh blue	$77\frac{1}{3}$	58	50
	Red or White	84	63	$54\frac{1}{2}$

" Now, if this table be compared with the third ſcheme, you will there ſee " the conſtitution of each colour, as to its ingredients, or the original colours, " of which it is compounded, and thence be enabled to judge of its intenſeneſs " or imperfection, which may ſuffice in explication of the fourth and eighteenth

THE HISTORY OF THE　　　[167⅘.

" obfervations, unlefs it be further defired to delineate the manner, how the
" colours appear, when the two objeét-glaffes are laid upon one another : to do
" which let there be defcribed a large arc of a circle and a ftrait line, which
" may touch that arc ; and parallel to that tangent feveral occult lines at fuch
" diftances from it, as the numbers fet againft the feveral colours in the table
" denote.　For the arc and its tangent will reprefent the fuperficies of the
" glaffes, terminating the interjacent air, and the places, where the occult lines
" cut the arc, will fhow at what diftances from the center, or point of the con-
" taét, each colour is refleéted.

" There are alfo other ufes for this table ; for by its affiftance the thicknefs
" of the bubble, in the nineteenth obfervation, was determined by the colours,
" which it exhibited.　And fo the bignefs of the parts of natural bodies may be
" conjeétured at by their colours, as fhall be hereafter fhown.　Alfo, if two
" or more very thin plates be laid one upon another, fo as to compofe one plate,
" equalling them all in thicknefs, the refulting colour may be hereby determined.
" For inftance, Mr. HOOKE, in his Micrographia, obferves, that a faint yellow
" plate of Mufcovy glafs, laid upon a blue one, conftituted a very deep purple.
" The yellow of the firft order is a faint one, and the thicknefs of the plate ex-
" hibiting it, according to the table, is $5\frac{1}{4}$, to which add $9\frac{1}{2}$, the thicknefs ex-
" hibiting blue of the fecond order, and the fum will be $14\frac{3}{4}$, which moft
" nearly approaches $14\frac{4}{5}$, the thicknefs exhibiting the purple of the third
" order.

" To explain, in the next place, the circumftances of the fecond and third
" obfervations, that is, how the colours (by turning the prifms about their com-
" mon axis the contrary way to that expreffed in thofe obfervations) may be con-
" verted into white and black rings, and afterwards into colours again in an
" inverted order ; it muft be remembered, that thofe colours are dilated by obli-
" quation of rays to the air, which intercedes the glaffes ; and that, according
" to the table in the feventh obfervation, their dilatation or refleétion from the
" common center is moft manifeft and fpeedy when they are obliqueft.　Now,
" the rays of yellow being more refraéted by the firft fuperficies of the faid air
" than thofe of red, are thereby made more oblique to the fecond fuperficies,
" at which they are refleéted. to produce the coloured rings ; and confequently,
" the yellow in each ring will be more dilated than the red ; and the excefs of
" its dilatation will be fo much the greater, by how much the greater is the obli-
" quity of the rays, until at laft it become of equal extent with the red of the
" fame ring.　And, for the fame reafon, the green, blue, and violet, will be
" alfo fo much dilated by the ftill greater obliquity of their rays, as to become
" all very nearly of equal extent with the red ; that is, equally diftant from the
" center of the rings.　And then all the colours of the fame feries muft be coinci-
" dent, and by their mixture exhibit a white ring ; and thefe white rings muft
" have black or dark rings between them, becaufe they do not fpread and inter-
" fere with one another as before ; and, for that reafon alfo, they muft become
" diftinéter, and vifible to far greater numbers.　But yet the violet, being
　　　　　　　　　　　　　　　　　　　　　　　　　　　" obliqueft,

" obliqueſt, will be ſomething more dilated in proportion than the other colours;
" and ſo very apt to appear at the exterior verges of the white.

" Afterwards, by a greater obliquity of the rays, the violet and the blue be-
" come ſenſibly more dilated than the red and yellow ; and ſo being further
" removed from the center of the rings, the colours muſt emerge out of the white
" in an order contrary to that which they had before, the violet and blue at the
" exterior limbs, and the red and yellow at the interior. And the violet, by
" reaſon of the greateſt obliquity of its rays, being, in proportion, moſt of all
" expanded, will ſooneſt appear at the exterior limb of each white ring, and
" become more conſpicuous than the reſt. And the ſeveral ſeries of colours, by
" their unfolding and ſpreading, will begin again to interfere, and thereby render
" the rings leſs diſtinct, and not viſible to ſo great numbers.

" If, inſtead of the priſms, the object-glaſſes be made uſe of, the rings, which
" they exhibit, become not white and diſtinct by the obliquity of the eye, by
" reaſon, that the rays, in their paſſage through that air, which interceded the
" glaſſes, are very nearly parallel to themſelves, when firſt incident on the glaſſes ;
" and conſequently, thoſe indued with ſeveral colours are not inclined one more
" than another to that air, as it happens in the priſms.

" There is yet another circumſtance of theſe experiments to be conſidered ;
" and that is, why the black and white rings, which, when viewed at a diſtance,
" appear diſtinct, ſhould not only become confuſed by viewing them near at
" hand, but alſo yield a violet colour at both the edges of every white ring :
" and the reaſon is, that the rays, which enter the eye at ſeveral parts of the
" pupil, have ſeveral obliquities to the glaſſes, and thoſe, which are moſt oblique,
" if conſidered apart, would repreſent the rings bigger than thoſe, which are the
" leaſt oblique. Whence the breadth of the perimeter of every white ring is ex-
" panded outwards by the obliqueſt rays, and inwards by the leaſt oblique. And
" this expanſion is ſo much the greater, by how much the greater is the difference
" of the obliquity ; that is, by how much the pupil is wider, or the eye nearer
" to the glaſſes : and the breadth of the violet muſt be moſt expanded, becauſe
" the rays, apt to excite a ſenſation of that colour, are moſt oblique to the
" ſecond or further ſuperficies of the thinned air, at which they are reflected ;
" and have alſo the greateſt variation of obliquity, which makes that colour
" ſooneſt emerge out of the edges of the white. And, as the breadth of every
" ring is thus augmented, the dark intervals muſt be diminiſhed, until the neigh-
" bouring rings become continuous, and are blended, the exterior firſt, and
" then thoſe nearer the center ; ſo that they can no longer be diſtinguiſhed a-part,
" but ſeem to conſtitute an even and uniform whiteneſs.

" Amongſt all the obſervations there is none accompanied with ſo odd circum-
" ſtances as the twenty-fourth. Of thoſe the principal are, that in thin plates,
" which, to the naked eye, ſeem of an even and uniform tranſparent whiteneſs,
" the refraction of a priſm ſhould make the rings of colours appear ; whereas it
" uſually makes objects to appear coloured only, where they are terminated with

P p 2   " ſhadows,

" fhadows, or have parts unequally luminous; and that it fhould make thofe
" rings exceedingly diftinct and white, although it ufually renders thofe objects
" confufed and coloured. The caufe of thefe things you will underftand by
" confidering, that all the rings of colours are really in the plate, when viewed
" by the naked eye, although, by reafon of the great breadth of their circum-
" ferences, they fo much interfere, and are blended together, that they feem to
" conftitute an even whitenefs. But, when the rays pafs through the prifm to
" the eye, the orbits of the feveral colours in every ring are refracted, fome more
" than others, according to their degree of refrangibility; by which means the
" colours on one fide of the ring become more unfolded and dilated, and on the
" other fide more complicated and contracted. And where, by a due refrac-
" tion, they are fo much contracted, that the feveral rings become narrower
" than to interfere with one another, they muft appear diftinct, and alfo white,
" if the conftituent colours be fo much contracted as to be wholly coinci-
" dent: but on the other fide, where every ring is made broader by the further
" unfolding its colours, it muft interfere more with other rings than before, and
" fo become lefs diftinct.

" To explain this a little further; fuppofe the concentric circles, A B and
" C D, reprefent the red and violet of any order, which, together with the in
" termediate colours, conftitute any one of thefe rings. Now, thefe being
" viewed through a prifm, the violet circle, B C, will, by a greater refraction, be
" further tranflated from its place than the red, A D, and fo approach nearer

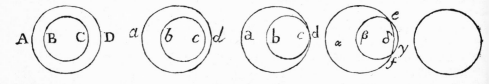

" to it on that fide towards which the refractions are made. For inftance, if
" the red be tranflated to a d, the violet may be tranflated to b c, fo as to ap-
" proach nearer to it at c than before; and, if the red be further tranflated to
" a d, the violet may be fo much further tranflated to b c, as to convene with
" it at c, and, if the red be yet further tranflated to a δ, the violet may be ftill
" fo much further tranflated to β γ, as to pafs beyond it at γ, and convene with it
" at e and f. And this being underftood, not only of the red and violet, but of
" all the other intermediate colours; and alfo of every revolution of thofe co-
" lours, you will eafily perceive, how thefe of the fame revolution or order, by
" their narrownefs at c d, and δ γ, and their coincidence at c d, e and f, ought
" to conftitute pretty diftinct arcs of circles, efpecially at c d, or at e and f, and
" that they will appear feveral at c d, at c d exhibit whitenefs by their coinci-
" dence, and again appear feveral at δ γ, but yet in a contrary order to that
" which they had before, and ftill retain beyond e and f. But, on the other
" fide, at a b, a b, or a β, thefe colours muft become much more confufed by
" being dilated, and fpread fo as to interfere with thofe of other orders. And
" the fame confufion will happen at δ γ between e and f, if the refraction be
                                         " very

" very great, or the prifm very diftant from the object-glaffes; in which cafe no
" parts of the ring will be feen, fave only two little arcs at *e* and *f*, whofe diftance
" from one another will be augmented by removing the prifm ftill further from
" the object-glaffes.   And thefe little arcs muft be diftincteft and whiteft at their
" middle ; and at their ends, where they grow confufed, they muft be coloured ;
" and the colours at one end of every arc muft be in a contrary order to thofe
" at the other end, by reafon that they crofs in the intermediate white ; namely,
" their ends, which verge towards δ γ, will be red, and yellow on that fide next
" the center, and blue and violet on the other fide.   But their other ends, which
" verge from δ γ, will, on the contrary, be blue and violet on that fide towards
" the center, and on the other fide red and yellow.

" For confirmation of all this, I need alledge no more, than that it is mathe-
" matically demonftrable from my former principles.   But I fhall add, that they,
" which pleafe to take the pains, may by the teftimony of their fenfes be affured,
" that thefe explications are not hypothetical, but infallibly true and genuine :
" for in a dark room, by viewing thefe rings through a prifm, by reflection of
" the feveral prifmatic colours, which an affiftant caufes to move to and fro
" upon a wall or paper, from whence they are reflected, whilft the fpectator's
" eye, the prifm, and object-glaffes (as in the thirteenth obfervation) are placed
" fteddy, the pofition of the circles, made fucceffively by the feveral colours,
" will be found fuch, in refpect of one another, as I have defcribed at *a b c d*, or
" *a b c d*, or *a β γ δ*.   And by the fame method the truth of the explications of
" the other obfervations is to be examined.

" By what hath been faid, the like phænomena of water-bubbles and thin
" plates of glafs may be underftood.   But in fmall fragments of thofe plates,
" there is this further obfervable, that, if they, lying flat upon a table, be turned
" about their center, whilft they are viewed through a prifm, fome of them ex-
" hibit waves in one or two pofitions only ; but the moft of them do in all pofi-
" tions exhibit thofe waves, and that for the moft part appearing almoft all over
" the glafs.   The reafon is, that the fuperficies of fuch plates are not even, but
" have many cavities and fwellings, which, how fhallow foever, do a little vary
" the thicknefs of the plate ; and by the feveral fides of thofe cavities there
" muft be produced waves in feveral poftures of the prifm.   Now, though it
" be but fome very fmall and narrow parts of the glafs, by which thefe waves
" for the moft part are caufed, yet they may feem to extend themfelves over the
" whole glafs, becaufe from the narroweft of thofe parts there are colours of feveral
" orders confufedly reflected, which by refraction of the prifm are unfolded, and
" difperfed to feveral places, fo as to conftitute fo many feveral waves as there
" were divers orders of the colours promifcuoufly reflected from that part of the
" glafs.

" Thefe are the principal phænomena of thin plates or bubbles, whofe expli-
" cations depend on the properties of light, that I have heretofore delivered :
" and thefe, you fee, do neceffarily follow from them, and agree with them even
" to their very leaft circumftances ; and not only fo, but do very much tend to
" their

" their proof. Thus, by the twenty-fourth obfervation, it appears, that the
" rays of feveral colours, made, as well by thin plates or bubbles, as by the re-
" fractions of a prifm, have feveral degrees of refrangibility, whereby thofe of
" each order, which, at their reflection from the plate or bubble, are intermixed
" with thofe of other orders, are feparated from them by refraction, and affoci-
" ated together, fo as to become vifible by themfelves, like arcs of circles. For,
" if the rays were all alike refrangible, it is impoffible, that the whitenefs, which
" to the naked fenfe appears uniform, fhould by refraction have its parts tranf-
" pofed, and ranged into thofe black and white arcs.

" It appears alfo, that the unequal refractions of difform rays proceed not
" from any contingent irregularities, fuch as are veins, an uneven polifh, or for-
" tuitous pofition of the pores of glafs, unequal motions in the air or æther,
" fpreading, breaking, or dividing the fame ray into many diverging parts, or
" the like. For, admitting any fuch irregularities, it would be impoffible for
" refractions to render thofe rings fo very diftinct and well defined, as they do
" in the twenty-fourth obfervation. It is neceffary therefore, that every ray have
" its proper and conftant degree of refrangibility connate with it; according to
" which its refraction is ever juftly and regularly performed, and that feveral
" rays have feveral of thofe degrees.

" And what is faid of their refrangibility may be underftood of their reflexi-
" bility; that is, of their difpofitions to be reflected, fome at a greater, and others
" at a lefs thicknefs of thin plates or bubbles, namely, that thofe difpofitions are
" alfo connate with the rays, and immutable, as may appear by the thirteenth,
" fourteenth, and fifteenth obfervations, compared with the fourth and eigh-
" teenth.

" By the precedent obfervations it appears alfo, that whitenefs is a diffimilar
" mixture of all colours, and that light is a mixture of rays endowed with all
" thofe colours. For, confidering the multitude of the rings of colours in the
" third, twelfth, and twenty-fourth obfervations, it is manifeft, that, although
" in the fourth and eighteenth obfervations there appear more than eight or nine
" of thofe rings, yet there are really a far greater number, which fo much inter-
" fere and mingle with one another, as, after thofe eight or nine revolutions, to
" dilute one another wholly, and conftitute an even and fenfible uniform white-
" nefs. And confequently, that whitenefs muft be allowed a mixture of all co-
" lours, and the light, which conveys it to the eye, muft be a mixture of rays
" endued with all thofe colours.

" But further, by the twenty-fourth obfervation it appears, that there is a con-
" ftant relation between colours and refrangibility, the moft refrangible rays being
" violet, the leaft refrangible red, and thofe of intermediate colours having pro-
" portionally intermediate degrees of refrangibility. And, by the thirteenth,
" fourteenth, and fifteenth obfervations, compared with the fourth or eighteenth,
" there appears to be the fame conftant relation between colour and refrangi-
" bility; the violet being on equal terms reflected at leaft thicknefs of any thin
" plate

" plate or bubble; the red at greateſt thickneſs, and the intermediate colours at
" intermediate thickneſſes : whence it] follows, that the colorific diſpoſitions of
" rays are alſo connate with them, and immutable ; and by conſequence, that all
" the productions and appearances of colours in the world are derived, not from
" any phyſical change cauſed in light by refraction or reflection, but only from
" the various mixtures or ſeparations of rays, by virtue of their different refran-
" gibility or reflexibility.   And, in this reſpect it is, that the ſcience of colours
" becomes a ſpeculation more proper for mathematicians than naturaliſts.

This being read, occaſion was taken to diſcourſe of Mr. NEWTON's theory
itſelf, and to debate, whether the rays of light, which, though alike incident in
the ſame medium, yet exhibit different colours, may not reaſonably be ſaid to
owe that exhibition of different colours to the ſeveral degrees of the velocity of
pulſes, rather than, as Mr. NEWTON thought, to the ſeveral connate degrees of
refrangibility in the rays themſelves ?

Mr. HOOKE was of opinion, that the former of theſe ways was ſufficient to give
a good account of the diverſity of colours.

February 10.   Dr. MAPLETOFT was elected and admitted.

Capt. SHEERES, Mr. HALL, and Signor TRAVAGINO were elected.

Mr. BERCHENSHAW preſented himſelf to the Society, and ſhewed them his
ſcale of muſic, wherein were contained,

1. A table of all conſonant and diſſonant intervals ſuitable to muſical harmony,
which are practicable, and may be expreſſed by the voice and other inſtruments.
To theſe reſpective intervals apt and proper numbers were aſſigned, by which
their ratio's and proportions were demonſtrated.

2. A ſyſtem of all the keys, by which the aforeſaid intervals were completed ;
of which keys ſome were natural ; ſome intended to the firſt degree of acute-
neſs ; ſome remitted to the firſt degree of gravity; ſome twice ſpiſſated; ſome
twice aſperated.

3. In this ſcale the magnitude, dimenſion, and proportion of the ſaid keys
were exactly demonſtrated according to the proportional parts of a chord, the
chord being ſuppoſed thirty-ſix inches long.

If it were demanded, whether there was any thing in this table and ſyſtem,
that was not to be found in the ſcales and writings of other muſicians ? he
anſwered,

1. That the intervals in this table were perfect and complete.   There was not
one too many, nor one wanting, which might conduce to the making of
harmony.
                                                                    2. That

2. That the founds or mufical numbers contained in this fyftem arofe out of the unifon, and from one another, according to the reafon of figurate, not fimple numbers, (as, he faid, he could demonftrate by numbers affigned to the refpective intervals in the table) for that fo the reafon of the ftate of mufic required.

3. That there are neither more or lefs keys in this fyftem, than would complete the aforefaid intervals.

4. That in this fcale all the tones are of the fame ratio, and that fo are all the femitones, femiditones, ditones, and other intervals.

5. That the true magnitude and dimenfion of every one of the faid keys are demonftrated according to the proportional parts of a chord.

6. That the natural, genuine, and true reafon of the excellency and fullnefs of the harmony of three, four, five, fix, and feven parts, may clearly be difcerned by the fyftem of feven parts.

He added, that many other things were to be found in this table and fcale, of which little or no mention is made in the fcales and writings of either modern or antient mufical authors; which, he faid, he intended to difcover, and to write of them at large, as he fhould be enabled thereunto.

He was exhorted to finifh this work, or at leaft to publifh this fyftem with an explanation thereof.

After this was read the laft part of Mr. NEWTON's *obfervations*, wherein he confidered in nine propofitions, how the phænomena of thin tranfparent plates ftand related to thofe of all other natural bodies : of which bodies having before mentioned, that they appear of divers colours, according as they are difpofed to reflect moft copioufly the rays indued with thefe colours, he now inquires after their conftitutions.

Here, among many other confiderable things, he fhews, how the bignefs of the component parts of natural bodies may be conjectured by their colours : as alfo, that the caufe of reflexion is not the impinging of light on the folid and impervious parts of bodies, as was commonly fuppofed.

This laft part was as follows:

" I am now come to the laft part of this defign; which is, to confider, how
" the phænomena of thin tranfparent plates ftand related to thofe of all other na-
" tural bodies. Of thefe bodies I have already told you, that they appear of di-
" vers colours, accordingly as they are difpofed to reflect moft copioufly the rays
" endued with thofe colours. But their conftitutions, whereby they reflect fome rays

2

" more

" more copioufly than others, remains to be inquired after. And this I fhall en-
" deavour in the following propofitions.

" Prop. 1. Thofe fuperficies reflect the greateft quantity of light, which have
" the greateft refracting power ; that is, which interceeds mediums, that differ moft
" in their refracting denfities ; and in the confines of equally denfe mediums there
" is no reflection.

" The analogy between reflection and refraction will appear by confidering, that
" when light paffeth obliquely out of one medium into another, which refracts
" from the perpendicular, the greater is the difference of their denfity, the lefs
" obliquity is requifite to caufe a total reflection ; becaufe as the fines are, which
" meafure the refraction, fo is the fine of incidence, at which the total reflection
" begins, to the radius of the circle ; and confequently that incidence is leaft,
" where there is the great difference of the fines. Thus in the paffing of light out
" of water into air, where the refraction is meafured by the ratio of the fines, 3 to
" 4, the total reflection begins, when the angle of the incidence is about forty-
" eight degrees and thirty-five minutes. In paffing out of glafs into air, where
" the refraction is meafured by the ratio of the fines 20 to 31, the total reflection
" begins, when the angle of incidence is forty degrees and ten minutes : and fo,
" in paffing out of cryftal, or more ftrongly refracting mediums, into air, there
" is ftill a lefs obliquity requifite to caufe a total reflection. Superficies therefore,
" which refract moft, do fooneft reflect all the light, which is incident on them,
" and fo muft be allowed moft ftrongly reflective.

" But the truth of this propofition will further appear, by obferving, that in
" the fuperficies, interceeding any two of thofe mediums, air or water, or other
" liquors, common glafs, cryftal, and metalline glaffes, the reflection is ftronger
" or weaker accordingly as the fuperficies hath a greater or lefs refracting power.
" Thus, when other mediums are contiguous to air, the reflection is ftronger
" in the fuperficies of glafs than of water, ftill ftronger in the fuperficies of cryf-
" tal, and ftrongeft in the fuperficies of metalline glafs. So, in the confine of
" water and common glafs, the reflection is very weak, but yet ftronger than in
" the confine of water and oil, or almoft any other two liquors, and ftill ftronger
" in the confine of water and cryftal, or metalline glafs : accordingly as thofe
" mediums differ more or lefs in denfity, fo in the confine of common glafs and
" cryftal there is a weak reflection, and a ftronger reflection in the confine of
" common and metalline glafs : but in the confine of two glaffes of equal den-
" fity, there is not any fenfible reflection, as was fhewn in the firft obfervation.
" And the fame may be underftood of the fuperficies of two cryftals or liquors,
" or any other fubftances, in which no refraction is caufed : whence it comes to
" pafs, that uniform mediums have no fenfible reflexion but in their external fu-
" perficies, where they are adjacent to their mediums of a different denfity.

" Prop. 2. The leaft parts of natural bodies are in fome meafure tranfparent ;
" and the opacities of thofe bodies arife from the multitude of reflections caufed
" in their internal parts.

Q q " That

" That this is fo, will eafily be granted by them, that have been converfant with
" microfcopes : and it may be alfo tried by applying any fubftance to a hole, through
" which the light is emitted into a dark room; for how opake foever that fub
" ftance may feem in the open air, it will, by that means, appear very manifeftly
" tranfparent, if it be of a fufficient thicknefs : only metalline bodies muft be ex-
" empted. which, by reafon of their exceffive denfity feem to reflect almoft all the
" light incident on their firft fuperficies.

" Prop. 3. Between the parts of opake or coloured bodies are many interftices,
" replenifhed with mediums of other denfities, as water between the tinging cor-
" pufcles, wherewith any liquor is impregnated; air between the aqueous globules
" that conftitute clouds or mifts; and for the moft part fpaces void of both air
" and water; but yet perhaps replenifhed with fome fubtiler medium between
" the parts of hard bodies.

" The truth of this is evinced by the two precedent propofitions : for by the
" fecond propofition there are many reflections from the internal part of bodies,
" which by the firft propofition would not happen, if the parts of thofe bodies
" were continued without any fuch interftices between them, becaufe reflections
" are caufed only in fuperficies, which interceed mediums of a different denfity.

" But further, that this difcontinuity of parts is the principal caufe of the opa-
" city of bodies, will appear by confidering, that opake fubftances become tranf
" parent by filling their pores with any fubftance of equal, or almoft equal denfity
" with their parts. Thus paper dipped in water or oil, the oculus mundi ftone
" fteeped in water, linen-cloth oiled or varnifhed, and many other fubftances foaked
" in fuch liquors, as will intimately pervade their little pores, become by that
" means more tranfparent than otherwife. So, on the contrary, the moft tranf-
" parent fubftances may, by feparating their parts, be rendered fufficiently opake;
" as glafs, by being reduced to powder, or otherwife flawed, water by being form-
" ed into many fmall bubbles, either alone in the form of froth, or by fhaking
" it together with oil of turpentine, or fome other convenient liquor, with which
" it will not incorporate, and horn by being fcraped.

" To the increafe of the opacity of thefe bodies it conduces fomething, that by
" the twenty third obfervation, the reflections of very thin tranfparent fubftances
" are confiderably ftronger than thofe made by the fame fubftances of a greater
" thicknefs. And to the reflection of folid bodies it may be further added, that
" the interftices of their parts are void of air. For that for the moft part they
" are fo, is reafonable to believe, confidering the ineptitude, which air hath to
" pervade fmall cavities, as appears by the afcenfion of water in flender glafs-
" pipes, paper, cloth, and other fuch like fubftances, whofe pores are found too
" fmall to be replenifhed with air, and yet large enough to admit water; and by
" the difficulty, wherewith air pervades the pores of a bladder, through which
" water find ready paffage. And according to the eleventh obfervation, the ca-
" vities thus void of air will caufe the fame kind of effects as to reflection, which
" thofe do, that are replenifhed with it; but yet fomething more manifeftly, be-
" caufe

" caufe the medium in relation to refractions is rareſt, when moſt empty of air"
" as Mr. Hooke hath proved in his Micrographia; in which book he hath alſo
" largely difcourſed of this and the precedent propoſition, and delivered many
" other very excellent things concerning the colours of thin plates, and other na-
" tural bodies, which I have not ſcrupled to make uſe of ſo far as they were ſor
" my purpoſe.

" Prop. 4. The parts of bodies and their interſtices muſt not be leſs than
" of ſome definitive bigneſs, to render them opake and coloured; for the opakeſt
" bodies, if their parts be ſubtilly divided (as metals by being diſſolved in acid
" menſtruums, &c.) become perfectly tranſparent.   And you may alſo remem-
" ber, that in the eighth obſervation there was no reflection at the ſuperficies of
" the object-glaſſes, where they were very near one another, though they did not
" abſolutely touch.   And in the ſeventeenth obſervation, the reflection of the
" water-bubble, where it became thinneſt, was almoſt inſenſible, ſo as to cauſe the
" apparitions of very black ſpots.

" On theſe grounds I conceive it is, that water, ſalt, glaſs, ſtones, and ſuch
" like ſubſtances, are tranſparent; for, upon divers conſiderations, they ſeem to
" be as porous as other bodies, but yet their pores and parts too ſmall to cauſe
" any opacity.

" Prop. 5. The tranſparent parts of bodies, according to their ſeveral ſizes,
" muſt *reflect* rays of one colour, and *tranſmit* thoſe of another, on the ſame
" grounds, that thin plates or bubbles do reflect or tranſmit thoſe rays: and this
" I take to be the ground of all their colours.

" For, if a thinned or plated body, which being of an even thickneſs appears
" all over of one uniform colour, ſhould be broken into fragments of the ſame
" thickneſs with the plate, I ſee no reaſon, why a heap of thoſe fragments ſhould
" not conſtitute a powder of the ſame colour, which the plate exhibited before it
" was broken.   And the parts of all natural bodies, being like ſo many fragments
" of a plate, muſt on the ſame grounds exhibit the ſame colours.

" Now, that they do ſo, will further appear by the affinity of their proper-
" ties: as that the infuſion of nephritic-wood, and many other ſubſtances reflect
" one colour, and tranſmit another, like thin bodies in the ninth and twentieth
" obſervations.   That the colours of ſilks, cloaths, and others ſubſtances, which
" water or oil can intimately penetrate, become more faint and obſcure by being
" emerged in thoſe liquors, and recover their vigour again by being dried, much
" after the manner declared of thin bodies, in the tenth and twenty firſt obſer-
" vations: and that ſome of thoſe coloured powders, which painters uſe, may have
" their colours a little changed, by being very elaborately and finely ground.
" Where I ſee not, what can be juſtly pretended for thoſe changes, beſides the
" breaking of their parts into leſs parts by that contrition, after the ſame manner
" that the colour of a plate is changed by varying its thickneſs.   For which rea-
" ſon alſo it is, that many flowers, by being bruiſed, become more tranſparent

" than before, or, at leaft, in fome degree or other, change their colours. Nor
" is it much lefs to my purpofe, that, by mixing divers liquors, very odd and
" remarkable productions and changes of colours may be effected, of which no
" caufe can be more obvious and natural, than that the faline corpufcles of one
" liquor do varioufly act upon, or unite with, the tinging corpufcles of another ;
" fo as to make them fwell or fhrink (whereby not only their bulk, but their
" denfity alfo may be changed) or to divide them into fmaller corpufcles, or make
" many of them affociate into one clufter ; for we fee how apt thofe faline men-
" ftruums are to penetrate and diffolve fubftances, to which they are applied ; and
" fome of them to precipitate what others diffolve.   In like manner, if we con-
" fider the various phænomena of the atmofphere, we may obferve, that when
" vapours are firft raifed, they hinder not the tranfparency of the air, being di-
" vided into parts too fmall to caufe any reflection in their fuperficies : but when,
" in order to compofe drops of rain, they began to coalefce and conftitute glo-
" bules of all intermediate fizes, thofe globules, when they become of a conveni-
" ent fize to reflect fome colours, and tranfmit others, may conftitute clouds of
" various colours, according to their fizes.   And I fee not what can be rationally
" conceived, in fo tranfparent a fubftance as water for the production of thefe
" colours, befides the various fizes of its parcels, which feem to affect a globular
" figure moft ; but yet perhaps not without fome inftability in the fmalleft of
" them, by reafon that thofe are moft eafily agitated by heat or any trembling mo-
" tions in the air.

" Prop. 6.   The parts of bodies, on which their colours depend, are denfer than
" the medium, which pervades their interftices.

" This will appear by confidering, that the colour of a body depends not only
" on the rays, which are incident perpendicularly or its parts, but on thofe alfo,
" which are incident at all other angles.   And that, according to the feventh
" obfervation, a very little variation of obliquity will change the reflected colour,
" where the thin body or fmall particle is rarer than the ambient medium, in
" fomuch that fuch a fmall particle will, at diverfly oblique incidents, reflect all
" forts of colours, in fo great a variety, that the colour, refulting from them all
" confufedly reflected from a heap of fuch particles, muft rather be a white or
" grey, than any other colour, or at beft it muft be but a very imperfect and
" dirty colour ; whereas, if the thin body or fmall particle be much denfer than
" the ambient medium, the colours, according to the nineteenth obfervation, are
" fo little changed by the variation of obliquity, that the rays, which are re-
" flected leaft obliquely, may predominate over the reft fo much, as to caufe a
" heap of fuch particles to appear very intenfly of their colour.

" It conduces alfo fomething to this propofition, that, according to the twenty-
" fecond obfervation, the colours exhibited by the denfer thin body within the
" rarer are more brifk than thofe exhibited by the rarer within the denfer.

" Prop. 7.   The bignefs of the component parts of natural bodies may be
" conjectured by their colours.

3   " For

" For fince the parts of thefe bodies, by propofition 5. do moft probably ex-
" hibit the fame colours with a plate of equal thicknefs, provided they have the
" fame refractive denfity; and fince their parts feem for the moft part to have
" much the fame denfity with water or glafs, as by many circumftances is obvious
" to collect: to determine the fizes of thefe parts, you need only have recourfe
" to the precedent tables, in which the thicknefs of water or glafs exhibiting any
" colour is expreffed. Thus, if it be defired to know the diameter of a cor-
" pufcle, which being of equal denfity with glafs, fhall reflect green of the third
" order; the number 17¼ fhows it to be about $\frac{17\frac{1}{4}}{1000000}$ parts of an inch.

" The greateft difficulty is here to know, of what order the colour of any
" body is; and for this end we muft have recourfe to the fourth and eighteenth
" obfervations, from whence may be collected thefe particulars.

" *Scarlets*, and other *reds*, *oranges* and *yellows*, if they be pure and intenfe, are
" moft probably of the fecond order. Thofe of the firft and third order alfo may
" be pretty good; only the orange and red of the third order have too great a
" mixture of violet and blue.

" There may be good *greens* of the fourth order, but the pureft are of the third:
" and of this order the green of all vegetables feems to be, partly by reafon of
" the intenfenefs of their colours, and partly becaufe when they wither, fome of
" them turn to a greenifh yellow, and others to a more perfect yellow or orange,
" or perhaps to red; paffing firft through all the aforefaid intermediate colours,
" which changes feem to be effected by the exhaling of the moifture, which may
" leave the tinging corpufcles more denfe, and fomething augmented by the ac-
" cretion of the oily and earthy part of that moifture. Now the green, without
" doubt, is of the fame order with thofe colours, into which it changeth, becaufe
" the changes are gradual, and thofe colours, though ufually not very pure, yet
" for the moft part are too pure and lively to be of the fourth order.

" *Blues* and *purples* may be either of the fecond or third order; but the beft are
" of the third. Thus the colour of *violet* feems to be of that order; becaufe
" their fyrup, by acid liquors, turns red, and by urinous and alkalazite turns
" green. For fince it is of the nature of acids to diffolve or attenuate, and of
" alcalis to precipitate or incraffate, if the purple colour of the fyrup was of
" the fecond order, an acid liquor by attenuating its tinging corpufcles would tinge
" it to a red of the firft order, and an alcali, by incraffating them, would change
" it to a green of the fecond order; which red and green, efpecially the green,
" feem too imperfect to be the colours produced by thefe changes. But if the
" faid purple be fuppofed of the third order, its change to red of the fecond
" and green of the third may, without any inconvenience, be allowed.

" If there be found any body of a deeper and lefs reddifh purple than that of
" violets, its colour moft probably is of the fecond order. But yet there being
" no body commonly known, whofe colour is conftantly more deep than theirs,
                                                        " I have

" I have made ufe of their name to denote the deepeft and leaft reddifh purples,
" fuch as manifeftly tranfcend their colour in purity.

" The *blue* of the firft order, though very faint and little, may poffibly be the
" colour of fome fubftances; and particularly the azure colour of the fkies
" feems to be of this order. For all vapours, when they begin to condenfe and
" coalefce into fmall parcels, become firft of that bignefs, whereby fuch an azure
" muft be reflected, before they can conftitute clouds of other colours. And fo
" this being the firft colour, which vapours begin to reflect, it ought to be the
" colour of the fineft and moft tranfparent fkies, in which vapours are not ar-
" rived to that groffnefs requifite to reflect other colours, as we find it is by ex-
" perience.

" Whitenefs, if it be intenfe, is either that in the firft ˜order of colours, of
" which fort perhaps is the colour of white lead; or elfe it is a mixture of
" thofe fucceeding the third or fourth order, fuch as is the colour of paper,
" linen, and moft white fubftances. If corpufcles of various fizes, exhibiting the
" colours of the fecond and third order, be mixed, they fhould rather conftitute
" an imperfect whitenefs or grey, of which I have already fpoken : but yet it feems
" not impoffible for them to exhibit an intenfe whitenefs, if they be difpofed to
" tranfmit all the light, which they reflect not, and do not retain and ftifle much
" of it. For thus I told you, that froth at a diftance hath appeared very white,
" and yet, near at hand, the feveral bubbles, of which it was conftituted, were
" feen tinged all over with rings of colours of the four or five firft orders.

" Laftly, for the production of *black*, the corpufcles muft be lefs than any of
" thofe, which exhibit colours. For at all greater fizes there is too much light re-
" flected to conftitute this colour. But if they be fuppofed a little lefs than is re-
" quifite to reflect the blue of the firft order, they will, according to the fourth,
" eight, feventeenth, and eighteenth obfervations, reflect fo very little light as
" to appear intenfely black, and yet may perhaps varioufly refract it to and fro
" within themfelves fo long, until it happen to be ftifled and loft; by which
" means they will appear black in all pofitions of the eye without any tranfpa-
" rency. And from hence may be underftood, why fire, and the more fubtil
" diffolver, putrefaction, turn fubftances to black ; why fmall quantities of black
" fubftances impart their colour very freely and intenfely to other fubftances, to
" which they are applied ; why glafs ground very elaborately, on a copper-plate,
" till it be well polifhed, makes the fand, together with what is worn off from
" the glafs, and copper, become very black; why black fubftances do fooneft of
" all others become hot and burn, which effect may proceed, partly from the
" multitude of refractions in a little room, and partly from the eafy commo-
" tion of fo very fmall corpufcles; and why blacks are ufually a little inclined to
" a bluifh colour. For that they are fo, may be feen by illuminating white
" paper by reflection from black fubftances, which will ufually appear of a bluifh
" white. And the reafon is, that black borders on the obfcure blue of the firft
" order, defcribed in the eighteenth obfervation, whence the corpufcles of black
" fubftances are moft apt to reflect that colour.

" In

" In thefe defcriptions I have been the more particular, becaufe it is not impof-
" fible, but that microfcopes may at length be improved to the difcovery of
" corpufcles of bodies, on which their colours depend.   For if thofe inftruments
" could be fo far improved, as with fufficient diftinctnefs to reprefent objects five
" or fix hundred times bigger than at a foot diftance they appear to our naked eyes.
" I fhould hope, that we might be able to difcover fome of the greateft of thofe
" corpufcles.   And by one, that would magnify three or four thoufand times, per-
" haps they might all be difcovered but thofe, which produce blacknefs.   In the
" mean while, I fee nothing material, that rationally can be doubted of, except-
" ing this pofition, that tranfparent corpufcles of the fame thicknefs and denfity
" with a plate do exhibit the fame colour.   And this I would have underftood
" not without fome latitude, as well becaufe thofe corpufcles may be of irregular
" figures, and many rays muft be obliquely incident, and fo have a fhorter way
" through them than the length of their diameter; as becaufe the ftraitnefs of
" the medium, pent in on all fides, may a little alter its motions, or other qua-
" lities, on which the reflexion depends.   But yet I cannot much fufpect the laft,
" becaufe I have obferved of fome fmall plates of Mufcovy-glafs, which were of
" an even thicknefs, that through a microfcope they have appeared of the fame
" colour at their edges and corners, where the included medium was terminated,
" which they appeared of in other places.   However, it would add much to our
" fatisfaction, if thofe corpufcles could be difcovered with microfcopes, which if
" we fhall ever attain to, I fear it will be the utmoft improvement of this fenfe;
" for it feems impoffible to fee the more fecret and noble works of nature within
" thofe corpufcles, by reafon of their tranfparency.

" This may fuffice concerning the conftitution of natural bodies, on which their
" colours depend.   But for further underftanding the nature of reflections, I
" fhall add thefe two following propofitions.

" Prop. 8.   The caufe of the reflection is not the impinging of light on the
" folid and impervious parts of bodies, as is commonly fuppofed.

" This will appear by the following confiderations: firft, that in the paffage of
" light out of glafs into air, there is a reflection as ftrong or ftronger than in its
" paffage out of air into glafs, and by many degrees ftronger than in its paffage
" out of glafs into water.   And it feems not probable, that air fhould have more
" reflecting parts than water or glafs.   But if that fhould poffibly be fuppofed, it
" will avail nothing; for the reflection is as ftrong, if not ftronger, when the air
" is drawn away from the glafs (fuppofe in the air-pump invented by Mr. BOYLE)
" as when it is adjacent to it.   Secondly, if light in its paffage out of glafs into
" air be incident more obliquely than at an angle of forty or forty-one degrees,
" it is wholly *reflected*; if lefs obliquely, it is in great meafure *tranfmitted*.   Now
" it is not to be imagined, that light at one degree of obliquity fhould meet with
" pores enough in the air to tranfmit the greater part of it, and at another degree
" of obliquity meet with nothing but parts to reflect it wholly; efpecially confi-
" dering, that in its paffage out of air into glafs, how oblique foever be its
" incidence, it finds pores enough in the glafs to tranfmit the greateft part of it.
" If

" If any man suppose, that it is not reflected by the air, but by the utmost su-
" perficial parts of the glass, there is still the same difficulty; besides, that such
" a supposition is unintelligible; and will also appear to be false, by applying wa-
" ter behind some part of the glass instead of air.   For so in a convenient obli-
" quity of the rays, suppose of forty-five or forty-six degrees, at which they are
" all *reflected*, where the air is adjacent to the glass, they shall be in great measure
" *transmitted*, where the water is adjacent to it; which argues, that their reflection
" or transmission depends on the constitution of the air and water behind the
" glass, and not on the parts of the glass.

" Thirdly, if the colours made by a prism, placed at the entrance of a beam
" of light into a darkened room, be successively cast on a second prism placed
" at a great distance from the former, in such manner that they are all alike in-
" cident upon it; the second prism may be so inclined to the incident rays, that
" those, which are of a blue colour, shall be all reflected by it; and yet those of a
" red colour pretty copiously transmitted.   Now if the reflection be caused by
" the parts of air or glass, I would ask, why at the same obliquity of incidence
" the blue should wholly impinge on those parts so as to be all reflected, and yet
" the red find pores enough to be in great measure transmitted.   Fourthly,
" where two glasses touch one another, there is no sensible reflection, as was de-
" clared in the first observation; and yet I see no reason, why the rays should not
" impinge on the parts of glass, when contiguous to another glass, a smuch as
" when contiguous to air.   Fifthly, when the top of a water-bubble (in the se-
" venteenth observation) by the continual subsiding and exhaling of the water
" grew very thin, there was such a little and almost insensible quantity of light
" reflected from it, that it appeared intensely black; whereas, round about that
" black spot, where the water was thicker, the reflection was so strong as to make
" the water seem very white.   Nor is it only at the least thickness of thin plates
" or bubbles that there is no manifest reflection, but at many other thicknesses
" continually greater and greater.   For in the fifteenth observation, the rays of the
" same colour were by turns transmitted at one thickness, and reflected at another
" thickness, for an intermediate number of successions.   And yet in the superfi-
" cies of the third body, where it is of any one thickness, there are as many
" parts for the rays to impinge on, as where it is of any other thickness.

" Lastly, if reflection were caused by the parts of reflecting bodies, it would
" be impossible for thin plates or bubbles, at the same place to reflect the rays of
" one colour, and transmit those of another, as they do according to the thirteenth
" and fifteenth observations.   For is is not to be imagined, that at one place the
" rays, which, for instance, exhibit a blue colour, should have the fortune to dash
" upon the *parts*, and those, which exhibit a red, to hit upon the pores of the
" body; and then at another place, where the body is either a little thicker, or a
" little thinner, that on the contrary the blue should hit upon its *pores*, and the
" red upon its *parts*.

" Prop. 9.   It is most probable, that the rays, which impinge on the solid
" parts of any body, are not reflected but stifled and lost in that body.

" This

167⅝.]   R O Y A L   S O C I E T Y   O F   L O N D O N.   305

" This is confentaneous to the precedent propofition, and will further appear
" by confidering, that if all the rays fhould be reflected, which impinge on the in-
" ternal parts of clear water or cryftal, thofe fubftances fhould rather have a cloudy
" than fo very clear tranfparency.

" And further, there would be no principle of the obfcurity or blacknefs, which
" fome bodies have in all pofitions of the eye.   For to produce this effect, it is ne-
" ceffary, that many rays be retained and loft in the body, and it feems not pro-
" bable, that any rays can be ftopped and retained in it, which do not impinge on
" its parts."

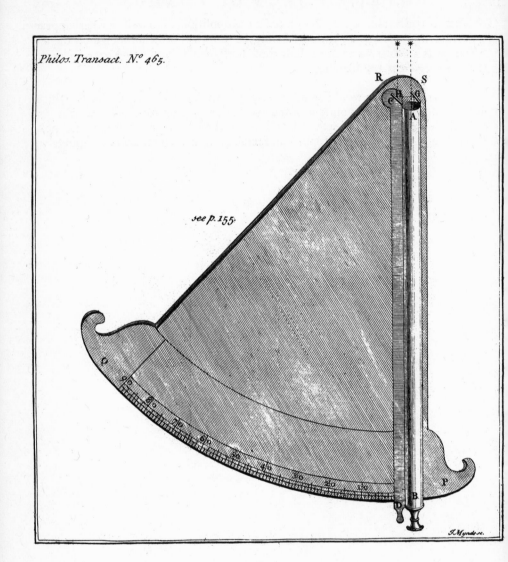

see p. 155.

[155]

I. *A true Copy of a* Paper *found,* in *the Hand Writing of Sir* Iſaac Newton, *among the* Papers *of the late* Dr. Halley, *containing a* Deſcription *of an* Inſtrument *for obſerving the* Moon's Diſtance *from the* Fixt Stars *at* Sea.

Read at a Meeting of the Royal Society, October 28, 1742.

IN the annexed Scheme, $PQRS$ denotes a Plate of Braſs, accurately divided in the Limb DQ, into $\frac{1}{2}$ Degrees, $\frac{1}{2}$ Minutes, and $\frac{1}{12}$ Minutes, by a Diagonal Scale; and the $\frac{1}{2}$ Degrees, and $\frac{1}{2}$ Minutes, and $\frac{1}{12}$ Minutes, counted for Degrees, Minutes, and $\frac{1}{6}$ Minutes.

A B, is a Teleſcope, three or four Feet long, fixt on the Edge of that Braſs Plate.

G, is a *Speculum*, fixt on the ſaid Braſs Plate perpendicularly, as near as may be to the Object-glaſs of the Teleſcope, ſo as to be inclined 45 Degrees to the Axis of the Teleſcope, and intercept half the Light which would otherwiſe come through the Teleſcope to the Eye.

C D, is a moveable Index, turning about the Centre *C*, and, with its fiducial Edge, ſhewing the Degrees, Minutes, and $\frac{1}{6}$ Minutes, on the Limb of the Braſs Plate PQ; the Centre *C*, muſt be over-againſt the Middle of the *Speculum G*.

H, is another *Speculum*, parallel to the former, when the fiducial Edge of the Index falls on oo^d oo′ oo″; ſo that the ſame Star may then appear through

X   the

[156]

the Telefcope, in one and the fame Place, both by
the direct Rays and by the reflex'd ones; but if the
Index be turned, the Star fhall appear in two Places,
whofe Diftance is fhewed, on the Brafs Limb, by the
Index.

By this Inftrument, the Diftance of the Moon from
any Fixt Star is thus obferved: View the Star through
the Perfpicil by the direct Light, and the Moon by
the Reflext (or on the contrary); and turn the Index
till the Star touch the Limb of the Moon, and the
Index fhall fhew upon the Brafs Limb of the Inftrument, the Diftance of the Star from the Limb of the
Moon; and though the Inftrument fhake, by the Motion of your Ship at Sea, yet the Moon and Star will
move together, as if they did really touch one another
in the Heavens; fo that an Obfervation may be made
as exactly at Sea as at Land.

And by the fame Inftrument, may be obferved,
exactly, the Altitudes of the Moon and Stars, by
bringing them to the Horizon; and thereby the Latitude, and Times of Obfervations, may be determined
more exactly than by the Ways now in Ufe.

In the Time of the Obfervation, if the Inftrument
move angularly about the Axis of the Telefcope, the
Star will move in a Tangent of the Moon's Limb, or
of the Horizon; but the Obfervation may notwithftanding be made exactly, by noting when the Line,
defcribed by the Star, is a Tangent to the Moon's
Limb, or to the Horizon.

To make the Inftrument ufeful, the Telefcope ought
to take in a large Angle: And to make the Obfervation true, let the Star touch the Moon's Limb, not on
the Outfide of the Limb, but on the Infide.

II. *The*

III.

Newton on Chemistry, Atomism, the Æther, and Heat

Newton's
Chemical Papers

MARIE BOAS

Newton's extraordinary achievements in physics have understandably overshadowed his chemical work; it is fortunate that the sale some years ago of his large collection of alchemical books and notes forced a renewed consideration of his overt preoccupation with alchemy, which in turn has led to the study of his place in the history of chemistry.[1] He has been found to have been a skilled, original, and painstaking chemist with a wide and profound influence.

A full understanding of Newton's chemical thinking and of the experimental basis of his conclusions will be reached only after a careful analysis of his extant chemical notebooks, now in the University Library, Cambridge. These have not been seriously studied since they were summarized by the group who compiled the *Cata-*

---

[1] See *Catalogue of the Newton Papers Sold by Order of the Viscount Lymington* (London, 1936). The most recent appraisal is by R. J. Forbes, "Was Newton an Alchemist?" *Chymia 2*, 27–36 (1949). The best general account is Douglas McKie, "Some Notes on Newton's Chemical Philosophy Written Upon the Occasion of the Tercentenary of his Birth," *Philosophical Magazine* [7] *33*, 847–70 (1942).

logue of the Portsmouth Collection in 1888.[2] There are three notebooks of considerable chemical interest containing chaotic records of experiments, proposed experiments, notes from books, recipes, topics for possible investigation—a fascinating laboratory record. But, important as these sources are for Newton's chemical development, they can safely be ignored in evaluating his chemical influence, since 18th-century Newtonians read the published works, not the manuscripts. Such Newtonian scientists were, as Mme. Metzger showed in her brilliant *Newton, Stahl, Boerhaave et la doctrine chimique* (Paris, 1930), profoundly influenced by the chemical implications of the theory of universal gravitation. More than that, they read and absorbed those of Newton's works that were wholly or partly chemical in nature.

Of the papers reprinted here, the "Letter to Boyle," dated 1678, was first published in Thomas Birch's "Life of Boyle" prefixed to the first edition, in 1744, of *The Works of the Honourable Robert Boyle,* which Birch edited. Though it can have had wide circulation only after Newton's death, it may have been known earlier, since Boyle or his executors could easily have shown it to interested scientists. Once printed, the letter was immediately reprinted in Bryan Robinson's *Sir Isaac Newton's Account of the Æther, with some additions by way of an appendix.*[3] Inevitably of greater influence was the "De natura acidorum," written in 1692 and first published in 1710 in the "Introduction" to volume II of the *Lexicon Technicum* of John Harris, F.R.S.[4] Harris is the authority for the date of composition; he stated that he printed the paper with Newton's permission and that the translation into English had been read and approved by Newton. The paper was subsequently printed, in a slightly different Latin version, in volume II of Newton's *Opuscula mathematica, philosophica et philologica* (Lausanne, 1744). This version, and that

---

[2] *A Catalogue of the Portsmouth Collection of Books and Papers Written by or Belonging to Sir Isaac Newton* (Cambridge, 1888). I have to thank the authorities of the University Library, Cambridge, who kindly allowed me access to the chemical notebooks mentioned.

[3] Dublin, 1745. This reprints not only the "Letter," but Queries 16–23 of the *Opticks.* Robinson had already published in 1743 *A Dissertation on the Æther of Sir Isaac Newton,* based on the *Opticks.*

[4] Cf. Douglas McKie: "John Harris and his *Lexicon Technicum* (1704)," *Endeavour* 4, 53–57 (1945).

later published by Samuel Horsley in *Isaaci Newtoni Opera quae exstant omnia* (1782), confirm the statement by Harris that more than one version of the paper was known to him; fragments, both in Newton's hand and in that of an amanuensis, are tucked into one of Newton's chemical notebooks.[5] The paper on heat was first published anonymously in the *Philosophical Transactions* for March-April 1701, and is the source for Newton's Law of Cooling. It is essentially a chemical paper, not only because of its interesting use of the melting points of mixtures of metals, but also because the related problems of heat and fire were considered to be a part of chemistry, rather than of physics, in the eighteenth century. There are a number of references to both chemical experiment and theory, particularly the nature of solubility and solution, in the paper on optics printed in this volume on page 177. Finally, there is one very important source for Newton's chemistry not reprinted here: the Queries, and more particularly the 31st Query, of the *Opticks*.

Even a cursory glance at Newton's chemical papers indicates that his approach to chemical problems was not that of an alchemist. His explanations are in the language and spirit of experimental natural philosophy, quite different from the usually cloudy and often mystic views of the alchemists whose works he bought or borrowed so avidly, as he did all books that had any pretensions to dealing with chemical theory or practice.[6] His library included scores of alchemical works; he read and was influenced by Van Helmont and his English follower George Starkey; but equally he read and was influenced by such natural philosophers as Robert Boyle who despised all mysticism in science. Actually Newton's chemical approach was far nearer to Boyle's than to Van Helmont's. Many of Newton's experiments on the colors of chemical solutions appear to be extensions of Boyle's experiments. And Newton always followed Boyle in treating chemistry

---

[5] S. I. Vavilov, "Newton and the Atomic Theory," in The Royal Society, *Newton Tercentenary Celebrations 15-19 July 1946* (Cambridge, 1947), 43–55, is in error in believing that Harris mistranslated the Latin; the divergence is so great that he can only have translated from another version.

[6] For a list of books owned by Newton, see R. de Villamil, *Newton: The Man* (London, n.d.).

as a physical science, rather than as a mystic art, and in using chemistry to suggest and confirm a molecular physics.

The "Letter to Boyle," the "De natura acidorum," and the 31st Query of the *Opticks* have much in common, although the exposition varies decidedly in works written over a period of more than twenty years. Basically, all three are concerned with the problems of chemical reactivity and the action of solvents as explicable in terms of a particulate theory of matter, which assumes a theory of universal attraction.

Underlying the whole of Newton's chemical (and physical) theory is the concept of matter as particulate. Almost all scientists of the later 17th century agreed that matter was composed of small, discrete particles, corpuscles, or atoms, and that the chemical and physical properties of bodies could be accounted for by means of the size, shape, *and motion* of the constituent particles. This is the so-called mechanical philosophy which rejected all "occult forces" such as sympathy, antipathy, congruity, incongruity, attraction, and hostility, and instead explained all the properties of matter in terms of the new science of dynamics.[7] One kind of mechanical explanation was the Cartesian: Descartes and his followers believed in an æther, a material substance composed of specially small, mobile particles which imparted motion and impulse to the naturally inert and gross particles of ordinary matter. Boyle on the other hand rejected even the æther, assuming random but constant motion of all particles to explain impulse; even chemical reaction he believed to be caused not by an æther nor by any attraction of one particle toward another, but by the fact that the size and shape of the particles of one substance happened to correspond to the size and shape of the pores between the particles of another substance.

Newton's addition to the mechanical philosophy was the assumption that particles moved mainly under the influence of what he at first called sociability and later called attraction. Attraction is, of course, the concept that made the *Principia* possible; the theory of universal gravitation is that all bodies in the universe, large or small, are mutually attracted to one another, and this theory Newton extended to both the physical and the chemical worlds. In using

[7] For a detailed account, see M. Boas, "The Establishment of the Mechanical Philosophy," *Osiris, 10,* 412–541 (1952).

a force like attraction Newton was, as Cartesian critics tirelessly insisted, something of a scientific reactionary, for the great prestige of the mechanical philosophers had been based chiefly upon the determined banishing of all such "occult" forces. But Newton found the concept uniquely useful, and made it as little occult as possible by treating it from the mechanical point of view.

Newton's ideas on the possible mechanism of attraction were never definitely worked out. When he spoke of attraction he sometimes, as in the "Letter to Boyle," immediately explained it in terms of impulse by an æther—sometimes, but by no means always. The *Principia* loftily and expressly avoided any explanation of the mechanism of gravitational attraction except for a suggestion in the final scholium added only in the second edition. In other works, especially in Queries 16–24 of the *Opticks,* Newton discussed ways in which the æther might account for chemical and gravitational attraction, but never did he offer a developed hypothesis. One is left with the feeling that Newton preferred a mechanical explanation in terms of an æther to the "action-at-a-distance" concept of pure attraction; this indeed is what he wrote Bentley. His avoidance of any decision in the *Principia* must have come chiefly from the absence of genuine experimental evidence. In fact, Boyle had published experiments that showed it unlikely that the æther as postulated by Descartes could exist; and Newton had demolished the Cartesian æther and its vortex action theoretically in the second book of the *Principia.* Any satisfactory æther had to be so different from that of Descartes as to be, essentially, experimentally undetectable, a most uncomfortable position for an empiricist to maintain.[8]

There is one further aspect of Newton's theory of matter that deserves mention, an aspect contained in the random notes at the end of the "De natura acidorum." Here—and it is the only place where he discussed the matter—Newton suggested that particles associate to form aggregates "of the first composition," that these associate to form aggregates "of the second composition," and so on. This led to a method of differentiating between reaction and transmutation. When gold reacts with mercury to form mercury amalgam

[8] Boyle, *The Spring and Weight of the Air, First Continuation,* in Thomas Birch, *The Works of the Honourable Robert Boyle* (second ed., London, 1772), III, 250 ff.; *Rarefaction of the Air; Works,* III, 495 ff.

the gold is recoverable, so presumably the mercury particles penetrated only to the particles of the "last" composition. But if mercury could get between the particles of the first composition, then and only then would gold be transmuted into some other substance. This is an intriguing suggestion, but analogies with modern atomic physics are not valid. The fact that this theory is not referred to in the *Opticks* must mean that Newton found this concept (which incidentally is not entirely original with him, for the notion of aggregates of particles is to be found in the work of many early 17th-century chemists writing on the nature of matter—for example, Sennert) not to be a useful enough hypothesis to be pursued; but it did convince him that transmutation was too difficult to be probable.

Unlike gravitational attraction, which was a universal force varying only objectively with mass and distance, chemical attraction was selective and varied subjectively with each pair of chemical compounds. So complex was the action of this kind of attraction that the addition of one chemical to another could alter the attraction or sociability of the latter to a third compound. This Newton pointed out as early as 1675 in one of the optical papers sent to the Royal Society, a letter which incidentally indicates Newton's current chemical interest.

Almost always Newton's discussion of sociability is a part of a search for a general theory of solution. The solvents that most interested him were the common strong acids and he repeatedly grappled with the difficult reactions between acids and metals. The most interesting of these he thought were the reactions of acid mixtures with gold and silver and he several times mentioned the specific nature of the ability of aqua regia to dissolve gold but not silver, and of aqua fortis to dissolve silver but not gold; this problem he tried to resolve by combining attraction and the relative size of the particles of acids and the pores between the particles of the metal as criteria of solubility.[9] His difficulties in this regard were not made easier by the necessity of defining clearly what substances should be classed as acids. In the mid 17th century there had been developed

[9] See Thomas S. Kuhn, "Newton's '31st Query' and the Degradation of Gold," *Isis 42*, 296–298 (1951), and M. Boas and T. S. Kuhn, "Newton and the Theory of Chemical Solution," *Isis 43*, 123–124 (1952).

a chemical theory based on the notion that all substances contained either acids or alkalies, so that all chemical reactions could be regarded as the combination of an acid and an alkali. Robert Boyle repeatedly attacked this view, in works which now have only the interest of controversy; but of lasting importance was his classification of acids and alkalies on the basis of their characteristic reactions: thus all acids turned syrup of violets red, all alkalies turned syrup of violets green, and some substances did neither.[10] Eighteenth-century chemists very frequently accepted this useful empirical classification. Newton used these tests in his own work; but he preferred to define acids theoretically, rather than empirically, as substances "endued with a great Attractive Force; in which Force their Activity consists." This definition, in the "De natura acidorum," was still assumed in the 31st Query of the *Opticks;* it was the chief explanation, for Newton, of the great solvent activity habitually displayed by acids. Another reaction involving acids which interested Newton, and which he also discussed in the 31st Query, was the replacement of one metal by another in an acid solution. He went so far as to list the six common metals in the order in which they would displace one another from a solution of aqua fortis (strong nitric acid). This is perhaps a forerunner of the tables of affinity so common in the eighteenth century, by which chemists tried to predict the course of a reaction.

Newton built no great chemical system comparable to his physical system of the universe, but by combining a particulate theory of matter with a profound experimental knowledge of chemistry he helped push chemistry one step nearer its acceptance as a true physical science. Newton is not less of a chemist because there is no positive chemical discovery associated with his name. Boerhaave, the great eighteenth-century physician and Newtonian chemist, more than once underlined the importance of chemistry as a part of natural philosophy with such remarks as, "*Sir Isaac Newton* gives us many chymical Experiments of the Attraction of Bodies" and "Isaac Newton . . . when he demonstrates by manifest effects the laws, actions, and forces of bodies does so not otherwise than by chem-

---

[10] *Reflections on the Hypothesis of Alkali and Acidum; Works,* IV, 284–292; cf. H. Metzger, *Les doctrines chimiques en France* (Paris, 1923), pp. 205–210. For Boyle's classification, see *The Experimental History of Colours; Works,* I, 744, 765–767.

istry." [11] Henry Pemberton, editor of the third edition of the *Principia* and author of a widely read popularization of Newtonian physics, in his chemical lectures, read at Gresham College about 1730, cited Newton's chemical achievements as laying the groundwork for greater discoveries: "Not only his general proofs, drawn from chemical experiments, of some active principles existing in nature, by which all natural effects are caused, but his more particular thoughts, concerning the nature of acids, cannot be sufficiently admired." [12] Many more examples could be cited; and a modern historian must agree that Newton's approach to chemical problems and his attempt to interpret and analyze chemical reactivity are very nearly as full of insight, as interesting, and as influential as the 18th-century chemists thought them to be. Or, as John Harris said in the *Lexicon Technicum*, introducing the "De natura acidorum," "The following Paper of Sir *Isaac Newton's* is excellently well worth the Philosophical Reader's most serious and repeated Perusal; for it containes in it the Reason of the Ways and Manner of all Chymical Operations, and indeed of almost all the Physical Qualities, by which Natural Bodies, by their small Particles, act one upon another."

[11] H. Boerhaave, *A Method of Studying Physick* (London, 1719), p. 101, and *Sermo academicus de chemia* (Leyden, 1718).

[12] *A Course of Chymistry . . . now first published from the Author's Manuscript by James Wilson* (London, 1771), pp. 13–14.

THE

WORKS

OF THE HONOURABLE

ROBERT BOYLE.

In FIVE VOLUMES.

To which is prefixed

The LIFE of the AUTHOR.

VOLUME I.

Ex rerum Causis Supremam noscere Causam.

LONDON:
Printed for A. MILLAR, oppofite *Catharine-Street*, in the *Strand.*
MDCCXLIV.

70   *The LIFE of the honourable* ROBERT BOYLE.

THE regard, which the great *Newton* had for Mr. *Boyle*, will appear from a very curious letter, which the former wrote to him, explaining his fentiments upon one of the moft abftrufe points of philofophy, with refpect to the ætherial medium, which in his *Optics* he propofes as the mechanical caufe of gravitation. This letter having never before feen the light, will be proper to be inferted here.

" Honoured Sir,

" I HAVE fo long deferred to fend you my thoughts about the phyfical qualities we
" fpake of, that did I not efteem myfelf obliged by promife, I think I fhould be afhamed
" to fend them at all.   The truth is, my notions about things of this kind are fo indigefted,
" that I am not well fatisfied my felf in them; and what I am not fatisfied in, I can fcarce
" efteem fit to be communicated to others; efpecially in natural philofophy, where there is
" no end of fancying.   But becaufe I am indebted to you, and yefterday met with a friend,
" Mr. *Maulyverer*, who told me he was going to *London*, and intended to give you the trou-
" ble of a vifit, I could not forbear to take the opportunity of conveying this to you by
" him.

" IT being only an explication of qualities, which you defire of me, I fhall fet down my
" apprehenfions in the form of fuppofitions, as follows.   And firft, I fuppofe, that there is
" diffufed through all places an æthereal fubftance, capable of contraction and dilatation,
" ftrongly elaftic, and, in a word, much like air in all refpects, but far more fubtile.

" 2. I SUPPOSE this æther pervades all grofs bodies, but yet fo as to ftand rarer in their
" pores than in free fpaces, and fo much the rarer, as their pores are lefs.   And this I fup-
" pofe (with others) to be the caufe, why light incident on thofe bodies is refracted towards
" the perpendicular; why two well polifhed metals cohere in a receiver exhaufted of air;
" why ☿ ftands fometimes up to the top of a glafs pipe, though much higher than 30 inches;
" and one of the main caufes, why the parts of all bodies cohere; alfo the caufe of filtration,
" and of the rifing of water in fmall glafs pipes above the furface of the ftagnating water they
" are dipped into: for I fufpect the æther may ftand rarer, not only in the infenfible pores of
" bodies, but even in the very fenfible cavities of thofe pipes.   And the fame principle may
" caufe menftruums to pervade with violence the pores of the bodies they diffolve, the fur-
" rounding æther, as well as the atmofphere, preffing them together.

" 3. I fuppofe the rarer æther within bodies, and the denfer without them, not to be ter-
" minated in a mathematical fuperficies, but to grow gradually into one another; the ex-
" ternal æther beginning to grow rarer, and the internal to grow denfer, at fome little
" diftance from the fuperficies of the body, and running through all intermediate degrees of
" denfity in the intermediate fpaces: And this may be the caufe, why light, in *Grimaldo*'s
" experiment, paffing by the edge of a knife, or other opake body, is turned afide, and as
" it were refracted, and by that refraction makes feveral colours.   Let ABCD be a denfe
" body, whether opake, or tranfparent, EFGH the outfide
" of the uniform æther, which is within it, IKLM the infide
" of the uniform æther, which is without it; and conceive the
" æther, which is between EFGH and IKLM, to run
" through all intermediate degrees of denfity between that of
" the two uniform æthers on either fide.   This being fuppofed,
" the rays of the fun SB, SK, which pafs by the edge of this
" body between B and K, ought in their paffage through
" the unequally denfe æther there, to receive a ply from
" the denfer æther, which is on that fide towards K, and that
" the more, by how much they pafs nearer to the body, and
" thereby to be fcattered through the fpace PQRST, as by
" experience they are found to be.   Now the fpace between the limits EFGH and IKLM
" I fhall call the fpace of the æther's graduated rarity.

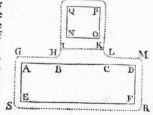

" 4. When two bodies moving towards one another come near together, I fuppofe the
" æther between them to grow rarer than before, and the fpaces of its graduated rarity to
" extend further from the fuperficies of the bodies to-
" wards one another; and this, by reafon, that the æther
" cannot move and play up and down fo freely in the
" ftrait paffage between the bodies, as it could before
" they came fo near together.   Thus, if the fpace of
" the æther's graduated rarity reach from the body
" ABCDFE only to the diftance GHLMRS, when
" no other body is near it, yet may it reach farther, as
" to IK, when another body NOPQ approaches: and
" as the other body approaches more and more, I fuppofe
" the æther between them will grow rarer and rarer.

" Thefe

The LIFE of the honourable ROBERT BOYLE. 71

" THESE fuppofitions I have fo defcribed, as if I thought the fpaces of graduated æther
" had precife limits, as is expreffed at I K L M in the firft figure, and G M R S in the
" fecond : for thus I thought I could better exprefs my felf. But really I do not think they
" have fuch precife limits, but rather decay infenfibly, and, in fo decaying, extend to a much
" greater diftance, than can eafily be believed, or need be fuppofed.

" 5. Now from the fourth fuppofition it follows, that when two bodies approaching one
" another, come fo near together, as to make the æther between them begin to rarefy, they
" will begin to have a reluctance from being brought nearer together, and an endeavour to
" recede from one another : which reluctance and endeavour will encreafe, as they come
" nearer together, becaufe thereby they caufe the interjacent æther to rarefy more and more.
" But at length, when they come fo near together, that the excefs of preffure of the exter-
" nal æther, which furrounds the bodies, above that of the rarefied æther, which is between
" them, is fo great, as to overcome the reluctance, which the bodies have from being brought
" together ; then will that excefs of preffure drive them with violence together, and make
" them adhere ftrongly to one another, as was faid in the fecond fuppofition. For inftance,
" in the fecond figure, when the bodies E D and N P are fo near together, that the fpaces
" of the æther's graduated rarity begin to reach to one another, and meet in the line I K ;
" the æther between them will have fuffered much rarefaction, which rarefaction requires
" much force, that is, much preffing of the bodies together : and the endeavour, which the
" æther between them has to return to its former natural ftate of condenfation, will caufe the
" bodies to have an endeavour of receding from one another. But on the other hand, to
" counterpoife this endeavour, there will not yet be any excefs of denfity of the æther, which
" furrounds the bodies, above that of the æther, which is between them at the line I K. But
" if the bodies come nearer together, fo as to make the æther in the mid-way-line I K grow
" rarer than the furrounding æther, there will arife from the excefs of denfity of the fur-
" rounding æther a compreffure of the bodies towards one another : which when by the
" nearer approach of the bodies it becomes fo great, as to overcome the aforefaid endeavour
" the bodies have to recede from one another, they will then go towards one another, and
" adhere together. And, on the contrary, if any power force them afunder to that diftance,
" where the endeavour to recede begins to overcome the endeavour to accede, they will again
" leap from one another. Now hence I conceive it is chiefly, that a fly walks on water
" without wetting her feet, and confequently without touching the water ; that two polifhed
" pieces of glafs are not without preffure brought to contact, no, not though the one be plain,
" the other a little convex ; that the particles of duft cannot by preffing be made to cohere,
" as they would do, if they did but fully touch ; that the particles of tinging fubftances and
" falts diffolved in water do not of their own accord concrete and fall to the bottom, but
" diffufe themfelves all over the liquor, and expand ftill more, if you add more liquor to
" them. Alfo, that the particles of vapours, exhalations, and air, do ftand at a diftance from
" one another, and endeavour to recede as far from one another, as the preffure of the in-
" cumbent atmofphere will let them : for I conceive the confufed mafs of vapours, air, and
" exhalations, which we call the atmofphere, to be nothing elfe but the particles of all forts
" of bodies, of which the earth confifts, feparated from one another, and kept at a diftance,
" by the faid principle.

" FROM thefe principles the actions of menftruums upon bodies may be thus explained.
" Suppofe any tinging body, as cochineal, or logwood, be put into water ; fo foon as the
" water finks into its pores and wets on all fides any particle, which adheres to the body
" only by the principle in the fecond fuppofition, it takes off, or at leaft much diminifhes
" the efficacy of that principle to hold the particle to the body, becaufe it makes the æther
" on all fides the particle to be of a more uniform denfity than before. And then the particle
" being fhaken off, by any little motion, floats in the water, and with many fuch others makes
" a tincture ; which tincture will be of fome lively colour, if the particles be all of the
" fame fize and denfity ; otherwife of a dirty one. For the colours of all natural bodies
" whatever feem to depend on nothing but the various fizes and denfities of their particles ;
" as I think you have feen defcribed by me more at large in another paper. If the particles
" be very fmall (as are thofe of falts, vitriols, and gums) they are tranfparent ; and as they
" are fuppofed bigger and bigger, they put on thefe colours in order, black, white, yellow,
" red ; violet, blue, pale green, yellow, orange, red ; purple, blue, green, yellow, orange,
" red, &c. as is difcerned by the colours, which appear at the feveral thickneffes of very thin
" plates of tranfparent bodies. Whence, to know the caufes of the changes of colours,
" which are often made by the mixtures of feveral liquors, it is to be confidered, how the
" particles of any tincture may have their fize or denfity altered by the infufion of another
" liquor.

" WHEN any metal is put into common water, the water cannot enter into its pores, to act
" on it and diffolve it. Not that water confifts of too grofs parts for this purpofe, but be-
" caufe it is unfociable to metal. For there is a certain fecret principle in nature, by which
" liquors are fociable to fome things, and unfociable to others. Thus water will not mix
" with oil, but readily with fpirit of wine, or with falts. It finks alfo into wood, which
" quickfilver will not ; but quickfilver finks into metals, which, as I faid, water will not.
" So aqua fortis diffolves ☽, not ☉, aqua regis ☉, not ☽, &c. But a liquor, which is of itfelf
" unfociable

3

72   The *LIFE of the honourable* ROBERT BOYLE.

" unfociable to a body, may, by the mixture of a convenient mediator, be made fociable.
" So molten lead, which alone will not mix with copper, or with regulus of Mars, by the
" addition of tin is made to mix with either. And water, by the mediation of faline
" fpirits, will mix with metal. Now when any metal is put in water impregnated with
" fuch fpirits, as into aqua fortis, aqua regis, fpirit of vitriol, or the like, the particles of
" the fpirits, as they, in floating in the water, ftrike on the metal, will by their fociablenefs
" enter into its pores, and gather round its outfide particles, and, by advantage of the con-
" tinual tremor the particles of the metal are in, hitch themfelves in by degrees between
" thofe particles and the body, and loofen them from it ; and the water entering into the
" pores together with the faline fpirits, the particles of the metal will be thereby ftill more
" loofed, fo as, by that motion the folution puts them into, to be eafily fhaken off, and
" made to float in the water : the faline particles ftill encompaffing the metallic
" ones as a coat or fhell does a kernel, after the manner expreffed in the annexed
" figure. In which figure I have made the particles round, though they may be
" cubical, or of any other fhape.
   " If into a folution of metal thus made be poured a liquor, abounding with particles,
" to which the former faline particles are more fociable than to the particles of the metal
" (fuppofe with particles of falt of tartar) then fo foon as they ftrike on one another in the
" liquor, the faline particles will adhere to thofe more firmly than to the metalline ones,
" and by degrees be wrought off from thofe to enclofe thefe. Suppofe A a metalline particle,
" enclofed with faline ones of fpirit of nitre, E a particle of falt of tartar,
" contiguous to two of the particles of fpirit of nitre b and c, and fuppofe
" the particle E is impelled by any motion towards d, fo as to roll about the
" particle c, till it touch the particle d, the particle b adhering more firmly to
" E than to A, will be forced off from A. And by the fame means the particle
" E, as it rolls about A, will tear off the reft of the faline particles from A, one
" after another, till it has got them all, or almoft all, about itfelf. And when
" the metallic particles are thus divefted of the nitrous ones, which, as a mediator between
" them and the water, held them floating in it ; the alcalizate ones crouding for the room the
" metallic ones took up before, will prefs thefe towards one another, and make them come
" more eafily together : fo that by the motion they continually have in the water, they fhall
" be made to ftrike on one another, and then, by means of the principle in the fecond fup-
" pofition, they will cohere and grow into clufters, and fall down by their weight to the bot-
" tom, which is called precipitation.
   " In the folution of metals, when a particle is loofing from the body, fo foon as it gets
" to that diftance from it, where the principle of receding defcribed in the fourth and fifth
" fuppofitions begins to overcome the principle of acceding, defcribed in the fecond fuppofi-
" tion, the receding of the particle will be thereby accelerated ; fo that the particle fhall as
" it were with violence leap from the body, and putting the liquor into a brifk agitation,
" beget and promote that heat we often find to be caufed in folutions of metals. And if
" any particle happen to leap off thus from the body, before it be furrounded with water,
" or to leap off with that fmartnefs, as to get loofe from the water ; the water, by the prin-
" ciple in the fourth and fifth fuppofitions, will be kept off from the particle, and ftand
" round about it, like a fpherically hollow arch, not being able to come to a full contact
" with it any more. And feveral of thefe particles afterwards gathering into a clufter, fo as
" by the fame principle to ftand at a diftance from one another, without any water between
" them, will compofe a bubble. Whence I fuppofe it is, that in brifk folutions there ufually
" happens an ebullition.
   " This is one way of tranfmuting grofs compact fubftances into aereal ones. Another
" way is, by heat. For as faft as the motion of heat can fhake off the particles of water
" from the furface of it, thofe particles, by the faid principle, will float up and down in the
" air, at a diftance both from one another, and from the particles of air, and make that fub-
" ftance we call vapour. Thus I fuppofe it is, when the particles of a body are very fmall
" (as I fuppofe thofe of water are) fo that the action of heat alone may be fufficient to
" fhake them afunder. But if the particles be much larger, they then require the greater
" force of diffolving menftruums, to feparate them, unlefs by any means the particles can
" be firft broken into fmaller ones. For the moft fixed bodies, even gold itfelf, fome have
" faid will become volatile, only by breaking their parts fmaller. Thus may the volatility
" and fixednefs of bodies depend on the different fizes of their parts.
   " And on the fame difference of fize may depend the more or lefs permanency of aereal
" fubftances, in their ftate of rarefaction. To underftand this, let us
" fuppofe A B C D to be a large piece of any metal, E F G H the
" limit of the interior uniform æther, and K a part of the metal at
" the fuperficies A B. If this part or particle K be fo little, that it
" reaches not to the limit E F, it is plain, that the æther at its centre
" muft be lefs rare, than if the particle were greater ; for were it
" greater, its centre would be further from the fuperficies A B, that
" is, in a place, where the æther (by fuppofition) is rarer. The lefs the particle K therefore,
" the denfer the æther at its centre, becaufe its centre comes nearer to the edge A B, where

2

the

The LIFE *of the honourable* ROBERT BOYLE. *73*

" the æther is denfer than within the limit E F G H. And if the particle were divided from
" the body, and removed to a diftance from it, where the æther is ftill denfer, the æther
" within it muft proportionally grow denfer. If you confider this, you may apprehend,
" how by diminifhing the particle, the rarity of the æther within it will be diminifhed, till
" between the denfity of the æther without, and the denfity of the æther within it, there be
" little difference; that is, till the caufe be almoft taken away, which fhould keep this and
" other fuch particles at a diftance from one another. For that caufe, explained in the fourth
" and fifth fuppofitions, was the excefs of denfity of the external æther above that of the
" internal. This may be the reafon then, why the fmall particles of vapours eafily come to-
" gether, and are reduced back into water, unlefs the heat, which keeps them in agitation, be
" fo great as to diffipate them as faft as they come together: but the groffer particles of ex-
" halations raifed by fermentation keep their aerial form more obftinately, becaufe the æther
" within them is rarer.
    " Nor does the fize only, but the denfity of the particles alfo, conduce to the permanency
" of aerial fubftances. For the excefs of denfity of the æther without fuch particles above
" that of the æther within them is ftill greater. Which has made me fometimes think,
" that the true permanent air may be of a metallic original; the particles of no fubftance
" being more denfe than thofe of metals. This, I think, is alfo favoured by experience, for I
" remember I once read in the Philofophical Tranfactions, how M. *Huygens* at *Paris* found,
" that the air made by diffolving falt of tartar included in two or three days time condenfe
" and fall down again, but the air made by diffolving a metal continued without con-
" denfing or relenting in the leaft. If you confider then, how by the continual fermentations
" made in the bowels of the earth there are aerial fubftances raifed out of all kinds of bodies,
" all which together make the atmofphere, and that of all thefe the metallic are the moft
" permanent, you will not, perhaps, think it abfurd, that the moft permanent part of the
" atmofphere, which is the true air, fhould be conftituted of thefe; efpecially fince they are
" the heavieft of all other, and fo muft fubfide to the lower parts of the atmofphere, and
" float upon the furface of the earth, and buoy up the lighter exhalation and vapours to float
" in greateft plenty above them. Thus, I fay, it ought to be with the metallic exhalations
" raifed in the bowels of the earth by the action of acid menftruums, and thus it is with
" the true permanent air; for this, as in reafon it ought to be efteemed the moft pon-
" derous part of the atmofphere, becaufe the loweft, fo it betrays its ponderofity, by mak-
" ing vapours afcend readily in it, by fuftaining mifts and clouds of fnow, and by buoying
" up grofs and ponderous fmoke. The air alfo is the moft grofs unactive part of the at-
" mofphere, affording living things no nourifhment, if deprived of the more tender exha-
" lations and fpirits, that float in it: and what more unactive and remote from nourifhment
" than metallic bodies?
    " I shall fet down one conjecture more, which came into my mind now as I was writ-
" ing this letter. It is about the caufe of gravity. For this end I will fuppofe æther to
" confift of parts differing from one another in fubtilty by indefinite degrees: that in the
" pores of bodies there is lefs of the groffer æther, in proportion to the finer, than in open
" fpaces; and confequently, that in the great body of the earth there is much lefs of the
" groffer æther, in proportion to the finer, than in the regions of the air: and that yet the
" groffer æther in the air affects the upper regions of the earth, and the finer æther in the
" earth the lower regions of the air, in fuch a manner, that from the top of the air to the
" furface of the earth, and again from the furface of the earth to the centre thereof, the
" æther is infenfibly finer and finer. Imagine now any body fufpended in the air, or lying
" on the earth: and the æther being by the hypothefis groffer in the pores, which are in the
" upper parts of the body, than in thofe which are in its lower parts, and that groffer æther
" being lefs apt to be lodged in thofe pores, than the finer æther below, it will endeavour to
" get out and give way to the finer æther below, which cannot be without the bodies
" defcending to make room above for it to go out into.
    " From this fuppofed gradual fubtilty of the parts of æther fome things above might
" be further illuftrated, and made more intelligible; but by what has been faid, you will
" eafily difcern, whether in thefe conjectures there be any degree of probability, which is all
" I aim at. For my own part, I have fo little fancy to things of this nature, that, had not
" your encouragement moved me to it, I fhould never, I think, have thus far fet pen to
" paper about them. What is amifs therefore, I hope, you will the more eafily pardon in

Cambridge, Feb. 28, 1678-9.   " Your moft humble fervant,

                                            " and honourer,

                                            " Isaac Newton.

This letter of our incomparable *Newton* may perhaps receive fome illuftration from another [*], which he wrote a few years before to Mr. *Oldenburg*, and was as follows.

                    [*] In the poffeffion of *William Jones*, Efq.

74 *The LIFE of the honourable* ROBERT BOYLE.

" S I R,

" I RECEIVED both yours, and thank you for your care in difpofing thofe things be-
" tween me and Mr. *Linus*. I fuppofe his friends cannot blame you at all for printing his
" firft letter, it being written, I believe, for that end, and they never complaining of the
" printing of that, but of the not printing that, which followed, which I take myfelf to
" have been *per accidens* the occafion of, by refufing to anfwer him. And though I think I
" may truly fay, I was very little concerned about it, yet I muft look upon it as the refult of
" your kindnefs to me, that you was unwilling to print it without an anfwer.

" As to the paper of Obfervations, which you move in the name of the Society to have
" printed, I cannot but return them my hearty thanks for the kind acceptance they meet
" with there, and know not how to deny any thing, which they defire fhould be done.
" Only I think it will be beft to fufpend the printing of them for a while, becaufe I have
" fome thoughts of writing fuch another fet of Obfervations for determining the manner of
" the productions of colours by the prifm, which, if done at all, ought to precede that now
" in your hands, and will do beft to be joined with it. But this I cannot do prefently, by
" reafon of fome incumbrances lately put upon me by fome friends, and fome other bufinefs
" of my own, which at prefent almoft take up my time and thoughts.

" THE additions, that I intended, I think I muft, after putting you to fo long expectations,
" difappoint you in ; for it puzzles me how to connect them with what I fent you ; and if I
" had thofe papers, yet I doubt the things I intended will not come in fo freely as I thought
" they might have done. I could fend them defcribed without dependance on thofe papers ;
" but I fear I have already troubled your Society and yourfelf too much with my fcribbling,
" and fo fuppofe it may do better to defer them till another feafon. I have therefore at
" prefent only fent you two or three alterations, though not of fo great moment, that I need
" have ftaid you for them ; and they are thefe :

" WHERE I fay, that *the frame of nature may be nothing but æther condenfed by a fermental
" principle*, inftead of thefe words write, that it may be nothing but various contextures of
" fome certain ætherial fpirits or vapours condenfed, as it were, by præcipitation, much af-
" ter the manner, that vapours are condenfed into water, or exhalations into groffer fub-
" ftances, though not fo eafily condenfable ; and after condenfation wrought into various
" forms, at firft by the immediate hand of the Creator, and ever fince by the power of na-
" ture, who, by virtue of the command, *Increafe and multiply*, became a complete imitator of
" the copies fet her by the Protoplaft. Thus perhaps may all things be originated from
" æther, &c.

A LITTLE after, when I fay, the ætherial fpirit may be *condenfed in fermenting or burning
" bodies, or otherwife infpiffated in the pores of the earth to a tender matter, which may be, as it
" were, the* fuccus nutritius *of the earth, or primary fubftance, out of which things generable
" grow :* inftead of this you may write, that that fpirit may be condenfed in fermenting or
" burning bodies, or otherwife coagulated in the pores of the earth and water into fome kind
" of humid active matter, for the continual ufes of nature, adhering to the fides of thofe
" pores after the manner, that vapours condenfe on the fides of a veffel.

" IN the fame paragraph there is, I think, a parenthefis, in which I mention volatile falt-
" petre. Pray ftrike out that parenthefis, left it fhould give offence to fomebody.

" Alfo where I relate the experiment of little papers made to move varioufly with a glafs
" rubbed, I would have all that ftruck out, which follows about trying the experiment with
" leaf-gold.

" SIR, I am interrupted by a vifit, and fo muft in hafte break off.

" Yours

Jan. 25, 1675-6.   " Is. NEWTON."

BUT to return to Mr. *Boyle*, in the year 1680, he gave the world the following tracts, *viz.*
The Aerial Noctiluca : or fome new Phænomena, and a procefs of a factitious felf-fhining fubftance ;
London, in 8vo. *A new Lamp*, printed in Mr. *Hooke's Philofophical Collections*, No. II. p.
33. and *Divers Experiments and Notes about the produciblenefs of chemical Principles*, fubjoined
to the fecond edition of his *Sceptical Chemift*, at *Oxford* 1680, in 8vo.

THE Royal Society, of which he had been fo long one of the greateft ornaments, now
thought proper at their annual election on St. *Andrew's* day, November 30, this year, to
choofe him for their prefident. But after a mature confideration he excufed himfelf from ac-
cepting that poft, for reafons, which fhew his extreme tendernefs and delicacy in all matters of
confcience, and were reprefented by him in the following letter to Mr. *Hooke*.

" *Pall-Mall,* Dec. 18, 1680.

SIR,

" THOUGH fince I laft faw you, I met with a lawyer, who has been a member of fe-
" veral parliaments, and found him of the fame opinion with my council in reference
" to the obligation to take the teft and oaths you and I difcourfed of ; yet not content with
" this,

Lexicon Technicum:

Or, An UNIVERSAL

Englifh Dictionary

OF

ARTS and SCIENCES:

EXPLAINING

Not only the TERMS of ART, but the
ARTS Themfelves.

VOL. II.

BY

JOHN HARRIS, D. D. Secretary to the
Royal-Society, and Chaplain to the *Lord High-
Chancellor* of GREAT-BRITAIN.

LONDON:

Printed for *Dan. Brown, Tim. Goodwin, J. Walthoe,
Joh. Nicholfon, Benj. Tooke, Dan. Midwinter,
M. Atkins,* and *T. Ward.* MDCCX.

INTRODUCTION.

DE

NATURA ACIDORUM.

Is. NEWTON. 1692.

ACidorum particulæ funt Aqueis Craſſiores, & propterea minus Volatiles, at Terreſtribus multo ſubtiliores & propterea multo minus fixæ. Vi magna Attractivâ pollent, & in hac vi conſiſtit earum Activitas, quâ & Corpora diſſolvunt & Organa Senſuum agitant & pungunt. Mediæ funt Naturæ inter Aquam & Corpora, & Utraque attrahunt. Per vim ſuam attractivam congregantur circum particulas corporum ſeu Lapideas ſeu Metallicas iiſq; undiq; adhærent arctiſſimè, ut ab iiſdem deinceps per Diſtillationem vel Sublimationem vix poſſint ſeparari, Attractæ vero & undique congregatæ, elevant, disjungunt & diſcutiunt particulas corporum ab invicem, id eſt corpora diſſolvunt ; & per vim Attractionis quâ ruunt in particulas commovent fluidum & ſic calorem excitant, particulaſq; nonnullas adeo diſcutiunt ut in Aerem convertant & ſic Bullas generant. Et hæc eſt Ratio Diſſolutionis & Fermentationis ; Acidum verò attrahendo Aquam æquè ac Terram efficit ut particulæ diſſolutæ prompte miſceantur cum Aquâ eique innatent ad modum ſalium. Et quem admodum Globus Terræ per vim Gravitatis attrahendo aquam fortiùs quam Corpora leviora, efficit ut leviora aſcendant in Aquâ, & fugiant de Terrâ. Sic particulæ Salium attrahendo Aquam fugant ſe mutuò & ab invicem quam maxime recedendo, per Aquam totam expanduntur.

Particulæ Salis Alkali ex Terreis & Acidis ſimilitèr Unitis conſtant ; ſed hæ Acidæ vi maxima Attractivâ pollent ut per ignem non ſeparentur à Sale ; utq; Metalla diſſoluta præcipitant attrahendo ab ipſis particulas Acidas quibus diſſolvebantur.

Si particulæ Acidæ in minori proportione cum Terreſtribus jungantur, hæ tam arctè retinentur à Terreſtribus, ut ab iis ſupprimi ac occultari videantur. Neq; enim ſenſum jam pungunt neq; attrahunt aquam, ſed corpora dulcia & quæ cum aquâ ægre miſcentur, hoc eſt pinguia, componunt ; ut fit in Mercurio dulci, Sulphure communi, Luna Cornea & Cupro quod Mercurius Snblimatus corroſit. Ab Acidi vero ſic ſuppreſſi vi attractivâ fit ut pinguia Corporibus prope Univerſis adhæreant & flammam facile concipiant, ſi modo Acidum calefactum inveniat alia Corpora in fumo accenſorum quæ fortius attrahat quam propria. Sed & Acidum in Sulphureis ſuppreſſum fortius attrahendo particulas aliorum Corporum (ſcilicet Terreas) quam proprias, Fermentationem lentam & Naturalem ciet & fovet uſq; ad Putrefactionem Compoſiti.

Quæ Putrefactio ſita eſt in eo quod Acidæ Fermentationem diu foventes tandem in interſtitia minima & primæ Compoſitionis partes interjacentia ſeſe inſinuant, intiméq; iis partibus Unitæ mixtionem Novam efficiunt non amovendam nec cum priore commutandam.

Cogitationes Variæ ejuſdem.

Flamma eſt Fumus Candens ; differtque à Fumo ut Ferrum rubens ab ignito ſed non rubente. Calor eſt Agitatio Partium quaqua verſum.

Nihil eſt abſolutè quieſcens ſecundum partes ſuas & ideo frigidum, præter atomos, vacui ſcilicet expertes.

Terra augetur, Aquâ in eam converſâ, & omnia in aquam [vi ignis] reduci poſſunt.

Nitrum abit diſtillatione magnam partem in Spiritum Acidum, relictâ terrâ, quia Acidum Nitri attrahit Phlegma ; & idcirco ſimul aſcendunt conſtituuntq; Spirstum : at Nitrum Carbone accenſum magnam partem abit in Sal Tartari, quia ignis eo modo applicatus partes Acidi & Terræ in ſeſe impingit fortiuſq; unit.

Spiritus ardentes ſunt Olea cum Phlegmate per Fermentationem Unita.

Tinctura Cochinellæ cum Spiritu Vini facta in aquæ magnam molem immiſſa, parva licet doſi, totam aquam inficit : Sc. quia particulæ Cochinellæ magis attrahuntur ab aquâ quam a ſe mutuo.

Aqua non habet magnum vim diſſolvendi quia pauco Acido gaudet. Acidum enim dicimus quod multum attrahit & attrahitur, videmus nempe ea cua in aquâ ſolvuntur lente & ſine Efferveſcentiâ ſolvi, at ubi eſt attractio fortis & particulæ menſtrui undiq; attrahuntur à particulâ Metalli, vel potius particula metalli undiq; attrahitur a particulis menſtrui, hæ illam abripiunt & circumſiſtunt, hoc eſt Metallum corrodunt : Hæ eadem particulæ ſenſorio applicatæ ejus partes eodem modo divellunt doloremq; inferunt ; à quo Acidæ appellantur, relictâ ſcilicet terrâ Subtili cui adhærebant ob majorem attractionem ad liquidum linguæ, & c.

In

INTRODUCTION.

In omni Solutione per Menstruum particulæ solvendæ magis attrahuntur apartibus Menstrui quam à se mutuo.

In omni Fermentatione est Acidum suppressum quod coagulat præcipitando.

Oleum cum nimis magnâ mole phlegmatis intime mixtum, fit Salinum quiddam & sic Acetum constituit, hic etiam Tartari seu Terræ admistæ habenda est ratio.

Mercurius attrahitur id est corroditur ab Acidis & sicut pondere Obstructiones tollit ita vi attractrice Acida infringit.

Mercurius est Volatilis & facile elevatur calore quia ejus particulæ ultimæ Compositionis sunt parvæ & facile separantur separatæq; sese fugant; ut fit in particulis Vaporis, fluidorumq; rarefactorum.

Aqua comprimi non potest quia ejus particulæ jamjam se tangunt. Et si se tangerent particulæ Aeris (nam Aer comprimi potest, quia ipsius particulæ nondum se tangunt) Aer evaderet in Marmor. Seq. ex Prop. 23. Lib. 2. Princ. Philosoph.

Aurum particulas habet se mutuo trahentes; minimarum summæ vocentur primæ Compositionis, harum summarum summæ secundæ Compositionis, &c.

Potest Mercurius, potest Aqua Regia poros pervadere, qui particulas ultimæ Compositionis interjacent at non alios.

Si posset Menstruum alios illos pervadere vel si auri partes primæ & secundæ Compositionis possent separari fieret Aurum, vel Fluidum, vel saltem magis malleabile. Si Aurum fermentescere posset in aliud quodvis corpus posset transformari.

Viscid tas est vel solum defectus fluiditatis, quæ sita est in partium parvitate & separabilitate (intellige partes ultimæ Compositionis) vel defectus lubricitatis seu lævioris partes unius supra alias labi impediens. Hujus visciditatis Acidum sæpe causa est; sæpe Spiritus alius lubricus terræ junctus, ut oleum Terebinthinæ capiti suo Mortuo redditum fit tenax.

Ratio cur Charta Oleo in uncta Transitum Oleo non Aquæ concedat est quia Aqua Oleo non miscetur sed fugatur ab eo.

Cum Acidæ partes, minores scilicet, aliquid dissolvunt, id faciunt, quia partem rei solvendæ includunt vndiq; utpote Majorem quàl bet Acidi partium.

Some Thoughts about the NATURE of ACIDS; By Sir ISAAC NEWTON.

THE Particles of Acids are of a Size grosser than those of Water, and therefore less volatile; but much smaller than those of Earth, and therefore much less fix'd than they. They are endued with a great Attractive Force; in which Force their Activity consists; and thereby also they affect and stimulate the Organ of Taste, and dissolve such Bodies as they can come at. They are of a middle Nature between Water and Terrestrial Bodies, and attract the Particles of both.

By this Attractive Force they get about the Particles of Bodies, whether they be of a metallick or stony Nature, and adhere to them most closely on all sides; so that they can scarce be separated from them by Distillation or Sublimation. When they are attracted and gather'd together about the Particles of Bodies, they raise, disjoyn and shake them one from another; that is, they dissolve those Bodies.

By their Attractive Force also, by which they rush towards the Particles of Bodies, they move the Fluid, and excite Heat; and they shake asunder some Particles, so much as to turn them into Air, and generate Bubbles: And this is the Reason of Dissolution, and all violent Fermentation; and in all Fermentation there is an Acid latent or suppress'd, which coagulates in Precipitation.

Acids also, by attracting Water as much as they do the Particles of Bodies, occasion that the dissolved Particles do readily mingle with Water, or swim or float in it, after the manner of Salts.

And as this Globe of Earth, by the Force of Gravity, attracting Water more strongly than it doth lighter Bodies, causes those lighter Bodies to ascend in the Water, and to go upwards from the Earth: So the Particles of Salts, by attracting the Water, do mutually avoid and recede from one another as far as they can, and so are diffused throughout the whole Water.

The Particles of Sal Alkali, do consist of Earthy and Acid united together, after the same manner: But these Acids have so great an Attractive Force, that they can't be separated from the Salt by Fire; they do also precipitate the Particles of Metals
dissolv'd

INTRODUCTION.

diffolv'd in *Menftrua*, by attracting from them the Acid Particles, which before had diffolved them, and kept them fufpended in the *Menftruum*.

If thefe Acid Particles be joyn'd with Earthy ones, in but a fmall Quantity, they are fo clofely retain'd by them, as to be quite fupprefs'd and hidden as it were by them; fo that they neither ftimulate the Organ of Senfe, nor attract Water, but compofe Bodies which are not Acid, *i. e.* Fat and Fufible Bodies, fuch as are *Mercurius dulcis, Common Brimftone, Luna Cornea,* and *Copper* corroded by *Mercury Sublimate.*

From the Attractive Force in thefe Acid Particles thus fupprefs'd, arifes that univerfal Property of almoft all Fat Bodies, that they adhere or ftick to others, and are eafily inflammable, if the heated Acid Particles meet with other Particles of Bodies in Fume, which the Acid attracts more ftrongly, than it doth the Particles to which it is united. And thus the Acid that lies fupprefs'd in fulphureous Bodies, by more ftrongly attracting the Particles of other Bodies (Earthy ones for Inftance) than its own, promotes a gentle Fermentation, produces and cherifhes Natural Heat, and carries it on fo far fometimes, as to the Putrefaction of the Compound : Which Putrefaction arifes hence, That the Acid Particles which have a long while kept up the Fermentation, do at long run infinuate themfelves into the leaft Interftices that lie between the Particles of the *firft Compofition,* and fo intimately uniting with thofe very Particles do produce a new Mixture or Compound, which cannot fall back again into the fame Form.

Note, *The Paper hitherto defcrib'd, feems to have been a continued Difcourfe; but what follows are fhort Minutes of Thoughts relating to the fame Subject.*

Nitre, in Diftillation, leaving its Earthy Part behind, turns moft of it into an Acid Spirit ; becaufe the Acid of the Nitre attracts the Phlegm, and therefore they afcend together, and conftitute a Spirit. But Nitre, kindled with a Coal, turns chiefly into a Salt of Tartar ; becaufe the Fire applied this Way, drives the Acid and Earthy Parts towards, and makes them impinge on, and more ftrongly unite one with another.

The Reafon why Water hath no great diffolving Force, is, becaufe there is but a fmall Quantity of Acid in it : For whatever doth ftrongly attract, and is ftrongly attracted, may be call'd an Acid : And fuch things as are diffolv'd in Water, we fee, become fo, *eafily,* without any Effervefcence : But where the Attraction is ftrong, and the Particles of the Menftruum are every where attracted by thofe of the Metal, or rather, where the Particles of the Metal are every way attracted by thofe of the Menftruum ; then the Particles of the Menftruum environ thofe of the Metal, tear them to pieces, and diffolve it.

So when thefe Acid Particles are applied to the Tongue, or to any excoriated Part of the Body, leaving the fubtile Earth in which they were before, they rufh into the liquid of the Senfory, tear and disjoint its Parts, and caufe a painful Senfation.

Mercury is attracted, and therefore corroded by Acids; and as it opens Obftructions by its great Weight ; fo it breaks and obtunds the Power of Acids (in the Body) by its attractive Force.

All Bodies have Particles which do mutually attract one another : The Summs of the leaft of which may be called Particles of the *firft Compofition,* and the Collections or Aggregates arifing from the, Primary Summs; or the Summs of thefe Summs may be call'd Particles of the *fecond Compofition, &c.*

Mercury and *Aqua Regis* can pervade thofe Pores of Gold or Tin, which lie between the Particles of *its laft Compofition ;* but they can't get any further into it; for if any Menftruum could do that, or if the Particles of the firft, or perhaps of the fecond Compofition of Gold could be feparated ; that Metal might be made to become a Fluid, or at leaft more foft. And if Gold could be brought once to ferment and putrefie, it might be turn'd into any other Body whatfoever.

And fo of Tin, or any other Bodies ; as common Nourifhment is turn'd into the Bodies of Animals and Vegetables.

N. B. *The fmall Difference which there is between this Tranflation and the* Latin *above, was its being taken from another Copy a little different from this* Latin *Paper. And having been fupervifed and approved of by the Illuftrious Author, I have not alter'd it fince.*

(824)

VII. *Scala graduum Caloris.*

Calorum Descriptiones & signa.

CAlor aeris hyberni ubi aqua incipit gelu rigescere. Innotescit hic calor accurate locando Thermometrum in nive compressa quo tempore gelu solvitur.

0,1,2,	Calores aeris hyberni.
2,3,4.	Calores aeris verni & autumnalis.
4,5,6.	Calores aeris æstivi.
6	Calor aeris meridiani circa mensem Julium.
12 1	Calor maximus quem Thermometer ad con- tactum

(825)

		tactum corporis humani concipit. Idem circiter eft calor avis ova incubantis.
$14 \frac{3}{11}$	$1 \frac{1}{4}$	Calor balnei prope maximus quem quis manu immerfa & conftanter agitata diutius perferre poteft. Idem fere eft calor fanguinis recens effufi.
17	1 1	Calor balnei maximus quem quis manu immerfa & immobili manente diutius perferre poteft.
$20 \frac{2}{11}$	$1 \frac{3}{4}$	Calor balnei quo cera innatans & liquefacta deferendo regifcit & diaphaneitatem amittit.
24	2	Calor balnei quo cera innatans incalefcendo, liquefcit & in continuo fluxu fine ebullitione confervatur.
$28 \frac{6}{11}$	$2 \frac{1}{4}$	Calor mediocris inter calores quo cera liquefcit & aqua ebullit.
34	$2 \frac{1}{2}$	Calor quo aqua vehementer ebullit & miftura duarum partium plumbi trium partium ftanni & quinque partium bifmuti defervendo rigefcit.Incipit aqua ebullire calore partium 33 & calorem partium plufquam $34 \frac{1}{2}$ ebulliendo vix concipit. Ferrum verò defervefcens calore partium 35 vel 36, ubi aqua calida & 37 ubi frigida in ipfum guttatim incidit, definit ebullitionem excitare.
$40 \frac{4}{11}$	$2 \frac{3}{4}$	Calor minimus quo miftura unius partisPlumbi quatuor partium Stanni & quinque partium Bifmuti incalefcendo liquefcit, & in continuo fluxu confervatur.
48	3	Calor minimus quo miftura æqualium partium ftanni & bifmuti liquefcit. Hæc miftura calore partium 47 defervendo coagulatur.
57	$3 \frac{1}{4}$	Calor quo miftura duarum partium ftanni & unius partis bifmuti funditur, ut & miftura trium partium ftanni & duarum plumbi fed miftura quinq; partium ftanni & duarum

N n n n n 2   partium

(826)

partium bifmuti hoc calore defervendo rigefcit. Et idem facit miftura æqualium
partium plumbi & bifmuti.

68 3 ½ Calor minimus quo miftura unius partis bifmuti & octo partium ftanni funditur. Stan-
num per fe funditur calore partium 72 &
Defervendo rigefcit calore partium 70.

81 3 ¾ Calor quo bifmutum funditur ut & miftura
quatuor partium plumbi & unius partis
ftanni. Sed miftura quinque partium plumbi & unius partis ftanni ubi fufa eft & de-
fervet in hoc calore rigefcit.

96 4 Calor minimus quo plumbum funditur. Plumbum incalefcendo funditur calore partium
96 vel 97 & defervendo rigefcit calore partium 95.

114 4 ¼ Calor quo corpora ignita defervendo penitus
definunt in tenebris nocturnis lucere, & vi-
ciffim incalefcendo incipiunt in iifdem tenebris lucere fed luce tenuiffima quæ fentiri
vix poffit. Hoc calore liquefcit miftura
æqualium partium Stanni & Reguli martis,
& miftura feptem partium bifmuti & quatuor partium ejufdem Reguli defervendo
rigefcit.

136 4 ½ Calor quo corpora ignita in tenebris nocturnis
candent, in crepufculo vero neutiquam.
Hoc calore tum miftura duarum partium reguli martis & unius partis Bifmuti tum etiam
miftura quinq; partium reguli martis & unius
partis Stanni defervendo rigefcit. Regulus per fe rigefcit calore partium 146.

161 4 ¾ Calor quo corpora ignita in crepufculo pro-
xime ante ortum folis vel poft occafum ejus
manifefto candent in clara vero diei luce
neutiquam, aut non nifi perobfcure.

Calor

(827)

192 | 5 | Calor prunarum in igne parvo culinari ex car-
bonibus fossilibus bituminofis conftructo &
abfq; ufu follium ardente. Idem eft calor
ferri in tali igne quantum poteft candentis.
Ignis parvi culinaris qui ex lignis conftat
calor paulo major eft nempe partium 200
vel 210. Et ignis magni major adhuc eft
calor, præfertim fi follibus cieatur.

In hujus Tabulæ columna prima habentur gradus caloris
in proportion e arithmetica computum inchoando a calore
quo aqua incipit gelu rigefcere tanquam ab infimo caloris
gradu feu commune termino caloris & frigoris, & ponendo
calorem externum corporis humani effe partium duodecim.
In fecunda columna habentur gradus caloris in ratione geometrica fic ut fecundus gradus fit duplo major primo, tertius
item fecundo & quartus tertio, & primus fit calcr exter-
nus corporis humani fenfibus æquatus. Patet autem per
hancTabulam quod calor aquæ bullientis fit fere triplo major quam calor corporis humani, & quod calor ftanni liquefcentis fit fextuplo major & calor plumbi liquefcentis
octuplo major & calor Reguli liquefcentis duodecuplo major & calor ordinarius ignis culinaris fexdecim vel feptem-
decim vicibus major quam calor idem corporis humani.
Conftructa fuit hæc Tabula ope Thermometri & ferri
candentis. Per Thermometrum inveni menfuram calorum
omnium ufq; ad calorem quo ftannum funditur & per ferrum calefactum inveni menfuram reli quorum. Nam calor
quem ferrum calefactum corporibus frigidis fibi contiguis
dato tempore communicat, hoc eft calor quem ferrum dato
tempore amittit eft ut calor totus ferri. Ideoq; fi tempora
refrigerii fumantur æqualia calores erunt in ratione geometrica, & propterea per tabulam logarithmorum facile in-
veniri poffunt.
Primum igitur per Thermometrum ex oleo lini con-
ftructum inveni quod fi oleum ubi Thermometer in nive
liquefcente locabatur occupabat fpatium partim 10000,
idem

(828)

i
dem oleum calore primi gradus feu corporis humani rarefactum occupabat fpatium 10256 & calore aquæ jamjam
ebullire incipientis fpatium 10705 & calore aquæ vehe-
menter ebullientis fpatium 10725 & calore ftanni lique-
facti de fervientis ubi incipit rigefcere & confiftentiam
amalgamentis induere fpatium 11516 & ubi omnino rigefcit fpatium 11496. Igitur oleum rarefactum fuit ac
dilatatum in ratione 40 ad 39 per calorem corporis humani, in ratione 15 ad 14 per calorem aquæ bullientis, in
ratione 15 ad 13 per calorem ftanni defervientis ubi incipit coagulari & rigefcere & in ratione 23 ad 20 per calorem
quo ftannum deferviens omnio rigefcit. Rarefactio aeris
æquali calore fuit decuplo major quam rarefactio olei, &
rarefactio olei quafi quindecim vicibus major quam rarefactio fpiritus vini. Et ex his inventis ponendo calores
olei ipfius rarefactioni proportionales & pro calore corporis
humani fcribendo partes 12 prodijt calor aquæ ubi incipit
ebullire partium 33 & ubi vehementius ebullit partium 34 ;
& calor ftanni ubi vel liquefcit vel deferviendo incipit rigefcere & confiftentiam amalgamatis induere prodijt partium 72, & ubi defervendo rigefcit & induratur partium 70.
His cognitis ut reliqua inveftigarem calefeci ferrum fatis
craffum donec fatis canderet & ex igne cum forcipe etiam
candente exemptum locavi ftatim in loco frigido ubi ventus
conftanter fpirabat & huic imponendo particulas diverforum metallorum & aliorum corporum liquabilium notavi
tempora refrigerij donec particulæ omnes amiffa fluiditate
rigefcerent & calor ferri æquaretur calori corporis humani.
Deinde ponendo quod exceffus calorum ferri & particula-
rum rigefcentium fupra calorem atmofphæræ Thermome-
tro inventum effent in progreffione geometrica ubi
tempora funt in progreffione Arithmetica, calores omnes innotuere. Locavi autem ferrum, non in aere tran-
quillo fed in vento uniformiter fpirante ut aer a ferro cale-
factus femper abriperetur a vento & aer frigidus in locum
ejus uniformi cum motu fuccederet. Sic enim aeris partes
æquales æqualibus temporibus calefactæ funt & calorem con-
ceperunt calori ferri proportionalem.   Ca-

(829)

Calores autem fic inventi eandem habuerunt rationem inter fe cum caloribus per Thermometrum inventis & propterea rarefactiones olei ipfius caloribus proportionales effe recte affumpfimus.

A Scale of the Degrees of Heat.   N° 270, p. 824.   *Translated from the Latin.*

0 ..0.. The heat of the air in winter, when the water begins to freeze; and it is discovered exactly by placing the thermometer in compressed snow, when it begins to thaw.

0,1,2 ..0 .. The heat of the air in winter.

2,3,4 ..0 .. The same in spring and autumn.

4,5,6 ..0 .. The same in summer.

6 ..0 .. Heat of the air at noon about the month of July.

12 ..1 .. Greatest heat the thermometer received on the contact of a man's body, as also that of a bird hatching her eggs.

$14\frac{3}{11}$..$1\frac{1}{4}$.. Almost the greatest heat of a bath, which a man can bear by moving his hand in it for some time ; also that of blood newly drawn.

17 .. 1 .. $1\frac{1}{4}$.. Greatest degree of heat of a bath, which a man can bear for some time without stirring his hand in it.

20$\frac{2}{11}$.. 1$\frac{3}{4}$.. Heat of a bath, by which melted wax swimming on it by cooling hardens and loses its transparency.

24 ..2.. Heat of a bath, by which wax swimming on it is melted by growing hot, and kept in continual fusion without ebullition.

28$\frac{6}{11}$.. 2$\frac{1}{4}$.. Mean heat between that by which wax melts and water boils.

34 ..2$\frac{1}{4}$.. Heat by which water has a strong ebullition, and a mixture of two parts of lead, three of tin, and five of bismuth, by cooling hardens; water begins to boil with a degree of heat of 33 parts, and by boiling scarcely acquires any greater degree than that of 34$\frac{1}{4}$; but iron growing cold with the heat of 35 or 36 parts, when hot water, and 37, when cold water is dropped on it, ceases to cause any ebullition.

40$\frac{4}{11}$.. 2$\frac{4}{5}$.. Least degree of heat by which a mixture of one part of lead, four parts of tin, and five parts of bismuth, by growing hot is melted and kept in continual fusion.

48 ..3.. Least degree of heat, by which a mixture of equal parts of tin and bismuth is melted; this mixture with the heat of 47 parts, by cooling coagulates.

57 ..3$\frac{1}{4}$.. Degree of heat, by which a mixture of two parts of tin and one part of bismuth is melted, as also a mixture of three parts of tin and two of lead; but a mixture of five parts of tin and two of bismuth, with this degree of heat, by cooling hardens, and in like manner a mixture of equal parts of lead and bismuth.

68 ..3$\frac{1}{2}$.. Least degree of heat, that melts a mixture of one part of bismuth and eight parts of tin; tin by itself is put into fusion with the heat of 72 parts, and by cooling hardens with the heat of 70 parts.

81 ..3$\frac{3}{4}$.. Degree of heat that melts bismuth, as also a mixture of four parts of lead and one part of tin; but a mixture of five parts of lead and one part of tin, when melted, and cooling again, it hardens with this heat.

96 ..4.. Least degree of heat that melts lead; lead, by growing hot, is melted with the heat of 96 or 97 parts, and cooling it hardens with 95 parts.

114 ..4$\frac{1}{4}$.. Degree of heat, by which ignited bodies in cooling quite cease to shine by night, and again, by growing hot begin to shine in the dark, but with a very faint light, which is scarcely perceptible; in such a degree of heat there melts a mixture of equal parts of tin and regulus martis, and a mixture of seven parts of bismuth and four parts of the said regulus by cooling hardens.

6

136   .. 4¼... Degree of heat with which ignited bodies glow by night, but not
at all in the twilight, and with this degree of heat both a
mixture of two parts of regulus martis and one part of bismuth, as also a mixture of five parts of the said regulus and
one part of tin, by cooling hardens; the regulus by itself
hardens with the heat of 146 parts.

161   .. 4¾... Degree of heat, by which ignited bodies manifestly glow in the
twilight immediately preceding the rising of the sun, or after
his setting, but not at all in a clear day, or but very faintly.

192   .. 5 .. Degree of heat of live coals in a small kitchen fire, made up of
bituminous pit-coals, and that burn without using bellows; as
also, the heat of iron made as hot as it can be in such a fire;
the degree of heat of a small kitchen fire made of faggots is
somewhat greater, viz. 200 or 210 parts, and that of a large
fire is still greater, especially if blown with bellows.

In the first column of this table are the degrees of heat in arithmetical proportion, beginning with that which water has when it begins to freeze, being
as it were the lowest degree of heat, or the common boundary between heat
and cold; and supposing that the external heat of the human body is 12 parts.
In the second column are set down the degrees of heat in geometrical proportion, so that the second degree is double the first, the third double the second,
and the fourth double the third; and making the first degree the external heat
of the human body in its natural state. It appears by this table, that the heat
of boiling water is almost 3 times that of the human body, of melted tin 6
times, of melted lead 8 times, of melted regulus 12 times, and the heat of an
ordinary kitchen fire is 16 or 17 times greater than that of the human body.

This table was constructed by means of the thermometer and red-hot iron.
By the thermometer were found all the degrees of heat, down to that which
melted tin; and by the hot iron were discovered all the other degrees; for the
heat which hot iron, in a determinate time, communicates to cold bodies near
it, that is, the heat which the iron loses in a certain time, is as the whole heat
of the iron; and therefore, if equal times of cooling be taken, the degrees of
heat will be in geometrical proportion, and therefore easily found by the tables
of logarithms. First it was found by the thermometer with linseed oil, that if,
when it was placed in melted snow, the oil possessed the space of 10000 parts;
then the same oil rarefied with the heat of the first degree, or that of a human
body, possessed the space of 10256 parts, with the heat of water just beginning to boil, the space of 10705; with that of water strongly boiling, the space
of 10725 parts; with that of melted tin, beginning to cool, and to be of the
consistence of an amalgama, the space of 11516; and when it is quite hardened

the space of 11496; therefore the rarefied oil was to the same expanded by the heat of the human body, as 40 is to 39; by that of boiling water, as 15 to 14; by that of tin beginning to cool, coagulate, and harden, as 15 to 13; and by the heat of cooling tin when quite hardened, as 23 is to 20; the rarefaction of air by an equal heat was 10 times greater than that of oil, and the rarefaction of oil was 15 times greater than that of spirits of wine. From these data, putting the degrees of the heat of the oil proportional to its rarefaction, and taking 12 parts for the heat of the human body, we then have the degree of the heat of water when it begins to boil, viz. 33 parts, and when it boils more vehemently 34; of tin when melted, or when it begins in cooling to harden, and have the consistence of an amalgama, 72 parts, and in cooling is quite hard, 70 parts.

Having discovered these things; in order to investigate the rest, there was heated a pretty thick piece of iron red-hot, which was taken out of the fire with a pair of pincers, which were also red-hot, and laid in a cold place, where the wind blew continually upon it, and putting on it particles of several metals, and other fusible bodies, the time of its cooling was marked, till all the particles were hardened, and the heat of the iron was equal to the heat of the human body; then supposing that the excess of the degrees of the heat of the iron, and the particles above the heat of the atmosphere, found by the thermometer, were in geometrical progression, when the times are in an arithmetical progression, the several degrees of heat were discovered; the iron was laid not in a calm air, but in a wind that blew uniformly upon it, that the air heated by the iron might be always carried off by the wind, and the cold air succeed it alternately; for thus equal parts of air were heated in equal times, and received a degree of heat proportional to the heat of the iron; the several degrees of heat thus found had the same ratio among themselves with those found by the thermometer: and therefore the rarefactions of the oil were properly assumed proportional to its degrees of heat.*

---

* A method if not more accurate, at least more expeditious than the above, of measuring high degrees of heat, was invented some years ago by the late Mr. Wedgewood ; founded on the property which argillaceous earth possesses, of contracting its dimensions when placed in the fire. See Phil. Trans. Vols. 72, 74, and 76.

IV.

Newton's Four Letters to Bentley, and the Boyle Lectures Related to Them

Bentley and Newton

Perry Miller

Richard Bentley was born in 1662 in a family of substantial Yorkshire yeomen.[1] He achieved fame (and left an impress on British scholarship that still is felt) as a classical scholar of prodigious erudition, and also a certain infamy as the tempestuous Master of Trinity College, Cambridge, which he ruled from 1700 until his death in 1742 with so tyrannical a hand that he excited repeated insurrections of the Fellows. He was a massive philologist, who found the supreme felicity of life in the emendation of a corrupted text or in the exposure of a forgery. He made a sensation among the learned in 1699 by demonstrating that a body of letters long attributed to a Sicilian tyrant of the 6th century B.C., named Phalaris, was a fabrication made some five or ten centuries later. These epistles had been publicly admired by gentlemen such as Sir

[1] See Bishop James Henry Monk, *The Life of Richard Bentley, with an account of his writings* (London, 1830); R. C. Jebb, *Bentley* (New York and London, 1901 [1882]: "English Men of Letters," edited by John Morley); Rev. Alexander Dyce, ed., *The Works of Richard Bentley* (3 vols., London, 1836–1838). Material concerning Bentley is also to be found in the standard literature on Newton; see, especially, Edleston's volume of Newton-Cotes correspondence and Brewster's two-volume biography of Newton.

William Temple who believed that the writers of antiquity were far superior to all moderns, including Shakespeare and Milton. By showing the letters to be spurious, Bentley impeached both the acumen and the taste of these "ancients." The greatest classicist of his time thus appeared a barbarous and ruthless modernist, and so was furiously attacked in a squib called *The Battle of the Books,* written by an erstwhile secretary of Sir William Temple, one Jonathan Swift.

In 1691, Bentley, having taken his degree at St. John's College, was chaplain to Bishop Stillingfleet of Worcester, a leader of liberal theologizing, who early said of Bentley that "had he but the gift of humility, he would be the most extraordinary man in Europe." On December 30 died Robert Boyle, a great physicist and chemist, a gentleman, and one who devoutly believed the new science to be a bulwark against the "atheism" so widely affected during the Restoration by the wits of the taverns and coffeehouses. He left funds sufficient to yield £ 50 a year for endowing an annual lectureship of eight discourses on the evidences of Christianity. There were four trustees, one of whom was John Evelyn; another was Bishop Tenison of Lincoln, who had encountered and appraised the chaplain of his colleague in Worcester. The trustees took what seemed a long chance, and nominated Bentley. He threw himself into the challenge with the same energy he expended upon Greek manuscripts or in opposing dons.

The principal source of the atheism Bentley had to counteract was Thomas Hobbes, who had been under fire from the pious and the orthodox for forty years. Platonists like Ralph Cudworth had belabored him with preëxistent ideas, Richard Cumberland with inherent moral law, and ecclesiastical authoritarians, most notably John Dryden, with general abuse. But, so far, it seemed to the guardians of Christianity that the tide of atheism had not been checked; clearly a new method was required. Bentley was exactly the man for the occasion, because he was one of the first to grasp the importance of a book published in 1690 by John Locke, *An Essay Concerning Human Understanding;* Bentley saw at once that thereafter nobody in the age would give credence to the notion of an innate idea. If his *a Confutation of Atheism* was really going to confute, it would need *proofs.* Bentley was the sort of bulldog who, ordered to find proofs, would bring back dozens of them between his jaws.

A mind that operated in this fashion would already have been thinking that if theological propositions were now to rest their defense exclusively on demonstrations satisfactory to reason, the defender would have to know something about a book that Isaac Newton of Trinity College had published in 1687, the *Principia.* So far, it appeared, few if any were able to understand it, and many said it was nonsense, but Bentley had to see for himself. However, he was a linguist and a literary scholar, and needed help; in the summer of 1691, before the lectureship was instituted, he had asked a Scottish mathematician, John Craige, to tell him what books he would need to master in order to qualify himself for following the *Principia.* Craige sent back, as an essential minimum, a bibliography so tremendous that even a Bentley was aghast; but characteristically he began to look about for short cuts, and, taking his courage in his hands, addressed Newton directly. From Trinity College came a much shorter list, encouraging directions, and apparently full sympathy. "At the first perusal of my Book," said Newton, "it's enough if you understand the propositions with some of the demonstrations which are easier than the rest." He thought Bentley should read the first sixty pages, then skip to the third book and get the design of that; then he might at leisure go back to such propositions as he had a desire to know. With the task thus cut down to manageable proportions, Bentley rapidly comprehended (so he thought) the whole design. When the call came, he was ready. He devoted the first six of his Boyle Lectures to proving the existence of God from such data as the faculties of the human soul and the structure of the body, but he triumphantly expounded in the last two (reprinted below) the new, difficult, and mathematically irrefutable physics. His success was immense, and in the opinion of many (including Bentley himself), *A Confutation of Atheism* so routed the atheists that they did not dare any longer show their faces openly, and so took refuge in the pretense of "deism."

The two sermons are important in the history of Western thought not only because they were the first popular attempt to lay open the "sublime discoveries" of Newton, but because they set the precedent for the entire Enlightenment. So far, neither the infidel nor the believer had been able to cope with the new wisdom; Bentley seized the initiative, and gave believers the assurance (or perhaps one should say the illusion) that the Newtonian physics, by conclusively showing that the order of the universe could not have been produced mechanically, was now the chief support of faith. Whether employed by Christians or deists, Bentley's technique for deducing religious propositions out of the equations of the *Principia* became an indispensable ingredient in the whole complex of 18th-century optimism.

But, for our purposes, the sermons are still more important because, whatever their merits as expositions of the system, they called forth from the great man himself four letters which are major declarations in modern history of the method and of the mentality of the scientist. While the manuscript was being printed, Bentley found himself worried for fear he had not sufficiently disposed of the theory of Lucretius (from whom Hobbes derived) that the cosmic system began with chance bumpings together of descending atoms, each endowed with an innate power of gravity. He wrote to Newton for further clarification, so that he could make last-minute changes in his proof. It took Newton four letters, from December 10 to February 25, to set Bentley straight (in fact, we may wonder whether Bentley fully got the point!), and Bentley appreciated their importance. He carefully preserved them, so that his executor could publish them in 1756. Dr. Johnson, observing that the questions had caused Newton to think out further consequences of his principles than he had yet anticipated, said of them about the finest thing that can be said, that they show "how even the mind of Newton gains ground gradually upon darkness."

The sermons show that Bentley had indeed perceived the general thesis, though the letters suggest that in the printed form Bentley made it more precise than he had done in the pulpit. This is the argument that, had gravity been the only force active at the moment of creation, the planets of our system would have fallen quickly into the sun. Hence must be assumed a specific intervention of force (only a divine force would do) which arrested the descents at the appropriate places and sent the planets spinning on their transverse orbits. Likewise, when one considers the spacing of these orbits, no principle of science will determine the relations of the distances except that "The Author of the system thought it convenient." Bentley seemed to Newton on the right track insofar as he argued that the operations of gravity over empty spaces could mean only that an "agent" was constantly guiding the stars and planets according to certain laws. Assuredly, this agent must have a volition, and must be "very well skilled in mechanics and geometry." Bentley was eager to call the agent God; Newton had no objection.

But evidently, either in the first draft of the sermons or in a letter, Bentley said something which implied that gravity was in some sense an inherent property of matter, implicit in the very substance, a sort of "occult quality," or a kind of eternal magnetism. The vehemence with which Newton rejects any such opinion is striking. Between the letters numbered II and III in this printing, Bentley wrote back a worried answer: he was so fully aware that in Newton's system universal gravitation could never be solved "mechanically" that he was surprised to have Newton warn him against the heresy. "If I used that word, it was only for brevity's sake." Well, brevity to a philologist might be one thing, but another to Newton. He wanted language exact, and certainly in the printed version Bentley took care that not even for brevity's sake should there be any suggestion that gravity is synonymous with material existence. Thus corrected, Bentley was able to conclude that mutual gravitation can operate at a distance only because it is simultaneously regulated by the "agent" and not by the system itself; here then was what he and the age most wanted, "a new and invincible argument for the being of God." From this point the sailing was clear, and Bentley goes ahead like a ship in full rig, to the joyous conclusion that everything concerning this system and particularly this globe, including the inclination of its axis and the irregular distribution of land and ocean, has been appointed for the best by a divine intelligence.

The letters show that Newton wanted to be helpful, and he was eager that Bentley should not misrepresent him; yet they are not prolix, they do not volunteer anything beyond replies to particular questions, and the careful reader does not get the impression of an outgoing enthusiasm. Newton was human enough to be eager for fame and almost pathologically jealous for his reputation; but he was shrewd enough to be able to utilize Bentley without being taken in by him. For years after the Boyle Lectures, Bentley made a public parade of his friendship with Newton, and took upon himself the office of urging a second edition of the *Principia*. When Newton at last consented in 1708 to allow Roger Cotes, Fellow of Trinity College (in whom Newton did have confidence), to prepare the text, Bentley officiously acted as middleman—and pocketed the profits! John Conduitt records that he was disgusted, and asked Newton point-blank why he let Bentley "print his *Principia*" when Bentley obviously did not understand it. "Why," replied the lordly Newton, "he was covetous, and I let him do it to get the money."

In the light of this revelation we may wonder what, back in February of 1693, Bentley made, if anything, of the extraordinary clause in the third letter, where Newton says that whether the agent who is the cause of gravity "be material or immaterial, I have left to the consideration of my readers." This hardly seems the tone of one who has joined a crusade against materialistic atheism! But still more startling is the sentence that comes in the next paragraph, where Newton shows Bentley that mathematically speaking he is entirely at sea in handling the concept of the infinite, and briefly informs him that, even though the mathematical language may seem to common sense an impropriety of speech, still "those things which men understand by improper and contradictious phrases may be sometimes really in nature without any contradiction at all." There is no suggestion in Bentley's two sermons that he had even a dim sense of what Newton tried in this passage to convey to him. For Bentley, the Newtonian system was clear, rational, simple; it could be translated at once and throughout into declarative affirmations of natural theology. That was its beauty and its utility. That there was any incongruity between the process of the human mind and those of the universe would henceforth be unthinkable. Newton had, Bentley was assured, linked them indissolubly.

This conviction, as I have said, became the major premise of the Age of Reason. Bentley's tactics were taken over by Voltaire in 1738 when he conquered the mind of the Continent by popularizing Newton. Actually, the assumption remained undisturbed—or indeed strengthened—by that revolution in sensibility which we call the Romantic movement. Even after the character of reason had been radically transformed from Bentley's solid prose to the inward intuitions of the poet, the assumption that there is a perfect "correspondence" between the structures of the psyche and those of physics endured. Emerson summarized the Romantic optimism by declaring that the laws of nature answer to those of mind as image in the mirror. Only recently, and mainly in our own distracted time, has science freed itself from the literary incubus that Bentley fastened upon it. But we should find this worth meditating upon, that Newton explicitly warned him that what men are apt to consider self-contradictory may, nevertheless, be the rule in nature.

There is a mystery in these letters—the enigma that is Newton himself. Nobody in 1692, nor for a century thereafter, noted that, when Bentley confidently brought God into action as the diverter of falling bodies into "this transverse and violent motion," the Creator became, in a sense, only a half-creator of the system. God's action was made once and once for all; it was that "first impulse impressed upon them, not only for five or six thousand years, but many millions of millions." But the gravitating motion, the descent toward the sun, is continuous; despite his effort to make clear his agreement with Newton, Bentley still calls it "a constant energy infused into matter by the Author of all things." Did Newton, in his secret heart, have the wit, which no contemporary possessed, to see that such toying with the notion that gravity was a constant energy infused into matter raised the question of whether the infusion really had been made by the author of all things? Might this not be only a gratuitous addition, made by a mind precommitted to the thesis, by one incapable properly of dealing with the meaning of the infinite? Whether Newton had read Pascal we do not know, but assuredly Bentley never had!

If the letters mean anything, then, they mean that Newton was not quite a Newtonian. He was holding something in reserve, not giving himself entirely to his own discoveries, stupendous as he realized them to be. As for ultimate causes, he knew how to say that he did not know. Our curiosity is aroused, but never shall be satisfied, by the evasive ending of the first letter: Isaac Newton had still another argument to prove the existence of God, potentially very strong, but because the principles on which it was grounded were not yet widely enough received, "I think it more advisable to let it sleep." What were those principles? Perhaps he meant simply the realm of optics into which he was now venturing, already musing upon ideas he was to let see the light only in the form of a question at the end of Query 31 in the 1717 edition of the *Opticks,* when even then he was "not yet satisfied about it for want of experiments." But we cannot help asking if in his subtle consciousness there was a sense of still more complex principles which would need to wait still longer before becoming "better received." And were these withheld principles possibly just those dark and inexplicable discrepancies between the mind of the creature and the methods of the creation which he could dare to contemplate, but of which the Bentleys of this world never attain even a rudimentary awareness?

FOUR
LETTERS
FROM
Sir Isaac Newton
TO
Doctor Bentley.
CONTAINING
Some ARGUMENTS
IN
Proof of a DEITY.

LONDON:
Printed for R. and J. DODSLEY, *Pall-Mall,*

M DCC LVI.

[1]

LETTERS, &c.

His concern w/
Religion is demonstrated
by his correspondence.

LETTER I.

To the Reverend Dr. RICHARD
BENTLEY, *at the Bishop of*
Worcester's *House in* Park-
street, Westminster.

SIR,

WHEN I wrote my Treatise about
our System, I had an Eye upon
such Principles as might work with considering Men, for the Belief of a Deity,
and nothing can rejoice me more than to
find it useful for that Purpose. But if I

B   have

[2]

have done the Public any Service this
way, it is due to nothing but Induſtry and
patient Thought.

As to your firſt Query, it ſeems to me
that if the Matter of our Sun and Planets,
and all the Matter of the Univerſe, were
evenly ſcattered throughout all the Heavens, and every Particle had an innate
Gravity towards all the reſt, and the
whole Space, throughout which this Matter was ſcattered, was but finite ; the
Matter on the outſide of this Space would
by its Gravity tend towards all the Matter
on the inſide, and by conſequence fall
down into the middle of the whole Space,
and there compoſe one great ſpherical
Maſs.   But if the Matter was evenly diſpoſed throughout an infinite Space, it
could never convene into one Maſs, but
ſome of it would convene into one Maſs
and ſome into another, ſo as to make an
infinite Number of great Maſſes, ſcattered
at great Diſtances from one to another
through-

[3]

throughout all that infinite Space. And thus might the Sun and fixt Stars be formed, fuppofing the Matter were of a lucid Nature. But how the Matter fhould divide itfelf into two forts, and that Part of it, which is fit to compofe a fhining Body, fhould fall down into one Mafs and make a Sun, and the reft, which is fit to compofe an opaque Body, fhould coalefce, not into one great Body, like the fhining Matter, but into many little ones; or if the Sun at firft were an opaque Body like the Planets, or the Planets lucid Bodies like the Sun, how he alone fhould be changed into a fhining Body, whilft all they continue opaque, or all they be changed into opaque ones, whilft he remains unchanged, I do not think explicable by meer natural Caufes, but am forced to afcribe it to the Counfel and Contrivance of a voluntary Agent.

The fame Power, whether natural or fupernatural, which placed the Sun in the

B 2

[4]

the Center of the fix primary Planets,
placed *Saturn* in the Center of the Orbs
of his five fecondary Planets, and *Jupiter*
in the Center of his four fecondary Planets,
and the Earth in the Center of the Moon's
Orb; and therefore had this Caufe been
a blind one, without Contrivance or Defign, the Sun would have been a Body
of the fame kind with *Saturn*, *Jupiter*, and
the Earth, that is, without Light and
Heat. Why there is one Body in our
Syftem qualified to give Light and Heat
to all the reft, I know no Reafon, but
becaufe the Author of the Syftem thought
it convenient; and why there is but one
Body of this kind I know no Reafon, but
becaufe one was fufficient to warm and
enlighten all the reft. For the *Cartefian*
Hypothefis of Suns lofing their Light,
and then turning into Comets, and Comets into Planets, can have no Place in
my Syftem, and is plainly erroneous; becaufe it is certain that as often as they
appear to us, they defcend into the Syftem

of

[5]

of our Planets, lower than the Orb of
Jupiter, and fometimes lower than the
Orbs of *Venus* and *Mercury*, and yet never
ftay here, but always return from the Sun
with the fame Degrees of Motion by
which they approached him.

To your fecond Query, I anfwer, that
the Motions which the Planets now have
could not fpring from any natural Caufe
alone, but were impreffed by an intelligent Agent. For fince Comets defcend
into the Region of our Planets, and here
move all manner of ways, going fometimes the fame way with the Planets,
fometimes the contrary way, and fometimes in crofs ways, in Planes inclined to
the Plane of the Ecliptick, and at all
kinds of Angles, 'tis plain that there is
no natural Caufe which could determine
all the Planets, both primary and fecondary, to move the fame way and in
the fame Plane, without any confiderable
Variation : This muft have been the Effect

[6]

fect of Counfel. Nor is there any natural Caufe which could give the Planets thofe juft Degrees of Velocity, in Proportion to their Diftances from the Sun, and other central Bodies, which were requifite to make them move in fuch concentrick Orbs about thofe Bodies. Had the Planets been as fwift as Comets, in Proportion to their Diftances from the Sun (as they would have been, had their Motion been caufed by their Gravity, whereby the Matter, at the firft Formation of the Planets, might fall from the remoteft Regions towards the Sun) they would not move in concentrick Orbs, but in fuch eccentrick ones as the Comets move in. Were all the Planets as fwift as *Mercury*, or as flow as *Saturn* or his Satellites; or were their feveral Velocities otherwife much greater or lefs than they are, as they might have been had they arofe from any other Caufe than their Gravities; or had the Diftances from the Centers about which they move, been greater or
                                lefs

[7]

leſs than they are with the ſame Velocities; or had the Quantity of Matter in
the Sun, or in *Saturn*, *Jupiter*, and the
Earth, and by conſequence their gravitating Power been greater or leſs than it is;
the primary Planets could not have revolved about the Sun, nor the ſecondary
ones about *Saturn*, *Jupiter*, and the Earth,
in concentrick Circles as they do, but
would have moved in Hyperbolas, or
Parabolas, or in Ellipſes very eccentrick.
To make this Syſtem therefore, with
all its Motions, required a Cauſe which
underſtood, and compared together, the
Quantities of Matter in the ſeveral Bodies of the Sun and Planets, and the
gravitating Powers reſulting from thence;
the ſeveral Diſtances of the primary
Planets from the Sun, and of the ſecondary ones from *Saturn*, *Jupiter*, and
the Earth; and the Velocities with which
theſe Planets could revolve about thoſe
Quantities of Matter in the central Bodies; and to compare and adjuſt all theſe

Things

[8]

Things together, in fo great a Variety of
Bodies, argues that Caufe to be not blind
and fortuitous, but very well fkilled in
Mechanicks and Geometry.

To your third Query, I anfwer, that
it may be reprefented that the Sun may,
by heating thofe Planets moft which are
neareft to him, caufe them to be better
concocted, and more condenfed by that
Concoction. But when I confider that
our Earth is much more heated in its
Bowels below the upper Cruft by fubterraneous Fermentations of mineral Bodies
than by the Sun, I fee not why the interior Parts of *Jupiter* and *Saturn* might
not be as much heated, concocted, and
coagulated by thofe Fermentations as our
Earth is ; and therefore this various Denfity fhould have fome other Caufe than
the various Diftances of the Planets from
the Sun. And I am confirmed in this
Opinion by confidering, that the Planets
of *Jupiter* and *Saturn*, as they are rarer
than

[9]

than the reſt, ſo they are vaſtly greater, and contain a far greater Quantity of Matter, and have many Satellites about them ; which Qualifications ſurely aroſe not from their being placed at ſo great a Diſtance from the Sun, but were rather the Cauſe why the Creator placed them at great Diſtance. For by their gravitating Powers they diſturb one another's Motions very ſenſibly, as I find by ſome late Obſervations of Mr. *Flamſteed,* and had they been placed much nearer to the Sun and to one another, they would by the ſame Powers have cauſed a conſiderable Diſturbance in the whole Syſtem.

To your fourth Query, I anſwer, that in the Hypotheſis of Vortices, the Inclination of the Axis of the Earth might, in my Opinion, be aſcribed to the Situation of the Earth's Vortex before it was abſorbed by the neighbouring Vortices, and the Earth turned from a Sun to a

C   Comet ;

[10]

Comet; but this Inclination ought to decreafe conftantly in Compliance with the
Motion of the Earth's Vortex, whofe
Axis is much lefs inclined to the Ecliptick, as appears by the Motion of the
Moon carried about therein. If the Sun
by his Rays could carry about the Planets, yet I do not fee how he could
thereby effect their diurnal Motions.

Laftly, I fee nothing extraordinary in
the Inclination of the Earth's Axis for
proving a Deity, unlefs you will urge it
as a Contrivance for Winter and Summer, and for making the Earth habitable towards the Poles; and that the
diurnal Rotations of the Sun and Planets,
as they could hardly arife from any Caufe
purely mechanical, fo by being determined all the fame way with the annual
and menftrual Motions, they feem to
make up that Harmony in the Syftem,
which, as I explaind above, was the
Effect of Choice rather than Chance.

There

[11]

There is yet another Argument for a Deity, which I take to be a very ſtrong one, but till the Principles on which it is grounded are better received, I think it more adviſable to let it ſleep.

I am,

   Your moſt humble Servant,

    to command,

Cambridge,
Decemb. 10, 1692.

    I S. N E W T O N.

[13]

LETTER II.

For Mr. BENTLEY, *at the Palace at* Worcefter.

SIR,

I Agree with you, that if Matter evenly diffufed through a finite Space, not fpherical, fhould fall into a folid Mafs, this Mafs would affect the Figure of the whole Space, provided it were not foft, like the old Chaos, but fo hard and folid from the Beginning, that the Weight of its protuberant Parts could not make it yield to their Preffure. Yet by Earth-quakes loofening the Parts of this Solid, the Protuberances might fometimes fink a little by their Weight, and thereby the Mafs might, by Degrees, approach a fpherical Figure.

The

[14]

The Reason why Matter evenly scattered through a finite Space would convene in the midst, you conceive the same
with me ; but that there should be a central Particle, so accurately placed in the
middle, as to be always equally attracted
on all Sides, and thereby continue without Motion, seems to me a Supposition
fully as hard as to make the sharpest
Needle stand upright on its Point upon a
Looking-Glass. For if the very mathematical Center of the central Particle be
not accurately in the very mathematical
Center of the attractive Power of the
whole Mass, the Particle will not be attracted equally on all Sides. And much
harder it is to suppose all the Particles in
an infinite Space should be so accurately
poised one among another, as to stand
still in a perfect Equilibrium. For I reckon
this as hard as to make not one Needle
only, but an infinite number of them (so
many as there are Particles in an infinite
Space) stand accurately poised upon their
Points.

[15]

Points. Yet I grant it poffible, at leaft by a divine Power; and if they were once to be placed, I agree with you that they would continue in that Pofture without Motion for ever, unlefs put into new Motion by the fame Power. When therefore I faid, that Matter evenly fpread through all Space, would convene by its Gravity into one or more great Maffes, I underftand it of Matter not refting in an accurate Poife.

But you argue, in the next Paragraph of your Letter, that every Particle of Matter in an infinite Space, has an infinite Quantity of Matter on all Sides, and by confequence an infinite Attraction every way, and therefore muft reft in Equilibrio, becaufe all Infinites are equal. Yet you fufpect a Paralogifm in this Argument; and I conceive the Paralogifm lies in the Pofition, that all Infinites are equal. The generality of Mankind confider Infinites no other ways than indefinitely;

and

[16]

and in this Senſe, they ſay all Infinites are equal; tho' they would ſpeak more truly if they ſhould ſay, they are neither equal nor unequal, nor have any certain Difference or Proportion one to another. In this Senſe therefore, no Concluſions can be drawn from them, about the Equality, Proportions, or Differences of Things, and they that attempt to do it uſually fall into Paralogiſms. So when Men argue againſt the infinite Diviſibility of Magnitude, by ſaying, that if an Inch may be divided into an infinite Number of Parts, the Sum of thoſe Parts will be an Inch; and if a Foot may be divided into an infinite Number of Parts, the Sum of thoſe Parts muſt be a Foot, and therefore ſince all Infinites are equal, thoſe Sums muſt be equal, that is, an Inch equal to a Foot.

The Falſeneſs of the Concluſion ſhews an Error in the Premiſes, and the Error lies in the Poſition, that all Infinites are equal.

[17]

equal. There is therefore another Way of confidering Infinites ufed by Mathematicians, and that is, under certain definite Reftrictions and Limitations, whereby Infinites are determined to have certain Differences or Proportions to one another. Thus Dr. *Wallis* confiders them in his *Arithmetica Infinitorum*, where by the various Proportions of infinite Sums, he gathers the various Proportions of infinite Magnitudes : Which way of arguing is generally allowed by Mathematicians, and yet would not be good were all Infinites equal. According to the fame way of confidering Infinites, a Mathematician would tell you, that tho' there be an infinite Number of infinite little Parts in an Inch, yet there is twelve times that Number of fuch Parts in a Foot, that is, the infinite Number of thofe Parts in a Foot is not equal to, but twelve Times bigger than the infinite Number of them in an Inch. And fo a Mathematician will tell you, that if a

D   Body

[18]

Body ftood in Equilibrio between any two
equal and contrary attracting infinite
Forces; and if to either of thefe Forces
you add any new finite attracting Force,
that new Force, how little foever, will
deftroy their Equilibrium, and put the
Body into the fame Motion into which
it would put it were thofe two contrary
equal Forces but finite, or even none at
all; fo that in this Cafe the two equal
Infinites by the Addition of a Finite to
either of them, become unequal in our
ways of Reckoning; and after thefe
ways we muft reckon, if from the
Confiderations of Infinites we would always draw true Conclufions.

To the laft Part of your Letter, I anfwer, Firft, that if the Earth (without
the Moon) were placed any where with
its Center in the *Orbis Magnus*, and ftood
ftill there without any Gravitation or Projection, and there at once were infufed
into it, both a gravitating Energy towards
the

[19]

the Sun, and a tranſverſe Impulſe of a
juſt Quantity moving it directly in a Tangent to the *Orbis Magnus*; the Compounds of this Attraction and Projection
would, according to my Notion, cauſe a
circular Revolution of the Earth about
the Sun. But the tranſverſe Impulſe
muſt be a juſt Quantity; for if it be too
big or too little, it will cauſe the Earth
to move in ſome other Line. Secondly,
I do not know, any Power in Nature
which would cauſe this tranſverſe Motion
without the divine Arm. *Blondel* tells us
ſomewhere in his Book of Bombs, that
Plato affirms, that the Motion of the
Planets is ſuch, as if they had all
of them been created by God in
ſome Region very remote from our
Syſtem, and let fall from thence towards the Sun, and ſo ſoon as they arrived
at their ſeveral Orbs, their Motion of
falling turned aſide into a tranſverſe
one. And this is true, ſuppoſing the
gravitating Power of the Sun was double

D 2   at

[20]

at that Moment of Time in which they all arrive at their feveral Orbs ; but then the divine Power is here required in a double refpect, namely, to turn the defcending Motions of the falling Planets into a fide Motion, and at the fame time to double the attractive Power of the Sun. So then Gravity may put the Planets into Motion, but without the divine Power it could never put them into fuch a circulating Motion as they have about the Sun ; and therefore, for this, as well as other Reafons, I am compelled to afcribe the Frame of this Syftem to an intelligent Agent.

You fometimes fpeak of Gravity as effential and inherent to Matter. Pray do not afcribe that Notion to me ; for the Caufe of Gravity is what I do not pretend to know, and therefore would take more Time to confider of it.

I fear what I have faid of Infinites, will feem obfcure to you ; but it is enough if
you

[21]

you underſtand, that Infinites when conſidered abſolutely without any Reſtriction
or Limitation, are neither equal nor unequal, nor have any certain Proportion one
to another, and therefore the Principle
that all Infinites are equal, is a precarious
one.

Sir, I am,

Your moſt humble Servant,

Trinity College,
Jan. 17, 1692-3.

I S. N E W T O N.

L E T-

[23]

LETTER III.

For Mr. BENTLEY, *at the Palace at* Worcefter.

SIR,

BEcaufe you defire Speed, I will anfwer your Letter with what Brevity I can. In the fix Pofitions you lay down in the Beginning of your Letter, I agree with you. Your affuming the *Orbis Magnus* 7000 Diameters of the Earth wide, implies the Sun's horizontal Parallax to be half a Minute. *Flamfteed* and *Caffini* have of late obferved it to be about 10″, and thus the *Orbis Magnus* muft be 21,000, or in a rounder Number 20,000 Diameters of the Earth wide. Either Computation I think

[24]

think will do well, and I think it not worth while to alter your Numbers.

In the next Part of your Letter you lay down four other Pofitions, founded upon the fix firft. The firft of thefe four feems very evident, fuppofing you take Attraction fo generally as by it to underftand any Force by which diftant Bodies endeavour to come together without mechanical Impulfe. The fecond feems not fo clear ; for it may be faid, that there might be other Syftems of Worlds before the prefent ones, and others before thofe, and fo on to all paft Eternity, and by confequence, that Gravity may be co-eternal to Matter, and have the fame Effect from all Eternity as at prefent, unlefs you have fomewhere proved that old Syftems cannot gradually pafs into new ones ; or that this Syftem had not its Original from the exhaling Matter of former decaying Syftems, but from a Chaos of Matter evenly
difperfed

[25]

difperfed throughout all Space ; for fomething of this Kind, I think, you fay was
the Subject of your fixth Sermon ; and
the Growth of new Syftems out of old
ones, without the Mediation of a divine
Power, feems to me apparently abfurd.

The laft Claufe of the fecond Pofition
I like very well. It is inconceivable, that
inanimate brute Matter fhould, without
the Mediation of fomething elfe, which is
not material, operate upon, and affect
other Matter without mutual Contact, as
it muft be, if Gravitation in the Senfe of
Epicurus, be effential and inherent in it.
And this is one Reafon why I defired you
would not afcribe innate Gravity to me.
That Gravity fhould be innate, inherent
and effential to Matter, fo that one Body
may act upon another at a Diftance thro'
a *Vacuum*, without the Mediation of any
thing elfe, by and through which their
Action and Force may be conveyed from
E   one

[26]

one to another, is to me fo great an Abfurdity, that I believe no Man who has in
philofophical Matters a competent Faculty
of thinking, can ever fall into it.   Gravity
muft be caufed by an Agent acting conftantly according to certain Laws ; but
whether this Agent be material or immaterial, I have left to the Confideration of
my Readers.

Your fourth Affertion, that the World
could not be formed by innate Gravity
alone, you confirm by three Arguments.
But in your firft Argument you feem to
make a *Petitio Principii* ; for whereas
many ancient Philofophers and others, as
well Theifts as Atheifts, have all allowed,
that there may be Worlds and Parcels of
Matter innumerable or infinite, you deny
this, by reprefenting it as abfurd as that
there fhould be pofitively an infinite arithmetical Sum or Number, which is a Contradiction *in Terminis* ; but you do not
prove

[27]

prove it as abſurd. Neither do you prove, that what Men mean by an infinite Sum or Number, is a Contradiction in Nature; for a Contradiction *in Terminis* implies no more than an Impropriety of Speech. Thoſe things which Men underſtand by improper and contradictious Phraſes, may be ſometimes really in Nature without any Contradiction at all: a Silver Inkhorn, a Paper Lanthorn, an Iron Whetſtone, are abſurd Phraſes, yet the Things ſignified thereby, are really in Nature. If any Man ſhould ſay, that a Number and a Sum, to ſpeak properly, is that which may be numbered and ſummed, but Things infinite are numberleſs, or, as we uſually ſpeak, innumerable and ſumleſs, or inſummable, and therefore ought not to be called a Number or Sum, he will ſpeak properly enough, and your Argument againſt him will, I fear, loſe its Force. And yet if any Man ſhall take the Words, Number and Sum, in a larger Senſe, ſo

[28]

as to underftand thereby Things, which
in the proper way of fpeaking are num-
berlefs and fumlefs (as you feem to do
when you allow an infinite Number of
Points in a Line) I could readily allow him
the Ufe of the contradictious Phrafes of
innumerable Number, or fumlefs Sum,
without inferring from thence any Abfurdity in the Thing he means by thofe
Phrafes. However, if by this, or any
other Argument, you have proved the
Finitenefs of the Univerfe, it follows, that
all Matter would fall down from the Out-
fides, and convene in the Middle. Yet
the Matter in falling might concrete into
many round Maffes, like the Bodies of
the Planets, and thefe by attracting one
another, might acquire an Obliquity of
Defcent, by means of which they might
fall, not upon the great central Body, but
upon the Side of it, and fetch a Compafs
about, and then afcend again by the fame
Steps and Degrees of Motion and Velocity
with

[29]

with which they defcended before, much
after the Manner that the Comets revolve
about the Sun; but a circular Motion in
concentrick Orbs about the Sun, they
could never acquire by Gravity alone.

And tho' all the Matter were divided at
firft into feveral Syftems, and every Syftem by a divine Power conftituted like
ours; yet would the Outfide Syftems defcend towards the Middlemoft; fo that
this Frame of Things could not always
fubfift without a divine Power to conferve
it, which is the fecond Argument; and
to your third I fully affent.

As for the Paffage of *Plato*, there is no
common Place from whence all the Planets being let fall, and defcending with
uniform and equal Gravities (as *Galileo*
fuppofes) would at their Arrival to their
feveral Orbs acquire their feveral Velocities, with which they now revolve in
them.

[30]

them. If we fuppofe the Gravity of all
the Planets towards the Sun to be of fuch
a Quantity as it really is, and that the Motions of the Planets are turned upwards,
every Planet will afcend to twice its
Height from the Sun. *Saturn* will afcend till he be twice as high from the Sun
as he is at prefent, and no higher; *Jupi-*
ter will afcend as high again as at prefent,
that is, a little above the Orb of *Saturn*;
Mercury will afcend to twice his prefent
Height, that is, to the Orb of *Venus*; and
fo of the reft; and then by falling down
again from the Places to which they afcended, they will arrive again at their feveral Orbs with the fame Velocities they
had at firft, and with which they now
revolve.

But if fo foon as their Motions by
which they revolve are turned upwards,
the gravitating Power of the Sun, by
which their Afcent is perpetually retarded,
be

[31]

be diminifhed by one half, they will now afcend perpetually, and all of them at all equal Diftances from the Sun will be equally fwift. *Mercury* when he arrives at the Orb of *Venus*, will be as fwift as *Venus*; and he and *Venus*, when they arrive at the Orb of the *Earth*, will be as fwift as the *Earth*; and fo of the reft. If they begin all of them to afcend at once, and afcend in the fameLine, they will conftantly in afcending become nearer and nearer together, and their Motions will conftantly approach to an Equality, and become at length flower than any Motion affign-able. Suppofe therefore, that they afcended till they were almoft contiguous, and their Motions inconfiderably little, and that all their Motions were at the fame Moment of Time turned back again ; or, which comes almoft to the fame Thing, that they were only deprived of their Motions, and let fall at that Time, they would all at once arrive at their feveral Orbs, each

with

[32]

with the Velocity it had at firſt; and if their Motions were then turned Side‑ways, and at the ſame Time the gravi‑tating Power of the Sun doubled, that it might be ſtrong enough to retain them in their Orbs, they would revolve in them as before their Aſcent. But if the gravitate‑ing Power of the Sun was not doubled, they would go away from their Orbs into the higheſt Heavens in parabolical Lines. Theſe Things follow from my *Princ. Math. Lib.* i. *Prop.* 33, 34, 36, 37.

I thank you very kindly for your de‑ſigned Preſent, and reſt

Your moſt

humble Servant

to command,

Cambridge,
Feb. 25, 1692-3.

I S. NEWTON.

[33]

LETTER IV.

To Mr. BENTLEY, *at the Palace at* Worcefter.

SIR,

THE Hypothefis of deriving the Frame of the World by mechanical Principles from Matter evenly fpread through the Heavens, being inconfiftent with my Syftem, I had confidered it very little before your Letters put me upon it, and therefore trouble you with a Line or two more about it, if this comes not too late for your Ufe.

In my former I reprefented that the diurnal Rotations of the Planets could not be derived from Gravity, but required a divine Arm to imprefs them. And tho'

F   Gravity

[34]

Gravity might give the Planets a Motion of Defcent towards the Sun, either directly or with fome little Obliquity, yet the tranfverfe Motions by which they revolve in their feveral Orbs, required the divine Arm to imprefs them according to the Tangents of their Orbs. I would now add, that the Hypothefis of Matter's being at firft evenly fpread through the Heavens, is, in my Opinion, inconfiftent with the Hypothefis of innate Gravity, without a fupernatural Power to reconcile them, and therefore it infers a Deity. For if there be innate Gravity, it is impoffible now for the Matter of the Earth and all the Planets and Stars to fly up from them, and become evenly fpread throughout all the Heavens, without a fupernatural Power; and certainly that which can never be hereafter without a fupernatural Power, could never be heretofore without the fame Power.

You

[35]

You queried, whether Matter evenly
fpread throughout a finite Space, of fome
other Figure than fpherical, would not in
falling down towards a central Body,
caufe that Body to be of the fame Figure
with the whole Space, and I anfwered,
yes. But in my Anfwer it is to be fuppofed that the Matter defcends directly
downwards to that Body, and that that
Body has no diurnal Rotation.

This, Sir, is all I would add to my
former Letters.

I am,

Your moſt humble

Servant,

Cambridge,
Feb. 11, 1693.

IS. NEWTON.

F I N I S.

A
Confutation of Atheism

FROM THE
Origin and Frame of the WORLD.

The Third and Laſt PART.

A
SERMON

Preached at

St Mary-le-Bow,

DECEMBER the 5th. 1692.

Being the *Eighth* of the Lecture Founded by the Honourable *ROBERT BOYLE*, Eſquire.

By *RICHARD BENTLEY*, M. A.
Chaplain to the Right Reverend Father in God,
EDWARD, Lord Biſhop of *Worceſter*.

LONDON,
Printed for *H. Mortlock* at the *Phœnix* in
St. *Paul's* Church-yard. 1693.

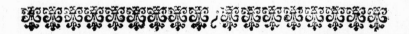

Imprimatur.

Ra. Barker, R^{mo} in Chriſto Patri ac D^{no} D^{no} *Johanni* Archiep. *Cantuar*. à Sacris Domeſt.

LAMBHITH,
Maij 30. 1693.

(3)

Acts XIV. 15, &c.

That ye should turn from these vanities unto the living God, who made Heaven and Earth and the Sea, and all things that are therein: Who in times past suffer'd all Nations to walk in their own ways. Nevertheless, he left not himself without witness, in that he did Good, and gave us Rain from Heaven, and fruitfull Seasons, filling our hearts with Food and Gladness.

WHen we firſt enter'd upon this Topic, the demonſtration of God's Exiſtence from the Origin and Frame of the World, we offer'd to prove four Propoſitions.

1. That this preſent Syſtem of Heaven and Earth cannot poſſibly have ſubſiſted from all Eternity.

2. That Matter conſider'd generally, and abſtractly from any particular Form and Concretion, cannot poſſibly have been eternal: Or, if Matter could be ſo; yet Motion cannot have coexiſted with it eternally, as an inherent property and eſſential attribute of Matter. Theſe two we have already eſtabliſhed

A 2   in

in the preceding Difcourfe ; we fhall now fhew in the third place,

3. That, though we fhould allow the Athe-ifts, that Matter and Motion may have been from everlafting ; yet if (as they now fuppofe) there were once no Sun nor Starrs nor Earth nor Planets ; but the Particles, that now con-ftitute them, were diffufed in the mundane Space in manner of a Chaos without any con-cretion and coalition ; thofe difperfed Particles could never of themfelves by any kind of Na-tural motion, whether call'd Fortuitous or Me-chanical, have conven'd into this prefent or any other like Frame of Heaven and Earth.

I. And firft as to that ordinary Cant of il-literate and puny Atheifts, the *fortuitous or ca-fual concourfe of Atoms*, that compendious and eafy Difpatch of the moft important and diffi-cult affair, the Formation of a World ; (befides that in our next undertaking it will be refuted all along) I fhall now briefly difpatch it, from

Serm. v. p. 6, 7.

what hath been formerly faid concerning the true notions of Fortune and Chance. Where-by it is evident, that in the Atheiftical Hypo-thefis of the World's production, Fortuitous and Mechanical muft be the felf-fame thing. Becaufe *Fortune* is no real entity nor phyfical effence, but a mere relative fignification, de-noting

Origin and Frame of the World.   5

noting only this; That fuch a thing faid to fall out by Fortune, was really effected by material and neceffary Caufes; but the Perfon, with regard to whom it is called Fortuitous, was ignorant of thofe Caufes or their tendencies, and did not defign nor forefee fuch an effect. This is the only allowable and genuine notion of the word Fortune. But thus to affirm, that the World was made *fortuitoufly*, is as much as to fay, That before the World was made, there was fome Intelligent Agent or Spectator; who defigning to do fomething elfe, or expecting that fomething elfe would be done with the Materials of the World, there were fome occult and unknown motions and tendencies in Matter, which mechanically formed the World befide his defign or expectation. Now the Atheifts, we may prefume, will be loth to affert a fortuitous Formation in this proper fenfe and meaning; whereby they will make Underftanding to be older than Heaven and Earth. Or if they fhould fo affert it; yet, unlefs they will affirm that the Intelligent Agent did difpofe and direct the inanimate Matter, (which is what we would bring them to) they muft ftill leave their Atoms to their mechanical Affections; not able to make one ftep toward the production

duction of a World beyond the neceffary Laws of Motion. It is plain then, that *Fortune*, as to the matter before us, is but a fynonymous word with Nature and Neceffity. It remains that we examin the adequate mean-
Serm. V. ing of *Chance* ; which properly fignifies, That
p. 12, 13. all events called Cafual, among inanimate Bodies, are mechanically and naturally produced according to the determinate figures and textures and motions of thofe Bodies; with this negation only, That thofe inanimate Bodies are not confcious of their own operations, nor contrive and caft about how to bring fuch events to pafs. So that thus to fay, that the World was made *cafually* by the concourfe of Atoms, is no more than to affirm, that the Atoms compofed the World mechanically and fatally; only they were not fenfible of it, nor ftudied and confider'd about fo noble an undertaking. For if Atoms formed the World according to the effential properties of Bulk, Figure and Motion, they formed it *mechanically*; and if they formed it mechanically without perception and defign, they formed it *cafually*. So that this negation of Confcioufnefs being all that the notion of Chance can add to that of Mechanifm; We, that do not difpute this matter with the Atheifts,

Origin and Frame of the World.   7

ifts, nor believe that Atoms ever acted by Counfel and Thought, may have leave to confider the feveral names of *Fortune* and *Chance* and *Nature* and *Mechanifm*, as one and the fame Hypothefis. Wherefore once for all to overthrow all poffible Explications which Atheifts have or may affign for the formation of the World, we will undertake to evince this following Propofition :

II. That the Atoms or Particles which now conftitute Heaven and Earth, being once fe- parate and diffufed in the Mundane Space, like the fuppofed *Chaos,* could never *without a God by their Mechanical affections* have con- vened into this prefent Frame of Things or any other like it.

Which that we may perform with the greater clearnefs and conviction; it will be neceffary, in a difcourfe about the Formation of the World, to give you a brief account of fome of the moft principal and fyftematical *Phænomena*, that occurr in the World now that it is formed.

(1.) The moft confiderable *Phænomenon* belonging to Terreftrial Bodies is the general action of *Gravitation,* whereby All known Bo- dies in the vicinity of the Earth do tend and prefs toward its Center ; not only fuch as are
fenfibly

8   *A Confutation of Atheism from the*

fenfibly and evidently Heavy, but even thofe that are comparatively the Lighteft, and even in their proper place, and natural Elements, (as they ufually fpeak) as Air gravitates even in Air and Water in Water. This hath been demonftrated and experimentally proved beyond contradiction, by feveral ingenious Perfons of the prefent Age, but by none fo perfpicuoufly and copioufly and accurately, as by the Honourable Founder of this Lecture in his incomparable Treatifes of the *Air* and *Hydroftaticks.*

Mr.*Boyle's* Phyfi-com.Exp. of Air. Hydro-ftat.Para-doxes.

(2.) Now this is the conftant Property of *Gravitation*; That the weight of all Bodies around the Earth is ever proportional to the Quantity of their Matter: As for inftance, a Pound weight (examin'd Hydroftatically) of all kinds of Bodies, though of the moft different forms and textures, doth always contain an equal quantity of folid Mafs or corporeal Subftance. This is the ancient Doctrine of the *Epicurean* Phyfiology, then and fince very probably indeed, but yet precarioufly afferted: But it is lately demonftrated and put beyond controverfy by that very excellent and divine Theorift Mr.*Ifaac Newton,* to whofe moft admirable fagacity and induftry we fhall frequently be obliged in this and the following Difcourfe.

Lucret. lib. 1.

Newton Philof. Natur. Princ. Math.lib. 3.prop.6.

I

Origin and Frame of the World.   9

I will not entertain this Auditory with an account of the Demonſtration; but referring the Curious to the Book it ſelf for full ſatisfaction, I ſhall now proceed and build upon it as a Truth ſolidly eſtabliſhed, *That all Bodies weigh according to their Matter*; provided only that the compared Bodies be at equal diſtances from the Center toward which they weigh. Becauſe the further they are removed from the Center, the lighter they are: decreaſing gradually and uniformly in weight, in a duplicate proportion to the Increaſe of the Diſtance.

(3.) Now ſince Gravity is found proportional to the Quantity of Matter, there is a manifeſt Neceſſity of admitting a *Vacuum*, another principal Doctrine of the *Atomical* Philoſophy. Becauſe if there were every-where an abſolute plenitude and denſity without any empty pores and interſtices between the Particles of Bodies, then all Bodies of equal dimenſions would contain an equal Quantity of Matter; and conſequently, as we have ſhewed before, would be equally ponderous: ſo that Gold, Copper, Stone, Wood, *&c.* would have all the ſame ſpecifick weight; which Experience aſſures us they have not: neither would any of them deſcend in the Air, as we all ſee they do; becauſe, if all Space was Full, even the Air would be as denſe and ſpecifically as

B   heavy

10   *A Confutation of Atheism from the*

heavy as they. If it be faid, that, though the
difference of fpecifick Gravity may proceed
from variety of Texture, the lighter Bodies
being of a more loofe and porous compofition, and the heavier more denfe and compact;
yet an æthereal fubtile Matter, which is in a
perpetual motion, may penetrate and pervade
the minuteft and inmoft Cavities of the clofeft
Bodies, and adapting it felf to the figure of e-
very Pore, may adequately fill them; and fo
prevent all Vacuity, without increafing the
weight: To this we anfwer; That that fubtile
Matter it felf muft be of the fame Subftance
and Nature with all other Matter, and therefore It alfo muft weigh proportionally to its
Bulk; and as much of it as at any time is comprehended within the Pores of a particular Body muft gravitate jointly with that Body: fo
that if the Prefence of this æthereal Matter
made an abfolute Fullnefs, all Bodies of equal
dimenfions would be equally heavy: which
being refuted by experience, it neceffarily follows, that there is a Vacuity; and that (notwithftanding fome little objections full of ca-
vil and fophiftry) mere and fimple Extenfion
or Space hath a quite different nature and notion from real Body and impenetrable Subftance.

(4.) This

Origin and Frame of the World.   II

(4.) This therefore being eſtabliſhed ; in the next place it's of great conſequence to our preſent enquiry, if we can make a computation, How great is the whole Summ of the Void ſpaces in our ſyſtem, and what proportion it bears to the corporeal ſubſtance. By many and ac- *Mr. Boyle* curate Trials it manifeſtly appears, that Refined of Air and Gold, the moſt ponderous of known Bodies, Porofity of Bodies. (though even that muſt be allowed to be porous too, being diſſoluble in *Mercury* and *Aqua Regis* and other Chymical Liquors ; and being naturally a thing impoſſible, that the Figures and Sizes of its conſtituent Particles ſhould be ſo juſtly adapted, as to touch one another in every Point,) I ſay, Gold is in ſpecifick weight to common Water as 19 to 1 ; and Water to common Air as 850 to 1 : ſo that Gold is to Air as 16150 to 1. Whence it clearly appears, ſeeing Matter and Gravity are always commenſurate, that (though we ſhould allow the texture of Gold to be intirely cloſe without any vacuity) the ordinary Air in which we live and reſpire is of ſo thin a compoſition, that 16149 parts of its dimenſions are mere emptineſs and Nothing ; and the remaining One only material and real ſubſtance. But if Gold it ſelf be admitted, as it muſt be, for a porous Concrete, the proportion of Void to Body in the texture of common Air will be ſo much the greater.

And

And thus it is in the loweſt and denſeſt region
of the Air near the ſurface of the Earth, where
the whole Maſs of Air is in a ſtate of violent
compreſſion, the inferior being preſs'd and
conſtipated by the weight of all the incumbent. But, ſince the Air is now certainly known
to conſiſt of elaſtick or ſpringy Particles, that
have a continual tendency and endeavour to
expand and diſplay themſelves; and the dimenſions, to which they expand themſelves, to
be reciprocally as the Compreſſion; it follows,
that the higher you aſcend in it, where it is leſs
and leſs compreſs'd by the ſuperior Air, the
more and more it is rarefied.   So that at the
hight of a few miles from the ſurface of the
Earth, it is computed to have ſome million
parts of empty ſpace in its texture for one of
ſolid Matter.   And at the hight of one Terreſtrial Semid. (not above 4000 miles) the Æther
is of that wonderfull tenuity, that by an exact calculation, if a ſmall Sphere of common
Air of one Inch Diameter (already 16149 parts
Nothing) ſhould be further expanded to the
thinneſs of that Æther, it would more than
take up the Vaſt Orb of *Saturn*, which is many
million million times bigger than the whole
Globe of the Earth.   And yet the higher you
aſcend above that region, the Rarefaction ſtill
gradually increaſes without ſtop or limit: ſo
that,

Mr. Boyle ibid.

Newton Philoſ. Nat.Prin- cipia. Math. p. 503.

Origin and Frame of the World.   13

that, in a word, the whole Concave of the Firmament, except the Sun and Planets and their Atmofpheres, may be confider'd as a mere Void.   Let us allow then, that all the Matter of the Syftem of our Sun may be 50000 times as much as the whole Mafs of the Earth; and we appeal to Aftronomy, if we are not liberal enough and even prodigal in this conceffion. And let us fuppofe further, that the whole Globe of the Earth is intirely folid and compact without any void interftices; notwithftanding what hath been fhewed before, as to the texture of Gold it felf.   Now though we have made fuch ample allowances; we fhall find, notwithftanding, that the void Space of our Syftem is immenfly bigger than all its corporeal Mafs. For, to proceed upon our fuppofition, that all the Matter within the Firmament is 50000 times bigger than the folid Globe of the Earth; if we affume the Diameter of the *Orbis Magnus* (wherein the Earth moves about the Sun) to be only 7000 times as big as the Diameter of the Earth (though the lateft and moft accurate Obfervations make it thrice 7000) and the Diameter of the Firmament to be only 100000 times as long as the Diameter of the *Orbis Magnus* (though it cannot poffibly be lefs than that, but may be vaftly and unfpeakably bigger) we muft pronounce, after fuch large conceffions

on

14   *A Confutation of Atheism from the*

on that fide and fuch great abatements on ours, That the Summ of Empty Spaces within the Concave of the Firmament is 6860 million million million times bigger than All the Matter contain'd in it.

Now from hence we are enabled to form a right conception and imagination of the fuppofed Chaos; and then we may proceed to determin the controverfy with more certainty and fatisfaction; whether a World like the Prefent could poffibly without a Divine Influence be formed in it or no?

(1.) And *firft*, becaufe every Fixt Star is fuppofed by Aftronomers to be of the fame Nature with our Sun; and each may very poffibly have Planets about them, though by reafon of their vaft diftance they be invifible to Us: we will affume this reafonable fuppofition, That the fame proportion of Void Space to Matter, which is·found in our Sun's Region within the Sphere of the Fixt Starrs, may competently well hold in the whole Mundane Space. I am aware, that in this computation we muft not affign the whole Capacity of that Sphere for the Region of our Sun; but allow half of its Diameter for the *Radii* of the feveral Regions of the next Fixt Starrs. So that diminifhing our former number, as this laft confideration requires; we may fafely affirm from cer-

ta·n

Origin and Frame of the World.   15

tain and demonftrated Principles, That the
empty Space of our Solar Region (compre-
hending half of the Diameter of the Firmament) is 8575 hundred thoufand million million times more ample than all the corporeal
fubftance in it.   And we may fairly fuppofe,
that the fame proportion may hold through
the whole Extent of the Univerfe.

(2.) And *fecondly* as to the ftate or condition
of Matter before the World was a-making,
which is compendioufly expreft by the word
Chaos ; they muft fuppofe, that either All the
Matter of our Syftem was *evenly* or well-nigh
evenly diffufed through the Region of the Sun,
this would reprefent a particular Chaos: or
All Matter univerfally fo fpread through the
whole Mundane Space ; which would truly
exhibit a General Chaos ; no part of the Univerfe being rarer or denfer than another.
Which is agreeable to the ancient
Defcription of it, That * *the Hea-*
vens and Earth had μίαν ἰδέαν, μίαν μορφὴν, *one form*, one texture and
conftitution: which could not be,
unlefs all the Mundane Matter
were *uniformly* and evenly diffufed.

* Diod. Sicul. lib. 1. Καὶα
τὴν ἐξ ἀρχῆς τῶν ὅλων συ-
ςάσιν μίαν ἔχειν ἰδέαν ὐρα-
νόντε κὶ γῆν, μεμιγμένης αὐ-
τῶν τῆς φύσεως. Apoll. Rho-
dius lib. 1. Ἥειδεν δ᾽ ὡς γαῖα
κὶ ὐρανὸς ἠδὲ θάλασσα, τὸ πρὶν
ἐπ᾽ ἀλλήλοισι μιῇ συναρηρό-
τα μορφῆ.

'Tis indifferent to our Difpute, whether they
fuppofe it to have continued a long time or
very little in the ftate of Diffufion.   For if
there

there was but one fingle Moment in all paft
Eternity, when Matter was fo diffufed : we
fhall plainly and fully prove, that it could never have convened afterwards into the prefent
Frame and Order of Things.

(3.) It is evident from what we have newly
proved, that in the Suppofition of fuch a Chaos
or fuch an even diffufion either of the whole
Mundane Matter or that of our Syftem (for it
matters not which they affume) every fingle Particle would have a Sphere of Void Space
around it 8575 hundred thoufand million million times bigger than the dimenfions of that
Particle. Nay further, though the proportion
already appear fo immenfe ; yet every fingle
Particle would really be furrounded with a
Void fphere Eight times as capacious as that
newly mention'd ; its Diameter being compounded of the Diameter of the Proper fphere,
and the Semi-diameters of the contiguous
Spheres of the neighbouring Particles. From
whence it appears, that every Particle (fuppofing
them globular or not very oblong) would be
above Nine Million times their own length
from any other Particle. And moreover in the
whole Surface of this Void fphere there can
only Twelve Particles be *evenly* placed (as the
Hypothefis requires) that is, at equal Diftances
from the Central one and each other. So that
if

Origin and Frame of the World.   17

if the Matter of our Syftem or of the Univerfe was equally difperfed, like the fuppofed Chaos ; the refult and iffue would be, not only that every Atom would be many Million times its own length diftant from any other : but if any One fhould be moved Mechanically (without direction or attraction) to the limit of that diftance; 'tis above a hundred million millions Odds to an unit, that it would not ftrike upon any other Atom, but glide through an empty interval without any contact.

(4.) 'Tis true, that while I calculate thefe Meafures, I fuppofe all the Particles of Matter to be at abfolute reft among themfelves, and fituated in an exact and mathematical evennefs ; neither of which is likely to be allowed by our Adverfaries, who not admitting the former, but afferting the eternity of Motion, will confequently deny the latter alfo : becaufe in the very moment that Motion is admitted in the Chaos, fuch an exact evennefs cannot poffibly be preferved. But this I do, not to draw any argument againft them from the Univerfal Reft or accurately equal diffufion of Matter ; but only that I may better demonftrate the great Rarity and Tenuity of their imaginary Chaos, and reduce it to computation. Which computation will hold with exactnefs enough, though we allow the Parti-

C   cles

cles of the Chaos to be varioufly moved, and to differ fomething in fize and figure and fituation. For if fome Particles fhould approach nearer each other than in the former Proportion; with refpect to fome other Particles they would be as much remoter. So that notwithftanding a fmall diverfity of their Pofitions and Diftances, the whole Aggregate of Matter, as long as it retain'd the name and nature of Chaos, would retain well-nigh an uniform tenuity of Texture, and may be confider'd as an homogeneous Fluid. As feveral Portions of the fame fort of Water are reckon'd to be of the fame fpecifick gravity; though it be naturally impoffible that every Particle and Pore of it, confider'd Geometrically, fhould have equal fizes and dimenfions.

We have now reprefented the true fcheme and condition of the Chaos; how all the Particles would be difunited; and what vaft intervals of empty Space would lye between each. To form a Syftem therefore, 'tis neceffary that thefe fquander'd Atoms fhould convene and unite into great and compact Maffes, like the Bodies of the Earth and Planets. Without fuch a coalition the diffufed Chaos muft have continued and reign'd to all eternity. But how could Particles fo widely difperfed combine into that clofenefs of Texture? Our Adverfaries

Origin and Frame of the World.   19

ries can have only thefe two ways of accounting for it. *Either* by the Common Motion of
Matter, proceeding from external Impulfe and
Conflict (without attraction) by which every
Body moves uniformly in a direct line according to the determination of the impelling force.
For, they may fay, the Atoms of the Chaos being varioufly moved according to this catholic Law, muft needs knock and interfere ; by
which means fome that have convenient figures for mutual coherence might chance to
ftick together, and others might join to thofe,
and fo by degrees fuch huge Maffes might be
formed, as afterwards became Suns and Planets: or there might arife fome vertiginous
Motions or Whirlpools in the Matter of the
Chaos ; whereby the Atoms might be thruft
and crowded to the middle of thofe Whirlpools, and there conftipate one another into
great folid Globes, fuch as now appear in the
World. Or *fecondly* by mutual Gravitation
or Attraction. For they may affert, that Matter hath inherently and effentially fuch an in-
trinfeck energy, whereby it inceffantly tends
to unite it felf to all other Matter: fo that feveral Particles placed in a Void fpace at any diftance whatfoever would without any external
impulfe fpontaneoufly convene and unite together. And thus the Atoms of the Chaos,

20   *A Confutation of Atheiſm from the*

though never ſo widely diffuſed, might by this innate property of Attraction ſoon aſſemble themſelves into great ſphærical Maſſes, and conſtitute Syſtems like the preſent Heaven and Earth. This is all that can be propoſed by Atheiſts, as an efficient cauſe of a World. For as to the *Epicurean* Theory, of Atoms deſcending down an infinite ſpace by an inherent principle of Gravitation, which tends not toward other Matter, but toward a *Vacuum* or Nothing; and verging from the Perpendicular * *no body knows why nor when nor where*; 'tis ſuch miſerable abſurd ſtuff, ſo repugnant to it ſelf, and ſo contrary to the known Phænomena of Nature (yet it contented ſupine unthinking Atheiſts for a thouſand years together) that we will not now honour it with a ſpecial refutation. But what it hath common with the other Explications, we will fully confute together with Them in theſe three Propoſitions.

* Lucret. *Nec regione loci certa, nec tempore certo.*

(1.) That by Common Motion (without attraction) the diſſever'd Particles of the Chaos could never make the World; could never convene into ſuch great compact Maſſes, as the Planets now are; nor either acquire or continue ſuch Motions, as the Planets now have.

(2.) That ſuch a mutual Gravitation or ſpontaneous Attraction can neither be inherent and eſſential to Matter; nor ever ſupervene to it, unleſs

Origin and Frame of the World.   21

unlefs imprefs'd and infufed into it by a Divine Power.

(3.) That though we fhould allow fuch Attraction to be natural and effential to all Matter ; yet the Atoms of a Chaos could never fo convene by it, as to form the prefent Syftem: or if they could form it, it could neither acquire fuch Motions, nor continue permanent in this ftate, without the Power and Providence of a Divine Being.

I. And firft, that by Common Motion the Matter of Chaos could never convene into fuch Maffes, as the Planets now are. Any man, that confiders the fpacious void Intervals of the Chaos, how immenfe they are in proportion to the bulk of the Atoms, will hardly induce himfelf to believe, that Particles fo widely diffeminated could ever throng and crowd one another into a clofe and compact texture. He will rather conclude, that thofe few that fhould happen to clafh, might rebound after the collifion ; or if they cohered, yet by the next conflict with other Atoms might be feparated again, and fo on in an eternal viciffitude of Faft and Loofe, without ever confociating into the huge condenfe Bodies of Planets ; fome of whofe Particles upon this fuppofition muft have travell'd many millions of Leagues through the gloomy regions of Chaos,

os, to place themſelves where they now are.
But then how rarely would there be any claſhing at all? how very rarely in compariſon to
the number of Atoms? The whole multitude
of them, generally ſpeaking, might freely move
and rove for ever with very little occurring or
interfering. Let us conceive two of the neareſt
Particles according to our former Calculation;
or rather let us try the ſame proportions in a-
nother Example, that will come eaſier to the
Imagination. Let us ſuppoſe two Ships, fitted with durable Timber and Rigging, but
without Pilot or Mariners, to be placed in the
vaſt *Atlantick* or the *Pacifique* Ocean, as far a-
ſunder as may be. How many thouſand years
might expire, before thoſe ſolitary Veſſels ſhould
happen to ſtrike one againſt the other? But let
us imagin the Space yet more ample, even the
whole face of the Earth to be covered with
Sea, and the two Ships to be placed in the oppoſite Poles: might not they now move long
enough without any danger of claſhing? And
yet I find, that the two neareſt Atoms in our
evenly diffuſed Chaos have ten thouſand times
leſs proportion to the two Void circular Planes
around them, than our two Ships would have
to the whole Surface of the Deluge. Let us
aſſume then another Deluge ten thouſand times
larger than *Noah's*. Is it not now utterly incredible,

Origin and Frame of the World.   23

credible, that our two Veffels, placed there Antipodes to each other, fhould ever happen to
concur? And yet let me add, that the Ships
would move in one and the fame Surface; and
confequently muft needs encounter, when they
either advance towards one another in direct
lines, or meet in the interfection of crofs ones;
but the Atoms may not only fly fide-ways, but
over likewife and under each other: wh.ch
makes it many million times more improbable,
that they fhould interfere than the Ships, even in
the laft and unlikelieft inftance. But they may
fay, Though the Odds indeed be unfpeakable
that the Atoms do not convene in any fet number of Trials, yet in an infinite Succeffion of
them may not fuch a Combination poffibly
happen? But let them confider, that the im-
probability of Cafual Hits is never diminifhed
by repetition of Trials; they are as unlikely to
fall out at the Thoufandth as at the Firft. So
that in a matter of mere Chance, when there
is fo many Millions odds againft any affign- Serm. V.
able Experiment; 'tis in vain to expect it fhould P. 32.
ever fucceed, even in endlefs Duration.

But though we fhould concede it to be fimply poffible, that the Matter of Chaos might
convene into great Maffes, like Planets: yet it's
abfolutely impoffible, that thofe Maffes fhould
acquire fuch revolutions about the Sun. Let
us

us suppose any one of those Masses to be the Present Earth. Now the annual Revolution of the Earth muft proceed (in this Hypothefis) *either* from the Summ and Refult of the feveral motions of all the Particles that formed the Earth, *or* from a new Impulfe from fome external Matter, after it was formed. The *former* is apparently abfurd, becaufe the Particles that form'd the round Earth muft needs convene from all points and quarters toward the middle, and would generally tend toward its Center; which would make the whole Compound to reft in a Poife: or at leaft that overplus of Motion, which the Particles of one Hemifphere could have above the other, would be very fmall and inconfiderable; too feeble and languid to propell fo vaft and ponderous a Body with that prodigious velocity. And *fecondly*, 'tis impoffible, that any external Matter fhould impell that compound Mafs, after it was formed. 'Tis manifeft, that nothing elfe could impell it, unlefs the Æthereal Matter be fuppofed to be carried about the Sun like a *Vortex* or Whirlpool, as a Vehicle to convey It and the reft of the Planets. But this is refuted from what we have fhewn above, that thofe Spaces of the Æther may be reckon'd a mere Void, the whole Quantity of their Matter fcarce amounting to the weight of a Grain. 'Tis refuted alfo

from

Origin and Frame of the World.   25

from Matter of Fact in the Motion of Comets; which, as often as they are visible to Us, are in the Region of our Planets; and there are observed to move, some in quite contrary courses to Theirs, and some in cross and oblique ones, in Planes inclined to the Plane of the Ecliptick in all kinds of Angles: which firmly evinces, that the Regions of the Æther are empty and free, and neither resist nor assist the Revolutions of Planets.   But moreover there could not possibly arise in the Chaos any *Vortices* or Whirlpools at all ; either to form the Globes of the Planets, or to revolve them when formed. 'Tis acknowledged by all, that inanimate unactive Matter moves always in a streight Line, nor ever reflects in an Angle, nor bends in a Circle (which is a continual reflexion) unless *either* by some external Impulse, that may divert it from the direct motion, *or* by an intrinsec Principle of Gravity or Attraction, that may make it describe a curve line about the attracting Body.   But this latter Cause is not now supposed: and the former could never beget Whirlpools in a Chaos of so great a Laxity and Thinness.   For 'tis matter of certain experience and universally allowed, that all Bodies moved circularly have a perpetual endeavour to recede from the Center, and every moment would fly out in right Lines, if they were

Newton
ibidem
p. 480.

D   not

not violently reftrain'd and kept in by contiguous Matter. But there is no fuch reftraint in a Chaos, no want of empty room there; no poffibility of effecting one fingle Revolution in way of a *Vortex*, which neceffarily requires either an abfolute Fulnefs of Matter, or a pretty clofe Conftipation and mutual Contact of its Particles.

And for the fame reafon 'tis evident, that the Planets could not *continue* their Revolutions about the Sun ; though they could poffibly acquire them. For to drive and carry the Planets in fuch Orbs as they now defcribe, that Æthereal Matter muft be compact and denfe, as denfe as the very Planets themfelves: otherwife they would certainly fly out in Spiral Lines to the very circumference of the *Vortex*. But we have often inculcated, that the wide Tracts of the Æther may be reputed as a mere extended Void. So that there is nothing (in this Hypothefis) that can retain and bind the Planets in their Orbs for one fingle moment; but they would immediately defert them and the neighbourhood of the Sun, and vanifh away in Tangents to their feveral Circles into the Abyfs of Mundane Space.

II. Secondly we affirm, that mutual Gravitation or fpontaneous Attraction cannot poffibly be innate and effential to Matter. By Attraction

traction we do not here underftand what is im-
properly, though vulgarly, called fo, in the operations of drawing, fucking, pumping, &c. which
is really Pulfion and Trufion; and belongs to
that Common Motion, which we have already
fhewn to be infufficient for the formation of a
World. But we now mean (as we have explain'd it before) fuch a power and quality,
whereby all parcels of Matter would mutually
attract or mutually tend and prefs to all others;
fo that (for inftance) two diftant Atoms *in va-
cuo* would fpontaneoufly convene together
without the impulfe of external Bodies. Now
we fay, if our Atheifts fuppofe this power to be
inherent and effential to Matter; they overthrow their own Hypothefis: there could never be a Chaos at all upon thefe terms, but the
prefent form of our Syftem muft have continued from all Eternity; againft their own Suppofition, and what we have proved in our Laft. *Vide* Serm.
For if they affirm, that there might be a Chaos VI. &
Serm. VIII.
notwithftanding innate Gravity; then let them
affign any Period though never fo remote,
when the diffufed Matter might convene.
They muft confefs, that before that affigned
Period Matter had exifted eternally, infepara-
bly endued with this principle of Attraction;
and yet had never attracted nor convened before, during that infinite duration: which is

fo monftrous an abfurdity, as even They will blufh to be charged with. But fome perhaps may imagin, that a former Syftem might be diffolved and reduced to a Chaos, from which the prefent Syftem might have its Original, as that Former had from another, and fo on: new Syftems having grown out of old ones in infinite Viciffitudes from all paft eternity. But we fay, that in the Suppofition of innate Gravity no Syftem at all could be diffolved. For how is it poffible, that the Matter of folid Maffes like Earth and Planets and Starrs fhould fly up from their Centers againft its inherent principle of mutual Attraction, and diffufe it felf in a Chaos? This is abfurder than the other: That only fuppofed innate Gravity not to be exerted; This makes it to be defeated, and to act contrary to its own Nature. So that upon all accounts this effential power of Gravitation or Attraction is irreconcilable with the Atheift's own Doctrine of a Chaos. And fecondly 'tis repugnant to Common Senfe and Reafon. 'Tis utterly unconceivable, that inanimate brute Matter (without the mediation of fome Immaterial Being) fhould operate upon and affect other Matter without mutual Contact; that diftant Bodies fhould act upon each other through a *Vacuum* without the intervention of fomething elfe by and through which the

Origin and Frame of the World. 29

the action may be conveyed from one to the other. We will not obscure and perplex with multitude of words, what is so clear and evident by its own light, and must needs be allowed by all, that have any competent use of Thinking, and are initiated into, I do not say the Mysteries, but the plainest Principles of Philosophy. Now mutual Gravitation or Attraction (in our present acception of the Words) is the same thing with This; 'tis an operation or vertue or influence of distant Bodies upon each other through an empty Interval, without any *Effluvia* or Exhalations or other corporeal Medium to convey and transmit it. This Power therefore cannot be innate and essential to Matter. And if it be not essential; it is consequently most manifest (seeing it doth not depend upon Motion or Rest or Figure or Position of Parts, which are all the ways that Matter can diversify it self) that it could never *supervene* to it, unless imprefs'd and infused into it by an immaterial and divine Power.

We have proved, that a Power of mutual Gravitation, without contact or impulse, can in no-wise be attributed to mere Matter: or if it could; we shall presently shew, that it would be wholly unable to form the World out of *Chaos.* But by the way; what if it be made appear, that there is really such a Power of
Gravity

Gravity perpetually acting in the conftitution
of the prefent Syftem? This would be a new
and invincible Argument for the Being of God:
being a direct and pofitive proof, that an immaterial living Mind doth inform and actuate
the dead Matter, and fupport the Frame of the
World. I will lay before you fome certain
Phænomena of Nature; and leave it to your
confideration from what Principle they can
proceed. 'Tis demonftrated, That the Sun,
Moon and all the Planets do reciprocally gravitate one toward another: that the Gravitating power of each of Thefe is exactly proportional to their Matter, and arifes from the feveral Gravitations or Attractions of every individual Particle that compofe the whole Mafs:
that all Matter near the Surface of the Earth,
for example, doth not only gravitate downwards, but upwards alfo and fide-ways and toward all imaginable Points; though the Tendency downwards be prædominant and alone
difcernible, becaufe of the Greatnefs and Near-
nefs of the attracting Body, the Earth: that e-
very Particle of the whole Syftem doth attract
and is attracted by all the reft, All operating
upon All: that this *Univerfal Attraction or Gra-*
vitation is an inceffant, regular and uniform
Action by certain and eftablifhed Laws according to Quantity of Matter and Longitude of
Diftance:

Origin and Frame of the World.   31

Diftance: that it cannot be deftroyed nor impair'd nor augmented by any thing, neither by Motion nor Reft, nor Situation nor Pofture, nor alteration of Form, nor diverfity of Medium: that it is not a Magnetical Power, nor the effect of a Vortical Motion; thofe common attempts toward the Explication of Gravity: Thefe things, I fay, are fully demonftra- *Newton* Philofo- ted, as matters of Fact, by that very ingenious phiæ Na- Author, whom we cited before.   Now how is Princ. it poffible that thefe things fhould be effected Math. lib. III. by any Material and Mechanical Agent? We have evinced, that mere Matter cannot operate upon Matter without mutual Contact.   It remains then, that thefe Phænomena are produced *either* by the intervention of Air or Æther or other fuch medium, that communicates the Impulfe from one Body to another; *or* by Effluvia and Spirits that are emitted from the one, and pervene to the other.   We can conceive no other way of performing them Mechanically.   But what impulfe or agitation can be propagated through the Æther from one Particle entombed and wedged in the very Center of the Earth to another in the Center of *Saturn?* Yet even thofe two Particles do reciprocally affect each other with the fame force and vigour, as they would do at the fame diftance in any other Situation imaginable. And becaufe

the

the Impulſe from this Particle is not directed
to That only ; but to all the reſt in the Univerſe, to all quatters and regions, at once invariably and inceſſantly : to do this mechanically; the ſame phyſical Point of Matter muſt
move all manner of ways equally and conſtant-
ly in the ſame inſtant and moment; which is
flatly impoſſible. But if this Particle cannot propagate Motion; much leſs can it ſend out Effluvia to all points without intermiſſion or variation; ſuch multitudes of Effluvia as to lay hold
on every Atom in the Univerſe without miſſing
of one. Nay every ſingle Particle of the very
Effluvia (ſeeing they alſo attract and gravitate)
muſt in this Suppoſition emit other ſecondary
Effluvia all the World over ; and thoſe others
ſtill emit more, and ſo *in infinitum.* Now if
theſe things be repugnant to human reaſon ;
we have great reaſon to affirm, That Univerſal Gravitation, a thing certainly exiſtent in Nature, is above all Mechaniſm and material Cauſes, and proceeds from a higher principle, a
Divine energy and impreſſion.

III. Thirdly we affirm ; That, though we
ſhould allow, that reciprocal Attraction is eſſential to Matter ; yet the Atoms of a Chaos could
never ſo convene by it, as to form the preſent
Syſtem ; or if they could form it, yet it could
neither acquire theſe Revolutions, nor ſubſiſt
in

Origin and Frame of the World.   33

in the prefent condition, without the Confervation and Providence of a Divine Being.

(1.) For firft, if the Matter of the Univerfe, and
confequently the Space through which it's diffufed, be fuppofed to be *Finite* (and I think it might
be demonftrated to be fo; but that we have already exceeded the juft meafures of a Sermon)
then, fince every fingle Particle hath an innate
Gravitation toward all others, proportionated by
Matter and Diftance: it evidently appears, that
the outward Atoms of the Chaos would neceffarily tend inwards and defcend from all quarters
toward the Middle of the whole Space (for in refpect to every Atom there would lie through the
Middle the greateft quantity of Matter and the
moft vigorous Attraction) and would there form
and conftitute one huge fphærical Mafs; which
would be the only Body in the Univerfe.   It is
plain therefore, that upon this Suppofition the
Matter of the Chaos could never compofe fuch
divided and different Maffes, as the Starrs and
Planets of the prefent World.

But allowing our Adverfaries, that The Planets might be compofed: yet however they could
not poffibly acquire fuch Revolutions in Circular Orbs, or (which is all one to our prefent purpofe) in Ellipfes very little Eccentric. For let them
affign any place where the Planets were formed.
Was it nearer to the Sun, than the prefent diftances are? But that is notorioufly abfurd: for then

E   they

they muſt have aſcended from the place of their Formation, againſt the eſſential property of mutual Attraction. Or were each formed in the ſame Orbs, in which they now move? But then they muſt have moved from the Point of Reſt, in an horizontal Line without any inclination or deſcent. Now there is no natural Cauſe, neither Innate Gravity nor Impulſe of external Matter, that could beget ſuch a Motion. For Gravity alone muſt have carried them downwards to the Vicinity of the Sun. And that the ambient Æther is too liquid and empty, to impell them horizontally with that prodigious celerity, we have ſufficiently proved before. Or were they made in ſome higher regions of the Heavens; and from thence deſcended by their eſſential Gravity, till they all arrived at their reſpective Orbs; each with its preſent degree of Velocity, acquired by the fall? But then why did they not continue their deſcent, till they were contiguous to the Sun; whither both Mutual Attraction and Impetus carried them? What natural Agent could turn them aſide, could impell them ſo ſtrongly with a tranſverſe Sideblow againſt that tremendous Weight and Rapidity, when whole Worlds are a falling? But though we ſhould ſuppoſe, that by ſome croſs attraction or other they might acquire an obliquity of deſcent, ſo as to miſs the body of the Sun, and to fall on one ſide of it: then indeed the force of their Fall would carry them quite
beyond

Origin and Frame of the World.   35

beyond it; and fo they might fetch a compafs about it, and then return and afcend by
the fame fteps and degrees of Motion and Velocity, with which they defcended before. Such
an eccentric Motion as this, much after the
manner that Comets revolve about the Sun, they
might poffibly acquire by their innate principle
of Gravity: but circular Revolutions in concentric Orbs about the Sun or other central Body
could in no-wife be attain'd without the power
of the Divine Arm. For the Cafe of the Planetary Motions is this. Let us conceive all the Planets to be formed or conftituted with their Centers in their feveral Orbs; and at once to be imprefs'd on them this Gravitating Energy toward
all other Matter, and a tranfverfe Impulfe of a
juft quantity in each, projecting them directly
in Tangents to thofe Orbs. The Compound
Motion, which arifes from this Gravitation and
Projection together, defcribes the prefent Revolutions of the Primary Planets about the Sun, and
of the Secondary about Thofe: the Gravity pro-
hibiting, that they cannot recede from the Centers of their Motions; and the tranfverfe Impulfe
with-holding, that they cannot approach to them.
Now although Gravity could be innate(which we
have proved that it cannot be) yet certainly this
projected, this tranfverfe and violent Motion can
only be afcribed to the Right hand of the *moſt high
God, Creator of Heaven and Earth.*

E 2   But

But finally, though we grant, that thefe Circular Revolutions could be naturally attained; or, if they will, that this very individual World in its prefent pofture and motion was actually formed out of Chaos by Mechanical Caufes: yet it requires a Divine Power and Providence to have conferved it fo long in the prefent ftate and condition. We have fhewed, that there is a Tranfverfe Impulfe imprefs'd upon the Planets, which retains them in their feveral Orbs, that they be not drawn down by their gravitating Powers toward the Sun or other central Bodies. Gravity we underftand to be a conftant Energy or Faculty (which God hath infufed into Matter) perpetually acting by certain Meafures and (naturally) inviolable Laws; I fay, a *Faculty* and Power: for we cannot conceive that the *Act* of Gravitation of this prefent Moment can propagate it felf or produce that of the next. But 'tis otherwife as to the Tranfverfe Motion; which (by reafon of the Inactivity of Matter and its inability to change its prefent State either of Moving or Refting) would from one fingle Impulfe continue for ever equal and uniform, unlefs changed by the refiftence of occurring Bodies or by a Gravitating Power; fo that the Planets, fince they move Horizontally (whereby Gravity doth not affect their fwiftnefs) and through the liquid and unrefifting Spaces of the Heavens (where either no Bodies at all or inconfiderable ones do occur) may

pre-

Origin and Frame of the World.   37

preferve the fame Velocity which the firft Impulfe
impreft upon them, not only for five or fix thoufand years, but many Millions of Millions. It
appears then, that if there was but One Vaft Sun
in the Univerfe, and all the reft were Planets, revolving around him in Concentric Orbs, at convenient Diftances: fuch a Syftem as that would
very long endure; could it but naturally have a
Principle of Mutual Attraction, and be once actually put into Circular Motions. But the Frame
of the prefent World hath a quite different ftructure: here's an innumerable multitude of Fixt
Starrs or Suns; all of which are demonftrated
(and fuppofed alfo by our Adverfaries) to have
Mutual Attraction: or if they have not; even
Not to have it is an equal Proof of a Divine Being, that hath fo arbitrarily indued Matter with
a Power of Gravity not effential to it, and hath
confined its action to the Matter of its own Solar Syftem: I fay, all the Fixt Starrs have a principle of mutual Gravitation; and yet they are
neither revolved about a common Center, nor
have any Tranfverfe Impulfe nor any thing elfe
to reftrain them from approaching toward each
other, as their Gravitating Powers incite them.
Now what Natural Caufe can overcome Nature
it felf? What is it that holds and keeps them in
fixed Stations and Intervals againft an inceffant
and inherent Tendency to defert them? Nothing
could hinder, but that the Outward Starrs with
their

38 *A Confutation of Atheiſm from the*

their Syſtems of Planets muſt neceſſarily have deſcended toward the middlemoſt Syſtem of the Univerſe, whither all would be the moſt ſtrongly attracted from all parts of a Finite Space. It is evident therefore that the preſent Frame of Sun and Fixt Starrs could not poſſibly ſubſiſt without the Providence of that almighty Deity, *who ſpake*
Pſal. 148. *the word and they were made, who commanded and they were created ; who hath made them Faſt for ever and ever, and hath given them a Law, which ſhall not be broken.*

(2.) And ſecondly in the Suppoſition of an *infinite* Chaos, 'tis hard indeed to determin, what would follow in this imaginary Caſe from an innate Principle of Gravity. But to haſten to a concluſion, we will grant for the preſent, that the diffuſed Matter might convene into an infinite Number of great Maſſes at great diſtances from one another, like the Starrs and Planets of this viſible part of the World. But then it is impoſſible, that the Planets ſhould naturally attain theſe circular Revolutions, either by intrinſec Gravitation or the impulſe of ambient Bodies. It is plain, here is no difference as to this ; whether the World be Infinite or Finite : ſo that the ſame Arguments that we have uſed before, may be equally urged in this Suppoſition. And though we ſhould concede, that theſe Revolutions might be acquired, and that all were ſettled and conſtituted in the preſent State and Poſture of Things ;
yet,

Origin and Frame of the World.   39

yet, we fay, the continuance of this Frame and Order for fo long a duration as the known ages of
the World muft neceffarily infer the Exiftence of
God. For though the Univerfe was Infinite, the
Fixt Starrs could not be fixed, but would naturally convene together, and confound Syftem with
Syftem: for, all mutually attracting, every one
would move whither it was moft powerfully
drawn. This, they may fay, is indubitable in the
cafe of a Finite World, where fome Syftems muft
needs be Outmoft, and therefore be drawn toward the Middle: but when Infinite Syftems fucceed one another through an Infinite Space, and
none is either inward or outward; may not all
the Syftems be fituated in an accurate Poife; and,
becaufe equally attracted on all fides, remain fixed and unmoved? But to this we reply; That unlefs the very mathematical Center of Gravity of
every Syftem be placed and fixed in the very mathematical Center of the Attractive Power of all
the reft; they cannot be evenly attracted on all
fides, but muft preponderate fome way or other.
Now he that confiders, what a mathematical Center is, and that Quantity is infinitly divifible; will
never be perfuaded, that fuch an Univerfal Equilibrium arifing from the coincidence of Infinite
Centers can naturally be acquired or maintain'd.
If they fay; that upon the Suppofition of Infinite
Matter, every Syftem would be infinitly, and
therefore equally attracted on all fides; and con-
                                                    fequently

ſequently would reſt in an exact Equilibrium, be the Center of its Gravity in what Poſition ſoever: This will overthrow their very Hypotheſis; at this rate in an *infinite Chaos* nothing at all could be formed; no Particles could convene by mutual Attraction; for every one there muſt have Infinite Matter around it, and therefore muſt reſt for ever being evenly balanced between Infinite Attractions. Even the Planets upon this principle muſt gravitate no more toward the Sun, than any other way: ſo that they would not revolve in curve Lines, but fly away in direct Tangents, till they ſtruck againſt other Planets or Starrs in ſome remote regions of the Infinite Space. An equal Attraction on all ſides of all Matter is juſt equal to no Attraction at all: and by this means all the Motion in the Univerſe muſt proceed from external Impulſe alone; which we have proved before to be an incompetent Cauſe for the Formation of a World.

And now, O thou almighty and eternal Creator, *having conſider'd the Heavens the work of thy* Pſal. 8. *fingers, the Moon and the Starrs which thou haſt ordained,* with all the company of Heaven we laud and magnify thy glorious Name, evermore praiſing thee and ſaying; Holy, Holy, Holy, Lord God of Hoſts, Heaven and Earth are full of thy Glory: Glory be to thee, O Lord moſt High.

F I N I S.

A
Confutation of Atheism
FROM THE
Origin and Frame of the WORLD.

PART II.

A
SERMON
Preached at
St. *Martin's* in the Fields,
NOVEMBER the 7[th.] 1692.
Being the *Seventh* of the Lecture Founded by
the Honourable ROBERT BOYLE, Esquire.

By *RICHARD BENTLEY*, M. A.
Chaplain to the Right Reverend Father in God,
E D W A R D, Lord Bishop of *Worcester*.

LONDON,
Printed for *H. Mortlock* at the *Phœnix* in
St. *Paul's* Church-yard. 1693.

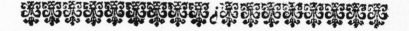

Imprimatur.

Ra. Barker, R^{mo} in Chriſto Patri
ac D^{no} D^{no} *Johanni* Archiep. *Cantuar.* à Sacris Domeſt.

LAMBHITH,
Novemb. 10.
1692.

(3)

Acts XIV. 15, &c.

That ye should turn from these vanities unto the living God, who made Heaven and Earth and the Sea, and all things that are therein: Who in times past suffer'd all Nations to walk in their own ways. Nevertheless, he left not himself without witness, in that he did Good, and gave us Rain from Heaven, and fruitfull Seasons, filling our hearts with Food and Gladness.

HAving abundantly proved in our Last Exercise, That the Frame of the present World could neither be made nor preserved without the *Power* of God; we shall now consider the structure and motions of our own System, if any characters of Divine *Wisdom* and *Goodness* may be discoverable by us. And even at the first and general View it very evidently appears to us (which is our FOURTH and Last Proposition,) That the Order and Beauty of the Systematical Parts of the World, the Discernible Ends and Final Causes of them, the τὸ βελτίον or Meliority above what was necessary to be, do evince by a reflex Argument, that it could not be produced by Mechanism or Chance, but by an

B 2   Intel-

4   *A Confutation of Atheifm from the*

Intelligent and Benign Agent, *that by his excellent Wifdom made the Heavens.*

But before we engage in this Difquifition, we muft offer one neceffary Caution; that we need not nor do not confine and determin the purpofes of God in creating all Mundane Bodies, merely to Human Ends and Ufes. Not that we believe it laborious and painfull to Omnipotence to create a World out of Nothing; or more laborious to create a great World, than a fmall one: fo as we might think it difagreeable to the Majefty and Tranquillity of the Divine Nature to take fo much pains for our fakes. Nor do we count it any abfurdity, that fuch a vaft and immenfe Univerfe fhould be made for the fole ufe of fuch mean and unworthy Creatures as the Children of Men. For if we confider the Dignity of an Intelligent Being, and put that in the fcales againft brute inanimate Matter; we may affirm, without over valuing Humane Nature, that the Soul of one vertuous and religious Man is of greater worth and excellency than the Sun and his Planets and all the Starrs in the World. If therefore it could appear, that all the Mundane Bodies are fome way conducible to the fervice of Man; if all were as beneficial to us, as the Polar Starrs were formerly for Navigation: as the Moon is for the flowing and ebbing of Tides, by which an ineftimable

Origin and Frame of the World.   5

mable advantage accrues to the World; for her
officious Courtefy on dark Winter nights, efpecially to the more Northern Nations, who in a
continual Night it may be of a whole month are
fo pretty well accommodated by the Light of the
Moon reflected from frozen Snow, that they do
not much envy their *Antipodes* a month's prefence
of the Sun: if all the Heavenly Bodies were thus
ferviceable to us, we fhould not be backward to
affign their ufefulnefs to Mankind, as the fole end
of their Creation.   But we dare not undertake to
fhew, what advantage is brought to Us by thofe
innumerable Starrs in the Galaxy and other parts
of the Firmament, not difcernible by naked eyes,
and yet each many thoufand times bigger than
the whole body of the Earth: If you fay, they
beget in us a great Idea and Veneration of the
mighty Author and Governer of fuch ftupendious
Bodies, and excite and elevate our minds to his
adoration and praife; you fay very truly and well.
But would it not raife in us a higher apprehen-
fion of the infinite Majefty and boundlefs Beneficence of God, to fuppofe that thofe remote and
vaft Bodies were formed, not merely upon Our
account to be peept at through an Optick Glafs,
but for different ends and nobler purpofes? And
yet who will deny, but that there are great multitudes of lucid Starrs even beyond the reach of the
beft

6   *A Confutation of Atheiſm from the*

beſt Teleſcopes; and that every viſible Starr may
have opake Planets revolve about them, which
we cannot diſcover? Now if they were not created for Our ſakes; it is certain and evident, that
they were not made for their own. For Matter
hath no life nor perception, is not conſcious of
its own exiſtence, nor capable of happineſs, nor
gives the Sacrifice of Praiſe and Worſhip to the
Author of its Being. It remains therefore, that
all Bodies were formed for the ſake of Intelligent
Minds: and as the Earth was principally deſigned
for the Being and Service and Contemplation of
Men; why may not all other Planets be created
for the like Uſes, each for their own Inhabitants
which have Life and Underſtanding? If any man
will indulge himſelf in this Speculation, he need
not quarrel with revealed Religion upon ſuch an
account. The Holy Scriptures do not forbid him
to ſuppoſe as great a Multitude of Syſtems and as
much inhabited, as he pleaſes. 'Tis true; there
is no mention in *Moſes*'s Narrative of the Creation, of any People in other Planets. But it plainly appears, that the Sacred Hiſtorian doth only
treat of the Origins of Terreſtrial Animals: he
hath given us no account of God's creating the
Angels; and yet the ſame Author in the enſuing
parts of the Pentateuch makes not unfrequent
mention of the *Angels of God*. Neither need we
be

Origin and Frame of the World.   7

be follicitous about the condition of thofe Planetary People, nor raife frivolous Difputes, how far
they may participate in the miferies of *Adam's* Fall,
or in the benefits of *Chrift's* Incarnation. As if,
becaufe they are fuppofed to be *Rational* they muft
needs be concluded to be *Men?* For what is
Man? not a *Reafonable Animal* merely, for that
is not an adequate and diftinguifhing Definition;
but a Rational Mind of fuch particular Faculties,
united to an Organical Body of fuch a certain
Structure and Form, in fuch peculiar Laws of
Connexion between the Operations and Affections of the Mind and the Motions of the Body?
Now God Almighty by the inexhaufted fecundity of his creative Power may have made innumerable Orders and Claffes of Rational Minds;
fome higher in natural perfections, others inferior
to Human Souls. But a Mind of fuperior or
meaner capacities than Human would conftitute
a different Species, though united to a Human
Body in the fame Laws of Connexion: and a
Mind of Human Capacities would make another
Species, if united to a different Body in different
Laws of Connexion: For this Sympathetical Union of a Rational Soul with Matter, fo as to produce a Vital communication between them, is an
arbitrary inftitution of the Divine Wifdom: there
is no reafon nor foundation in the feparate natures
of

8   *A Confutation of Atheism from the*

of either fubftance, why any Motion in the Body
fhould produce any Senfation at all in the Soul ;
or why This motion fhould produce That particular Senfation, rather than any other. God therefore may have join'd Immaterial Souls, even of
the fame Clafs and Capacities in their feparate
State, to other kinds of Bodies and in other Laws
of Union ; and from thofe different Laws of Union there will arife quite different affections and
natures and fpecies of the compound Beings. So
that we ought not upon any account to conclude,
that if there be Rational Inhabitants in the *Moon*
or *Mars* or any unknown Planets of other Syftems,
they muft therefore have Human Nature, or be
involved in the Circumftances of Our World.
And thus much was neceffary to be here inculcated (which will obviate and preclude the moft
confiderable objections of our Adverfaries) that
we do not determin the Final Caufes and Ufefulnefs of the Syftematical parts of the World, merely as they have refpect to the Exigencies or Conveniencies of Human Life.

Let us now turn our thoughts and imaginations to the Frame of our Syftem, if there we may
trace any vifible footfteps of Divine Wifdom and
Beneficence. But we are all liable to many mi-
ftakes by the prejudices of Childhood and Youth,
which few of us ever correct by a ferious fcru-
tiny

Origin and Frame of the World. 9

tiny in our riper years, and a Contemplation of the *Phænomena* of Nature in their Caufes and Beginnings. What we have always feen to be done in one conftant and uniform manner ; we are apt to imagin there was but that one way of doing it, and it could not be otherwife. This is a great error and impediment in a difquifition of this nature : to remedy which, we ought to confider every thing as not yet in Being ; and then diligently examin, if it muft needs have been at all, or what other ways it might have been as poffibly as the prefent ; and if we find a greater Good and Utility in the prefent conftitution, than would have accrued either from the total Privation of it, or from other frames and ftructures that might as poffibly have been as It: we may then reafonably conclude, that the prefent conftitution proceeded neither from the neceffity of material Caufes nor the blind fhuffles of an imaginary Chance, but from an Intelligent and Good Being, that formed it that particular way out of choice and defign. And efpecially if this Ufefulnefs be confpicuous not in one or a few only, but in a long train and feries of Things, this will give us a firm and infallible affurance, that we have not pafs'd a wrong Judgment.

B

I. Let

I. Let us proceed therefore by this excellent Rule in the contemplation of Our Syſtem. 'Tis evident that all the Planets receive Heat and Light from the body of the Sun. Our own Earth in particular would be barren and deſolate, a dead dark lump of Clay, without the benign influence of the Solar Rayes; which without queſtion is true of all the other Planets. It is *good* therefore, that there ſhould be a Sun to warm and cheriſh the Seeds of Plants, and excite them to Vegetation; to impart an uninterrupted Light to all parts of his Syſtem for the Subſiſtence of Animals. But how came the Sun to be Luminous? not from the neceſſity of natural Cauſes, or the conſtitution of the Heavens. All the Planets might have moved about him in the ſame Orbs and the ſame degrees of Velocity as now; and yet the Sun might have been an opake and cold Body like Them. For as the ſix Primary Planets revolve about Him, ſo the Secondary ones are moved about Them, the Moon about the Earth, the Satellites about *Jupiter*, and others about *Saturn*; the one as regularly as the other, in the ſame Seſquialteral proportion of their Periodical motions to their Orbs. So that, though we ſuppoſe the preſent Exiſtence and Conſervation of the Syſtem, yet the Sun might have been a Body without Light or Heat of the ſame kind with the

Earth

Origin and Frame of the World. 11

Earth and *Jupiter* and *Saturn*. But then what horrid darkneſs and deſolation muſt have reign'd in the World? It had been unfit for the Divine purpoſes in creating vegetable and ſenſitive and rational Creatures. It was therefore the contrivance and choice of a *Wiſe and Good* Being; that the Central Sun ſhould be a Lucid Body, to communicate warmth and light and life to the Planets around him.

II. We have ſhewed in our Laſt, that the concentric Revolutions of the Planets about the Sun proceed from a compound Motion; a Gravitation toward the Sun, which is a conſtant Energy infuſed into Matter by the Author of all things, and a projected tranſverſe Impulſe in Tangents to their ſeveral Orbs, that was impreſs'd at firſt by the Divine Arm, and will carry them around till the end of the World. But now admitting that Gravity may be eſſential to Matter; and that a tranſverſe Impulſe might be acquired too by Natural Cauſes, yet to make all the Planets move about the Sun in circular Orbs; there muſt be given to each a determinate Impulſe, theſe preſent particular degrees of Velocity which they now have, in proportion to their Diſtances from the Sun and to the quantity of the Solar Matter. For had the Velocities of the ſeveral Planets been greater or leſs than they are now, at the ſame di-

ſtances

12   *A Confutation of Atheism from the*

Newton
Phil. Na-
tur. Prin-
cip. Math.
ſtances from the Sun ; or had their Diſtances
from the Sun, or the quantity of the Sun's Matter and conſequently his Attractive Power been
greater or leſs than they are now, with the ſame
Velocities: they would not have revolved in concentric Circles as they do, but have moved in
Hyperbola's or Parabola's or in Ellipſes very Eccentric.   The ſame may be ſaid of the Velocities
of the Secondary Planets with reſpect to their Diſtances from the Centers of Their Orbs, and to
the Quantities of the Matter of thoſe Central Bodies.   Now that all theſe Diſtances and Motions
and Quantities of Matter ſhould be ſo accurately and harmoniouſly adjuſted in this great Variety of our Syſtem, is above the fortuitous Hits of
blind material Cauſes, and muſt certainly flow
from that eternal Fountain of Wiſdom, the Crea-
ὁ Θεὸς ἀ-
εἰ γεωμε-
τρεῖ. Plat. tor of Heaven and Earth, who *always acts Geome-*
trically, by juſt and adequate numbers and weights
and meaſures.   And let us examin it further by
our Critical Rule : Are the preſent Revolutions
in circular Orbs more beneficial, than the other
would be ?   If the Planets had moved in thoſe
Lines above named ; ſometimes they would have
approached to the Sun as near as the Orb of *Mer-*
cury, and ſometimes have exorbitated beyond the
diſtance of *Saturn :* and ſome have quite left the
Sun without ever returning.   Now the very conſtitution

Origin and Frame of the World.   1 3

ſtitution of a Planet would be corrupted and de-
ſtroyed by ſuch a change of the Interval between
it and the Sun: no living thing could have endured ſuch unſpeakable exceſſes of Heat and Cold:
all the Animals of our Earth muſt inevitably have
periſhed, or rather never have been.   So that as
ſure as it is *good, very good,* that Human Nature Gen. 1.
ſhould exiſt; ſo certain it is that the circular Revolutions of the Earth (and Planets) rather than
thoſe other Motions which might as poſſibly have
been, do declare not only the Power of God, but
his *Wiſdom and Goodneſß.*

III.   It is manifeſt by our laſt Diſcourſe, that
the Æthereal Spaces are perfectly fluid; they neither aſſiſt nor retard, neither guide nor divert the
Revolutions of the Planets; which rowl through
thoſe Regions as free and unreſiſted, as if they
moved in a *vacuum.*   So that any of them might
as poſſibly have moved in oppoſite Courſes to
the preſent, and in Planes croſſing the Plane of
the Eccliptic in any kind of Angles.   Now if the
Syſtem had been fortuitouſly formed by the convening Matter of a Chaos; how is it conceivable,
that all the Planets both Primary and Secondary,
ſhould revolve the ſame Way from the Weſt to
the Eaſt, and that in the ſame Plane too without
any conſiderable variation? No natural and neceſſary Cauſe could ſo determin their motions;
and

and 'tis millions of millions odds to an unit in ſuch a Caſt of a Chance. Such an apt and regular Harmony, ſuch an admirable Order and Beauty muſt deſervedly be aſcribed to Divine Art and Conduct. Eſpecially if we conſider, that the ſmalleſt Planets are ſituated neareſt the Sun and each other; whereas *Jupiter* and *Saturn*, that are vaſtly greater than the reſt and have many Satellites about them, are wiſely removed to the extreme Regions of the Syſtem, and placed at an immenſe Diſtance one from the other. For even now at this wide interval they are obſerved in their Conjunctions to diſturb one anothers motions a little by their gravitating Powers: but if ſuch vaſt Maſſes of Matter had been ſituated much nearer to the Sun or to each other (as they might as eaſily have been, for any mechanical or fortuitous Agent) they muſt neceſſarily have cauſed a conſiderable diſturbance and diſorder in the whole Syſtem.

IV. But let us conſider the particular Situation of our Earth and its diſtance from the Sun. It is now placed ſo conveniently, that Plants thrive and flouriſh in it, and Animals live: this is matter of fact, and beyond all diſpute. But how came it to paſs at the beginning, that the Earth moved in its preſent Orb? We have ſhewed before, that if Gravity and a Projected Motion be

fitly

Origin and Frame of the World.   1 5

fitly proportion'd, any Planet would freely revolve at any affignable diftance within the Space
of the whole Syftem.   Was it mere Chance then,
or Divine Counfel and Choice, that conftituted
the Earth in its prefent Situation? To know this;
we will enquire, if this particular Diftance from
the Sun be better for our Earth and its Creatures,
than a greater or lefs would have been.   We may
be mathematically certain, That the Heat of the
Sun is according to the denfity of the Sun-beams,
and is reciprocally proportional to the fquare of
the diftance from the Body of the Sun.   Now by
this Calculation, fuppofe the Earth fhould be re
moved and placed nearer to the Sun, and revolve
for inftance in the Orbit of *Mercury* ; there the
whole Ocean would even boil with extremity of
Heat, and be all exhaled into Vapors ; all Plants
and Animals would be fcorched and confumed in
that fiery Furnace.   But fuppofe the Earth fhould
be carried to the great Diftance of *Saturn* ; there
the whole Globe would be one *Frigid Zone*, the
deepeft Seas under the very Equator would be
frozen to the bottom ;   there would be no Life,
no Germination ; nor any thing that comes now
under our knowledge or fenfes.   It was much better therefore, that the Earth fhould move where
it does, than in a much greater or lefs Interval
from the body of the Sun.   And if you place it at
any

Newton
ibidem,
p. 415.

any other Diftance, either lefs or more than *Sa-turn* or *Mercury*; you will ftill alter it for the worfe proportionally to the Change. It was fituated therefore where it is, by the Wifdom of fome voluntary Agent ; and not by the blind motions of Fortune or Fate. If any one fhall think with himfelf, How then can any thing live in *Mercury* and *Saturn* in fuch intenfe degrees of Heat and Cold? Let him only confider, that the Matter of each Planet may have a different denfity and texture and form, which will difpofe and qualifie it to be acted on by greater or lefs degrees of Heat according to their feveral Situations ; and that the Laws of Vegetation and Life and Suftenance and Propagation are the arbitrary pleafure of God, and may vary in all Planets according to the Divine Appointment and the Exigencies of Things, in manners incomprehenfible to our Imaginations. 'Tis enough for our purpofe, to difcern the tokens of Wifdom in the placing of our Earth ; if its prefent conftitution would be fpoil'd and deftroy'd, if we could not wear Flefh and Blood, if we could not have Human Nature at thofe different Diftances.

V. We have all learnt from the Doctrine of the Sphere, that the Earth revolves with a double motion. For while it is carried around the Sun in the *Orbis Magnus* once a year, it perpetually wheels about

Origin and Frame of the World. 17

about its own Axis once in a day and a night: fo that in 24 hours fpace it hath turn'd all the parts of the Equinoctial to the rayes of the Sun. Now the Ufes of this vertiginous motion are very confpicuous; for this is it, that gives Day and Night fucceffively over the face of the whole Earth, and makes it habitable all around: without this Diurnal Rotation one Hemifphere would lye dead and torpid in perpetual Darknefs and Froft, and the beft part of the Other would be burnt up and depopulated by fo permanent a Heat. It is better therefore, that the Earth fhould move about its own Center, and make thefe ufefull Viciffitudes of Night and Day, than expofe always the fame fide to the action of the Sun. But how came it to be fo moved? not from any neceffity of the Laws of Motion or the Syftem of the Heavens. It might annually have compaffed the Sun, and yet never have once turned upon its own Axis. This is matter of Fact and Experiment in the motion of the Moon; which is carried about the Earth in the very fame manner as the Earth about the Sun, and yet always fhews the fame face to Us, not once wheeling upon her own Center. She indeed, notwithftanding this, turns all her globe to the Sun by moving in her menftrual Orb, and enjoys Night and Day alternately, one day of Hers being equal to about 14 Days

and

and Nights of Ours. But fhould the Earth be deprived of its Diurnal Motion; one half of it could never fee the Day, but muft eternally be condemned to Solitude and Darknefs. That the Earth therefore revolves about its own Center, is another eminent token of the Divine Wifdom and Goodnefs.

VI. But let us compare the mutual proportion of thefe Diurnal and Annual Revolutions ; for they are diftinct from one another, and have a different degree of Velocity. The Earth rowls once about its Axis in a natural day : in which time all the parts of the Equator move fomething more than 3 of the Earths Diameters ; which makes about 1100 in the fpace of a year. But within the fame annual time the Center of the Earth is carried above 50 times as far once round the *Orbis Magnus*, whofe widenefs we now affume to be 20000 Terreftrial Diameters. So that the annual motion is more than 50 times fwifter than the Diurnal Rotation, though we meafure the latter from the Equator, where the Celerity is the greateft. But it muft needs be acknowledged, since the Earth revolves not upon a material and rugged but a geometrical Plane, that their proportions may be varied in innumerable degrees ; any of which might have happen'd as probably as the prefent. What was it then that prefcribed this

Tacquet de Circulorum volutionibus.

Origin and Frame of the World.   19

this particular Celerity to each Motion, this proportion and temperament between them both?
Let us examin it by our former Rule : if there be
any *Meliority* in the prefent conftitution ; if any
confiderable Change would be for the worfe. We
will fuppofe then, that the *Annual* Motion is accelerated doubly ; fo that a periodical Revolution
would be performed in 6 Months. Such a Change
would be pernicious ; not only becaufe the Earth
could not move in a Circular Orb, which we have
confider'd before ; but becaufe the Seafons being
then twice as fhort as they are now, the cold Winter would overtake us, before our Corn and Fruits
could poffibly be ripe.   But fhall this Motion be
as much retarded, and the Seafons lengthen'd in
the fame proportion? This too would be as fa-
tal as the other : for in moft Countries the Earth
would be fo parched and effete by the drought of
the Summer, that it would afford ftill but one
Harveft, as it doth at the prefent : which then
would not be a fufficient ftore for the confumpti-
on of a double Year. But let us fuppofe, that the
Diurnal Rotation is either confiderably fwifter or
flower.   And firft let it be retarded ; fo as to
make (for example) but 12 Circuits in a year :
then every day and night would be as long as
Fifteen are now, not fo fitly proportion'd neither
to the common affairs of Life, nor to the exigen-

cies of Sleep and Suſtenance in a conſtitution of
Fleſh and Blood.   But let it then be accelerated;
and wheel a thouſand times about its Center,
while the Center deſcribes one circle about the
Sun : then an Equinoctial day would conſiſt but
of four Hours, which would be an inconvenient
Change to the inhabitants of the Earth; ſuch
haſty Nights as thoſe would give very unwelcome
interruptions to our Labours and Journeys and
other Tranſactions of the World.   It is *better*
therefore, that the Diurnal and Annual Motions
ſhould be ſo proportion'd as they are.   Let it
therefore be aſcribed to the tranſcendent Wiſdom
and Benignity of that God, *who hath made all things*
very good, and loveth all things that he hath made.

VII. But let us conſider not the Quantity and
Proportion only but the Mode alſo of this Diurnal Motion.   You muſt conceive an imaginary
Plane, which paſſing through the Centers of the
Sun and the Earth extends it ſelf on all ſides as
far as the Firmament : this Plane is called the E-
cliptic; and in this the Center of the Earth is
perpetually carried without any deviation.   But
then the Axis of the Earth, about which its Diurnal Rotation is made, is not erect to this Plane of
the Ecliptick, but inclines toward it from the Per-
pendiculum in an Angle of 2 3 degrees and a half.
Now why is the Axis of the Earth in this particular

Origin and Frame of the World.

cular pofture, rather than any other? did it happen by Chance, or proceed from Defign? To
determin this queftion, let us fee, as we have done
before, if This be more beneficial to us, than any
other Conftitution. We all know from the very
Elements of Aftronomy, that this inclined Pofition
of the Axis, which keeps always the fame Direction and a conftant Parallelifm to it felf, is the fole
caufe of thefe gratefull and needfull Viciffitudes of
the four Seafons of the Year, and the Variation in
length of Days. If we take away the *Inclination*;
it would abfolutely undo thefe Northern Nations;
the Sun would never come nearer us, than he
doth now on the tenth of *March* or the twelfth of
September. But would we rather part with the *Parallelifm?* Let us fuppofe then that the Axis of the
Earth keeps always the fame inclination toward
the body of the Sun: this indeed would caufe a
variety of Days and Nights and Seafons on the
Earth; but then every particular Country would
have always the fame diverfity of Day and Night
and the fame conftitution of Seafon without any
alternation: fome would always have long Nights
and fhort Days, others again perpetually long
Days and fhort Nights: one Climate would be
fcorched and fwelter'd with everlafting Dog-days;
while an eternal *December* blafted another. This
furely is not quite fo good as the prefent Order
of

of Seafons. But fhall the Axis rather obferve no conftant inclination to any thing, but vary and waver at uncertain times and places? This would be a happy Conftitution indeed. There could be no health, no life nor fubfiftence in fuch an irregular Syftem; by thofe furprizing Nods of the Pole we might be toffed backward or forward from *January* to *June*, nay poffibly from the *January* of *Greenland* to the *June* of *Abeffinia*. It is *better* therefore upon all accounts that the Axis fhould be continued in its prefent pofture and direction: fo that This alfo is a fignal Character of Divine Wifdom and Goodnefs.

But becaufe feveral have imagin'd, that this skue pofture of the Axis is a moft unfortunate and pernicious thing; that if the Poles had been erect to the Plane of the Ecliptic, all mankind would have enjoyed a very Paradife upon Earth; a perpetual Spring, an eternal Calm and Serenity, and the Longævity of *Methufelah* without pains or difeafes; we are obliged to confider it a little further. And firft as to the *Univerfal and Perpetual Spring*, 'tis a mere Poetical Fancy, and (bating the equality of Days and Nights, a thing of fmall value) as to the other properties is naturally impoffible, being repugnant to the very form of the Globe. For to thofe People that dwell under or near the Æquator, this Spring would be a moft peftilent and

Origin and Frame of the World.   23

and infupportable Summer; and as for thofe Countries that are nearer the Poles, in which number are our own and the moft confiderable Nations of the World, a Perpetual Spring will not do their bufinefs; they muft have longer Days, a nearer approach of the Sun, and a lefs Obliquity of his Rayes; they muft have a Summer and a Harveft-time too to ripen their Grain and Fruits and Vines, or elfe they muft bid an eternal adieu to the very beft of their fuftenance. For it is plain, that the Center of the Earth muft move all along in the *Orbis Magnus*; whether we fuppofe a Perpetual Æquinox, or an oblique Pofition of the Axis. So that the whole Globe would continue in the fame Diftance from the Sun, and receive the fame quantity of Heat from him in a Year or any affignable time, in either Hypothefis. Though the Axis then had been perpendicular; yet take the whole Year about, and we fhould have had the fame meafure of Heat, that we have now. So that here lies the queftion; Whether is more beneficial, that we fhould have the fame Yearly quantity of Heat diftributed equally every day, or fo difpofed as it is, a greater fhare of it in Summer and in Winter a lefs? It muft needs be allowed, that we have no Heat to fpare in Summer; 'tis very well if it be fufficient for the maturation of Fruits. Now this being granted; 'tis as certain and manifeft, that

an

an even diftribution of the fameYearly Heat would
never have brought thofe Fruits to maturity, as
this is a known and familiar experiment, That
fuch a quantity of Fewel all kindled at once will
caufe Water to boil, which being lighted gradually and fucceffively will never be able to do it. It
is clear therefore, that in the conftitution of a Perpetual Æquinox the beft part of the Globe would
be defolate and ufelefs : and as to that little that
could be inhabited, there is no reafon to expect,
that it would conftantly enjoy that admired *Calm
and Serenity*. If the affertion were true; yet fome
perhaps may think, that fuch a Felicity, as would
make Navigation impoffible, is not much to be
envied. But it's altogether precarious, and has no
neceffary foundation neither upon Reafon nor Experience. For the Winds and Rains and other affections of the Atmofphere do not folely depend
(as that affertion fuppofeth) upon the courfe of
the Sun; but partly and perhaps moft frequently
upon Steams and Exhalations from fubterraneous
Heat, upon the Pofitions of the Moon, the Situations of Seas or Mountains or Lakes or Woods,
and many other unknown or uncertain Caufes.
So that, though the Courfe of the Sun fhould be
invariable, and never fwerve from the Equator;
yet the temperament of the Air would be mutable neverthelefs, according to the abfence or prefence

Origin and Frame of the World.   25

fence or various mixture of the other Caufes. The ancient Philofophers for many ages together unanimoufly taught, that the Torrid Zone was not habitable. The reafons that they went upon were very fpecious and probable; till the experience of thefe latter ages evinced them to be erroneous. They argued from cœleftial Caufes only, the conftant Vicinity of the Sun and the directnefs of his Rayes; never fufpecting, that the Body of the Earth had fo great an efficiency in the changes of the Air; and that then could be the coldeft and rainieft feafon, the Winter of the Year, when the Sun was the neareft of all, and fteer'd directly over mens heads. Which is warning fufficient to have deterred any man from expecting fuch eternal Serenity and Halcyon-days from fo incompetent and partial a Caufe, as the conftant Courfe of the Sun in the Æquinoctial Circle. What general condition and temperament of Air would follow upon that Suppofition, we cannot poffibly define ; for 'tis not caufed by certain and regular Motions, nor fubject to Mathematical Calculations. But if we may make a conjecture from the prefent Conftitution; we fhall hardly wifh for a Perpetual Æquinox to fave the charges of Weatherglaffes : for 'tis very well known, that the Months of *March* and *September,* the two Æquinoxes of Our year, are the moft windy and tempeftuons,

D

the

the most unsettled and unequable of Seasons in
most Countries of the World.   Now if this notion of an uniform Calm and Serenity be false or
precarious; then even the last supposed advantage,
the *constant Health and Longævity* of Men must be
given up also, as a groundless conceit: for this (according to the Assertors themselves) doth solely,
as an effect of Nature, depend upon the other.
Nay further, though we should allow them their
Perpetual Calm and Æquability of Heat ; they
will never be able to prove, that therefore Men
would be so vivacious as they would have us believe.   Nay perhaps the contrary may be inferr'd,
if we may argue from the present experience : For
the Inhabitants of the Torrid Zone, who suffer
the least and shortest recesses of the Sun, and are
within one step and degree of a Perpetual Æquinox, are not only shorter lived (generally speaking) than other Nations nearer the Poles; but inferior to them in Strength and Stature and Courage, and in all the capacities of the Mind.   It
appears therefore, that the gradual Vicissitudes of
Heat and Cold are so far from shortning the
thread of man's Life, or impairing his intellectual
Faculties ; that very probably they both prolong
the one in some measure and exalt and advance
the other.   So that still we do profess to adore
the Divine Wisdom and Goodness for this variety

Origin and Frame of the World.   27

riety of Seafons, for *Seed-time and harveft, and cold* Gen. 8. *and heat, and fummer and winter.*

VIII. Come we now to confider the Atmof-phere, and the exterior Frame and Face of the Globe; if we may find any tracks and footfteps of Wifdom in the Conftitution of Them. I need not now inform you, that the Air is a thin fluid Body, endued with Elafticity or Springinefs, and capable of Condenfation and Rarefaction. Neither Can you be ignorant, that if the Air See Mr. fhould be much more expanded or condenfed the Air. *Boyle* of than it naturally is, no Animals could live and breath: it is probable alfo, that the Vapors could not be duly raifed and fupported in it; which at once would deprive the Earth of all its ornament and glory, of all its living Inhabitants and Vege-tables too. But 'tis certainly known and demon-ftrated, that the Condenfation and Expanfion of any portion of the Air, is always proportional to the weight and preffure incumbent upon it: fo that if the Atmofphere had been either much grea-ter or lefs than it is, as it might eafily have been, it would have had in its loweft region on the Surface of the Earth a much greater denfity or tenuity of texture; and confequently have been unferviceable for Vegetation and Life. It muft needs therefore be an Intelligent Being that could fo juftly adapt it to thofe excellent purpofes. 'Tis

D 2

con-

concluded by Aftronomers, that the Atmofphere
of the Moon hath no Clouds nor Rains, but a
perpetual and uniform ferenity : becaufe nothing
difcoverable in the Lunar Surface is ever covered and abfconded by the interpofition of any
clouds or mifts, but fuch as rife from our own
Globe. Now if the Atmofphere of Our Earth
had been of fuch a Conftitution ; there could nothing, that now grows or breaths in it have been
formed or preferved ; Human Nature muft have
been quite obliterated out of the Works of the Creation. If our Air had not been a fpringy elafti-
cal Body, no Animal could have exercifed the
very function of Refpiration : and yet the ends
and ufes of Refpiration are not ferved by that
Springinefs, but by fome other unknown and fingular Quality.   For the Air, that in exhaufted Re-
ceivers of Air-pumps is exhaled from Minerals
and Flefh and Fruits and Liquors, is as true and
genuine as to Elafticity and Denfity or Rarefaction, as that we refpire in : and yet this factitious
Air is fo far from being fit to be breathed in, that
it kills Animals in a moment, even fooner than
the very abfence of all Air, than a Vacuum it felf.
All which do inferr the moft admirable Providence of the Author of Nature ; who foreknew
the neceffity of Rains and Dews to the prefent
ftructure of Plants, and the ufes of Refpiration

to

Mr. Boyle's Second Continuation of Phyfico-mechanical Exp. about the Air.

Origin and Frame of the World.   29

to Animals; and therefore created thofe corre-
fpondent properties in the Atmofphere of the
Earth.

IX. In the next place let us confider the ample provifion of Waters, thofe inexhaufted Treafures of the Ocean: and though fome have grudg-
ed the great fhare that it takes of the Surface of
the Earth, yet we fhall propofe this too, as a confpicuous mark and character of the Wifdom of
God. For that we may not now fay, that the
vaft *Atlantick* Ocean is really greater Riches and
of more worth to the World, than if it was changed into a fifth Continent ; and that the Dry
Land is as yet much too big for its Inhabitants ;
and that before they fhall want Room by increafing and multiplying, there may be *new Heavens
and a new Earth:* We dare venture to affirm, that
thefe copious Stores of Waters are no more than
neceffary for the prefent conftitution of our Globe.
For is not the whole Subftance of all Vegetables
mere modified Water ? and confequently of all
Animals too ; all which either feed upon Vegetables or prey upon one another ? Is not an immenfe quantity of it continually exhaled by the
Sun, to fill the Atmofphere with Vapors and
Clouds, and feed the Plants of the Earth with the
balm of Dews and the fatnefs of Showrs ? It
feems incredible at firft hearing, that all the Blood

Lucret.
Et mare,
quod late
terrarum
diftinet o-
ras.

in

in our Bodies fhould circulate in a trice, in a very few minutes : but I believe it would be more
furprizing, if we knew the fhort and fwift periods
of the great Circulation of Water, that vital Blood
of the Earth which compofeth and nourifheth all
things.   If we could but compute that prodigious Mafs of it, that is daily thrown into the channel of the Sea from all the Rivers of the World :
we fhould then know and admire how much is
perpetually evaporated and caft again upon the
Continents to fupply thofe innumerable Streams.
And indeed hence we may difcover not only the
Ufe and *Neceffity* but the *Caufe* too of the vaft-
nefs of the Ocean.   I never yet heard of any
Nation, that complained they had too broad or
too deep or too many Rivers, or wifhed they
were either fmaller or fewer : they underftand
better than fo, how to value and efteem thofe
ineftimable gifts of Nature.   Now fuppofing
that the multitude and largenefs of Rivers ought
to continue as great as now ; we can eafily prove,
that the extent of the Ocean could be no lefs than
it is.   For it's evident and neceffary, if we follow
the moft fair and probable Hypothefis, that the
Origin of Fountains is from Vapors and Rain, that
the Receptacle of Waters, into which the mouths
of all thofe Rivers muft empty themfelves, ought
to have fo fpacious a Surface, that as much Water
may

Origin and Frame of the World.   31

may be continually brufhed off by the Winds and
exhaled by the Sun, as (befides what falls again
in Showers upon its own Surface) is brought into
it by all the Rivers.   Now the Surface of the O-
cean is juft fo wide and no wider : for if more
was evaporated than returns into it again, the Sea
would become lefs; if lefs was evaporated, it
would grow bigger. So that, becaufe fince the memory of all ages it hath continu'd at a ftand without
confiderable variation,   and if it hath gain'd ground
upon one Country, hath loft as much in another;
it muft confequently be exactly proportioned to
the prefent conftitution of Rivers. How rafh therefore and vain are thofe bufy Projectors in Speculation, that imagin they could recover to the World
many new and noble Countries, in the moft
happy and temperate Climates, without any da-
mage to the old ones, could this fame Mafs of
the Ocean be lodged and circumfcribed in a much
deeper Channel and within narrower Shores !
For by how much they would diminifh the prefent extent of the Sea, fo much they would impair the Fertility and Fountains and Rivers of the
Earth: becaufe the quantity of Vapors, that muft
be exhaled to fupply all thefe, would be leffened
proportionally to the bounds of the Ocean ; for
the Vapors are not to be meafured from the bulk
of the Water but from the fpace of the Surface. So
that

32   *A Confutation of Atheiſm from the*

that this alſo doth inferr the ſuperlative Wiſdom
and Goodneſs of God, that he hath treaſured up
the Waters in ſo deep and ſpacious a Storehouſe, *the*
place that he hath founded and appointed for them.

Pſal. 104.

Nequaquam nobis divinitus eſſe creatam
Naturam rerum, tanta ſtat prædita culpa.
Principio, quantum cœli tegit impetus ingens,
Inde avidam partem montes Sylvæq; ferarum
Poſſedere, tenent rupes, vaſtæq; paludes,
Et mare, quod late terrarum diſtinet oras.
　　Lucret *lib.* 5.

X. But ſome men are
out of Love with the fea-
tures and meen of our Earth;
they do not like this rugged
and irregular Surface, theſe
Precipices and Valleys and the gaping Channel of
the Ocean.   This with them is Deformity, and
rather carries the face of a Ruin or a rude and
indigeſted Lump of Atoms that caſually convened ſo, than a Work of Divine Artifice.   They
would have the vaſt Body of a Planet to be as
elegant and round as a factitious Globe repreſents
it; to be every where ſmooth and equable, and
as plain as the *Elyſian Fields.*   Let us examin, what
weighty reaſons they have to diſparage the preſent
conſtitution of Nature in ſo injurious a manner.
Why, if we ſuppoſe the Ocean to be dry, and
that we look down upon the empty Channel from
ſome higher Region of the Air, how horrid and
ghaſtly and unnatural would it look? Now admitting this Suppoſition; Let us ſuppoſe too that the
Soil of this dry Channel is covered with Graſs and
Trees in manner of the Continent, and then ſee
what would follow.   If a man could be carried
aſleep

Origin and Frame of the World.   33

afleep and placed in the very middle of this dry
Ocean; it muft be allowed, that he could not diftinguifh it from the inhabited Earth; for if the
bottom fhould be unequal with Shelves and Rocks
and Precipices and Gulfs; thefe being now appa-
rel'd with a vefture of Plants, would only refem-
ble the Mountains and Valleys that he was accuf-
tomed to before; but very probably he would
wake in a large and fmooth Plain: for though
the bottom of the Sea were gradually inclin'd and
floping from the Shore to the middle: yet the
additional Acclivity, above what a Level would
feem to have, would be imperceptible in fo fhort
a profpect as he could take of it. So that to
make this Man fenfible what a deep Cavity he
was placed in; he muft be carried fo high in the
Air, till he could fee at one view the whole Breadth
of the Channel, and fo compare the depreffion
of the Middle with the elevation of the Banks.
But then a very fmall skill in Mathematicks is
enough to inftruct us, that before he could arrive
to that diftance from the Earth, all the inequality
of Surface would be loft to his View: the wide
Ocean would appear to him like an even and
uniform Plane (uniform as to its Level, though
not as to Light and Shade) though every Rock of
the Sea was as high as the *Pico* of *Teneriff*. But
though we fhould grant, that the dry Gulf of the

E   Ocean

34   *A Confutation of Atheiſm from the*

Ocean would appear vaſtly hollow and horrible
from the top of a high Cloud: yet what a way
of reaſoning is this from the freaks of Imagination, and impoſſible Suppoſitions? Is the Sea ever
likely to be evaporated by the Sun, or to be
emptied with Buckets? Why then muſt we fancy
this impoſſible dryneſs; and then upon that ficti-
tious account calumniate Nature, as deformed
and ruinous and unworthy of a Divine Author?
Is there then any phyſical deformity in the Fabric
of a Human Body; becauſe our Imagination can
ſtrip it of its Muſcles and Skin, and ſhew us the
ſcragged and knotty Backbone, the gaping and
ghaſtly Jaws, and all the Sceleton underneath?
We have ſhewed before, that the Sea could not be
much narrower than it is, without a great loſs to
the World: and muſt we now have an Ocean of
mere Flats and Shallows, to the utter ruin of Navigation; for fear our heads ſhould turn giddy
at the imagination of gaping Abyſſes and unfa-
thomable Gulfs? But however the Sea-ſhores at
leaſt ſhould have been even and uniform, not
crooked and broken as they are into innumerable
Angles and Creeks and In-lets and Bays, without
Beauty or Order, which carry the Marks more
of Chance and Contuſion, than of the production
of a wiſe Creator. This would be a fine bargain
indeed; to part with all our commodious Ports
                                                    and

and Harbours, which the greater the In-let is, are fo much the better, for the imaginary pleafure of an open and ftreight Shore without any retreat or fhelter from the Winds; which would make the Sea of no ufe at all as to Navigation and Commerce. But what apology can we make for the horrid deformity of Rocks and Crags, of naked and broken Cliffs, of long Ridges, of barren Mountains; in the convenienteft Latitudes for Habitation and Fertility, could thofe rude heaps of Rubbifh and Ruins be removed out of the way? We have one general and fufficient anfwer for all feeming defects or diforders in the conftitution of Land or Sea; that we do not contend to have the Earth pafs for a Paradife, or to make a very Heaven of our Globe, we reckon it only as the Land of our *peregrination,* and afpire after *a better,* Heb. 11. *and a cœleftial Country.* 'Tis enough, if it be fo framed and conftituted, that by a carefull Contemplation of it we have great reafon to acknowledge and adore the Divine Wifdom and Benignity of its Author. But to wave this general Reply; let the Objectors confider, that thefe fuppofed irregularities muft have neceffarily come to pafs from the eftablifh'd Laws of Mechanifm and the ordinary courfe of Nature. For fuppofing the Exiftence of Sea and Mountains; if the Banks of that Sea muft never be jagged and torn by the

impe-

impetuous affaults or the filent underminings of
Waves ; if violent Rains and Tempefts muft not
wafh down the Earth and Gravel from the tops
of fome of thofe Mountains, and expofe their naked Ribbs to the face of the Sun ; if the Seeds of
fubterraneous Minerals muft not ferment, and
fometimes caufe Earthquakes and furious erupti-
ons of *Volcano's*, and tumble down broken Rocks,
and lay them in confufion : then either all things
muft have been over-ruled miraculoufly by the
immediate interpofition of God without any mechanical Affections or fettled Laws of Nature, or
elfe the body of the Earth muft have been as fixed
as Gold or as hard as Adamant and wholly unfit
for Our habitation.   So that if it *was good* in the
fight of God, that the prefent Plants and Animals,
and Human Souls united to Flefh and Blood
fhould be upon this Earth under a fettled conftitution of Nature : thefe fuppofed Inconveniences,
as they were forefeen and permitted by the Author
of that Nature, as neceffary confequences of
fuch a conftitution ; fo they cannot inferr the leaft
imperfection in his Wifdom and Goodnefs. And
to murmure at them is as unreafonable, as to
complain that he hath made us Men and not Angels, that he hath placed us upon this Planet, and
not upon fome other in this or another Syftem
which may be thought better than Ours. Let them
                                                    alfo

Gen. 1.

Origin and Frame of the World.   37

alfo confider, that this objected Deformity is in our Imaginations only, and not really in the Things themfelves. There is no Univerfal Reafon (I mean fuch as is not confined to Human Fancy, but will reach through the whole Intellectual Univerfe) that a Figure by us called Regular, which hath equal Sides and Angles, is abfolutely more beautifull than any irregular one. All Pulchritude is relative; and all Bodies are truly and phyfically beautifull under all poffible Shapes and Proportions; that are good in their Kind, that are fit for their proper ufes and ends of their Natures. We ought not then to believe, that the Banks of the Ocean are really deformed, becaufe they have not the form of a regular Bulwark; nor that the Mountains are mifhapen, becaufe they are not exact Pyramids or Cones; nor that the Starrs are unskilfully placed, becaufe they are not all fituated at uniform diftances. Thefe are not Natural Irregularities, but with refpect to our Fancies only; nor are they incommodious to the true Ufes of Life and the Defigns of Man's Being on the Earth. Let them confider, that thefe Ranges of barren Mountains by condenfing the Vapors and producing Rains and Fountains and Rivers, give the very Plains and Valleys themfelves that Fertility they boaft of. Let them confider, that thofe Hills
and

and Mountains fupply Us and the Stock of Nature with a great variety of excellent Plants. If there were no inequalities in the Surface of the Earth, nor in the Seafons of the Year; we fhould lofe a confiderable fhare of the Vegetable Kingdom : for all Plants will not grow in an uniform Level and the fame temper of Soil, nor with the fame degree of Heat. Let them confider, that to thofe Hills and Mountains we are obliged for all our Metals, and with them for all the conveniencies and comforts of Life. To deprive us of Metals is to make us mere Savages; to change our Corn or Rice for the old *Arcadian* Diet, our Houfes and Cities for Dens and Caves, and our Cloathing for Skins of Beafts : 'tis to bereave us of all Arts and Sciences, of Hiftory and Letters, nay of Revealed Religion too that ineftimable favour of Heaven, by making the whole Gofpel a mere Tradition and old Cabala without certainty, without authority. Who would part with thefe Solid and Subftantial Bleffings for the little fantaftical pleafantnefs of a fmooth uniform Convexity and Rotundity of a Globe? And yet the misfortune of it is, that the pleafant View of this imaginary Globe, as well as the deformed Spectacle of the true one, is founded upon impoffible Suppofitions. For this equal Convexity could never be feen and enjoyed by any

man

Origin and Frame of the World.   39

man living. The Inhabitants of fuch an Earth could have only the fhort profpect of a little Circular Plane about three Miles around them; tho' neither Woods nor Hedges nor artificial Banks fhould intercept it: which little too would appear to have an Acclivity on all fides from the Spectators; fo that every man would have the Satisfaction of fancying himfelf the loweft, and that he always dwelt and moved in a Bottom. Nay, confidering that in fuch a conftitution of the Earth they could have no means nor inftruments of Mathematical Knowledg; there is great reafon to believe, that the period of the final Diffolution might overtake them, ere they would have known or had any Sufpicion that they walked upon a round Ball. Muft we therefore, to make this Convexity of the Earth difcernible to the Eye, fuppofe a man to be lifted up a great hight in the Air, that he may have a very fpacious Horizon under one View? But then again, becaufe of the diftance, the convexity and gibboufnefs would vanifh away; he would only fee below him a great circular Flat, as level to his thinking as the face of the Moon. Are there then fuch ravifhing Charms in a dull unvaried Flat, to make a fufficient compenfation *for the chief things of the an-* Deut. 33. *cient Mountains, and for the precious things of the laft-* 15. *ing Hills?* Nay we appeal to the fentence of Mankind;

40 *A Confutation of Atheism from the*

kind ; if *a land of Hills and Valleys* with an infinite Variety of Scenes and Profpects, befides the Profit that accrues from it, have not more of Beauty too and Pleafantnefs than a wide uniform Plain; which if ever it may be faid to be very delightfull, is then only, when 'tis viewed from the top of a Hill. What *vide Æli-* were the *Tempe* of *Theffaly*, fo celebrated in ancient *an. var.* *Hift. lib.* ftory for their unparallelled pleafantnefs, but a Vale **III.** divided with a River & terminated with Hills ? Are not all the defcriptions of Poets embellifh'd with fuch Ideas, when they would reprefent any places of fuperlative Delight, and blisfull Seats of the Mu- fes or the Nymphs, any facred habitations of Gods or Goddeffes? They will never admit that a wide Flat can be pleafant, no not in the very *Elyfian Fields* *; but thofe too

* Virg. Æn. 6. *At pater Anchifes penitus convalle virenti.* & ibid. *Hoc fuperate jugum.* & ib. *Et tumulum cœpit.*

muft be diverfified with depreffed Valleys and fwelling Afcents.

† Flours worthy of Paradife, which not nice Art In Beds and curious Knots, but Nature boon Powr'd forth profufe on Hill and Dale and Plain. *Paradife Loft, lib.* 4.

They cannot imagin even † Paradife to be a place of Pleafure nor

‖ For Earth hath this variety from Heaven Of Pleafure fituate in Hill and Dale. *Ibid. lib.* 6.

Heaven it felf to be ‖ Heaven without them.

Let this therefore be another Argument of the Divine Wifdom & Good- nefs, that the Surface of the Earth is not uniformly Convex (as many think it would naturally have been, if mechanically formed by a Chaos) but di- ftinguifhed

Origin and Frame of the World.   41

ftinguifhed with Mountains and Valleys, and furrowed from Pole to Pole with the Deep Channel of the Sea ; and that becaufe of the τὸ βέλτιον, it is better that it fhould be fo.

Give me leave to make one fhort Inference from what has been faid, which fhall finifh this prefent Difcourfe, and with it our Task for the Year. We have clearly difcovered many Final Caufes and Characters of Wifdom and Contrivance in the Frame of the inanimate World; as well as in the Organical Fabrick of the Bodies of Animals. Now from hence arifeth a new and invincible Argument, that the prefent Frame of the World hath not exifted from all Eternity. For fuch an ufefulnefs of things or a fitnefs of means to Ends, as neither proceeds from the neceffity of their Beings, nor can happen to them by Chance, doth neceffarily inferr. that there was an Intelligent Being, which was the Author and Contriver of that Ufefulnefs. We have formerly demonftrated, that the Body of a Man, Serm. 5 which confifts of an incomprehenfible variety of Parts all admirably fitted for their peculiar Functions and the Confervation of the Whole, could no more be formed fortuitoufly ; than the *Æneis* of *Virgil* or any other long Poem with good Senfe and juft Meafures could be compofed by

F   the

42   *A Confutation of Atheiſm*, &c.

the Caſual Combinations of Letters. Now to purſue this Compariſon; as it is utterly impoſſible to be believed, that ſuch a Poem may have been eternal, tranſcribed from Copy to Copy without any firſt Author and Original: ſo it is equally incredible and impoſſible, that the Fabrick of Human Bodies, which hath ſuch excellent and Divine Artifice, and if I may ſo ſay, ſuch good Senſe and true Syntax and harmonious Meaſures in its Conſtitution, ſhould be propagated and tranſcribed from Father to Son without a firſt Parent and Creator of it. An eternal uſefulneſs of Things, an eternal Good Senſe, cannot poſſibly be conceived without an eternal Wiſdom and Underſtanding. But that can be no other than that eternal and omnipotent God; *that by Wiſdom hath*

Prov. 3. *founded the Earth, and by Underſtanding hath eſtabliſhed the Heavens*: To whom be all Honour and Glory and Praiſe and Adoration from henceforth and for evermore. *AMEN.*

F I N I S.

V.

Halley and the *Principia*

Halley and the *Principia*

ROBERT E. SCHOFIELD

The association of Edmond Halley and Isaac Newton was long and happy, both for them and for us. From 1684 until Newton's death, Halley seems to have participated in some way in every one of the important developments of Newton's career. In addition to the major role that Halley played in the publication of the *Principia*, we find his name associated with Newton's in connection with the Mint, the *Opticks*, the administration of the Royal Society, and even Newton's work on Biblical chronology. From Brewster, we gather that Halley was involved in the effort to obtain for Newton a position at the Mint.[1] Shortly after Newton began his work as Warden, Halley also began a period of service at the Mint and, from 1696, for two years was Deputy Comptroller of the Mint at Chester, one of five branch mints set up to facilitate the recoinage that took place during the reign of William III. Halley left that position in 1698, when the branch mints were broken up, to sail as Master of H.M.S. *Paramour Pink* on a scientific expedition to study the variation of magnetic declination in various parts of the

[1] Sir David Brewster, *Memoirs of the Life, Writings, and Discoveries of Sir Isaac Newton* (Edinburgh, 1855), vol. 2, pp. 190–192.

world. When Newton presented a copy of the *Opticks* to the Royal Society in 1704, it was Halley who "was desired to peruse it and give an abstract of it" to the Society.[2] Newton was president of the Royal Society from 1703 to his death in 1727. For eight years of that presidency (1713–1721), Halley was one of the Secretaries of the Royal Society and was editor and publisher of the *Philosophical Transactions* from 1714 to 1719 (he had earlier been editor-publisher of the *Phil. Trans.* from 1685 to 1692). He appears to have been almost as jealous of Newton's reputation as Newton himself, and in 1727, shortly after Newton's death, when an article appeared questioning Newton's chronology, Halley even undertook a partial defense of that, explaining and, in some measure, attempting to justify the method by which Newton had arrived at the dates in question.[3]

The frequently told story of our debt to Halley for promoting the publication of the *Principia* cannot better be epitomized than in the statements Newton made in his Preface signed May 8, 1686:

> In the publication of this work the most acute and universally learned Mr. *Edmund Halley* not only assisted me in correcting the errors of the press and preparing the geometrical figures, but it was through his solicitations that it came to be published; for when he had obtained of me my demonstrations of the figure of the celestial orbits, he continually pressed me to communicate the same to the *Royal Society,* who afterwards, by their kind encouragement and entreaties, engaged me to think of publishing them.[4]

From August 1684, when Halley visited Newton at Cambridge and encouraged the work that resulted in the *Principia,* through the period before the presentation of the first book to the Royal So-

[2] Quoted from the Journal book of the Royal Society, 16th February 1703/4, by Isaac Weld, *A History of the Royal Society* (London, 1848), vol. 1, p. 375.

[3] *Phil. Trans. 34,* p. 205 (1727).

[4] Sir Isaac Newton, *Mathematical Principles of Natural Philosophy . . . ,* Cajori edition of the English translation of Andrew Motte (Berkeley, California, 1947), p. xviii. See also Brewster, *Memoirs,* vol. 1, pp. 296–299, 304–307; and the contemporary and authoritative information supplied by the letter of June 29, 1686 from Halley to Newton, excerpt quoted by Brewster, vol. 1, pp. 446–447; and printed in entirety by W. W. Rouse Ball, *An Essay on Newton's Principia* (London, 1893), pp. 162–163; and by Stephen P. Rigaud, *Historical Essay on the First Publication of Sir Isaac Newton's Principia* (Oxford, 1838), pp. 35–39.

ciety, the discovery that the council of the Royal Society was financially unable to pay for its publication, and Halley's decision to undertake the "business of looking after it, and printing it at his own charge," [5] Halley was almost as important in the publication as was Newton himself. Moreover, not only did Halley pay for the publication, correct the proofs, check the calculations, and work with the printer; it was even necessary for him to persuade Newton to submit a major portion of the work for publication.[6] There is considerable justification for the belief, frequently expressed, that but for Halley the *Principia* would never have been published.

Under the circumstances, it is not unreasonable that Halley should have made the first public announcement of the publication of the *Principia*. This announcement took the form of a book review in the *Philosophical Transactions*. According to Ball, this was the only real book review of the *Principia* to appear at the time, since the other contemporary review, in the *Acta Eruditorum* for June 1688 (pp. 305–315), is and purports to be little more than a synopsis of the contents.[7] That the publisher and, in a sense, editor of the work should be the one to write a review of it may in-

[5] T. Birch, *The History of the Royal Society of London* (London, 1756), vol. 4, p. 486. The finances of the Royal Society appear to have been in serious danger owing to their publication of Willughby's *De historia piscium*. While there seems general agreement that Halley was not ultimately a loser because of his undertaking, in spite of the initial risk involved, there is some disagreement as to Halley's ability, at the time, to afford such a risk. Both Ball, *Essay,* pp. 67–68, and Rigaud, *Historical Essay,* p. 36, seem to feel (in Rigaud's words) that Halley undertook to meet the expense of publishing the *Principia* "precisely at that period of his life when he could least afford it." Sir Henry Lyons, *The Royal Society* (Cambridge, 1944), p. 103, states that Halley was "in fairly comfortable circumstances when he undertook to finance . . . the 'Principia'." Though it is not easy at this point to resolve this difference, some support is given to the opinion of Rigaud and Ball by the fact that a large portion of Halley's income up to 1684 had been an allowance from his father. The death intestate of his father in 1684 instituted a long litigation between Halley and his stepmother over Halley's patrimony, which was not settled until 1693.

[6] Newton had taken offense at some claims to priority made by Hooke and suggested, in a letter to Halley, that the third book, "De Systemate Mundi," be suppressed. This letter, quoted by Rigaud, p. 63, by Ball, pp. 158–159, and by Brewster, vol. 1, pp. 439–445, contains that familiar passage: "Philosophy is such an impertinently litigious lady, that a man had as good be engaged in lawsuits, as have to do with her. I found it so formerly, and now I am no sooner come near her again, but she gives me warning."

[7] Ball, *Essay,* p. 68.

deed seem odd. It is true, however, that next to Newton few other persons were more capable of reviewing a book of that scope—and certainly Halley is not the last reviewer to have an interest, personal or financial, in the success of a book he reviews.[8]

It is not surprising that the publication of the *Principia* should today be regarded as one of the most important events in the history of science. For over two hundred fifty years the work has been tested and, in that time, its real stature has scarcely been reduced. What is perhaps surprising, and is certainly to their credit, is that large numbers of Newton's contemporaries, scientific and not, recognized its importance. While the *Principia* was being written, the Royal Society was kept informed of its progress and frequently expressed its interest. Only the serious depletion of its treasury prevented the Society from financing the publication. Because of the printing laws of the period, a book could not be published without a license and the first edition of the *Principia* bears the imprimatur of Samuel Pepys, as President of the Royal Society.[9] From at least as early as a Star Chamber decree of 1637, the English government had made a formal attempt to control book publishing by a licensing procedure. The Commonwealth adopted its own technics of censorship, but after the Restoration the decree of 1637 was renewed, in substance, by parliament in 1662 (13 and 14 Car. II, c. 33) and again in 1685 (1 Jac. II, c. 8, §15). In spite of the zeal of some of its enforcers, this attempt at control was never wholly effective; books were published and new printers established themselves without regard for the law. But Newton was not the person nor the *Principia* the type of book to publish outside the law. By provision of the act of 1685, the *Principia* could be licensed by the Archbishop of Canterbury, the Bishop of London, the Chancellors or Vice-chancellors of Oxford or Cambridge, or the representatives of any of these. Finally, though not listed in act of 1662 or of 1685, the President, Council, and Fellows of the

[8] Sherman B. Barnes, "The Editing of Early Learned Journals," *Osiris 1,* 160 (1936), note 27, states: "There were instances of authors sending reviews of their own books to editors. Leibniz publicized himself through the journals of the time."

[9] Samuel Pepys, though best known to us as the author of a charming but indiscreet diary, was a highly efficient administrator, secretary to the admiralty, and a dedicated president to the Royal Society for two years, December 1, 1684 to November 30, 1686.

Royal Society could license it by the authority granted them in their charters.[10]

Probably none of the persons legally competent to sign an imprimatur was capable of reading and understanding the full significance of the *Principia,* but, under the circumstances, there is no doubt that the proper authority for licensing it would be the Council and President of the Royal Society. The *Philosophical Transactions* was regularly issued under the imprimatur of the President of the Society and Halley, as publisher of the *Phil. Trans.,* was acquainted with the Royal Society printers, with editing and printing procedures, and with the licensing problems.

There is no indication that any other licensing authority was considered, but we may reasonably ask what would have happened had the Society failed to approve the publication of the *Principia.* Scientific books were licensed and published through trade channels throughout this period, the licensing being done on application of the publisher and usually because he stood responsible for the contents of the book. But English booksellers were notoriously reluctant to publish scientific books of a mathematical nature,[11] and one may reasonably doubt that a trade bookseller would have solicited a publishing license for the *Principia.* Neither Oxford nor Cambridge was interested in books of this sort, and, in any event, the problem of getting an imprimatur outside the Society might well seem to present complications beyond even Halley's enthusiasm. In this sense, one can suggest that, without the approval of a society of men most of whom were probably unable to read and understand it, and the signature of a man who, able as he was in many respects, certainly did not understand it, the publication of the *Principia* might not have been possible.

[10] For the provisions of the licensing acts, see, for example, *The Term Catalogues, 1668–1709 A.D.,* ed. Edward Arber (London, 1903), vol. 1, pp. x ff; *A Transcript of the Registers of the Company of Stationers of London; 1554–1640,* ed. Edward Arber (London, 1875), vol. 1, pp. xvi ff; or any standard work on English printing history, as Henry R. Plomer, *Short History of English Printing* (New York, 1927). For the provisions of the charters of the Royal Society, see, for example, Lyons, *Royal Society,* pp. 329–338.

[11] See A. N. L. Munby, "The Distribution of the First Edition of Newton's *Principia,*" *Notes and Records of the Royal Society of London 10,* 29–31, (1952) for a discussion of this problem.

Indeed, one of the most striking things about the *Principia* is the interest of nonscientists in a book that they could not read. Not that every physical scientist could understand it either; then, as today, there were probably many more scientists who claimed to have read it than there were who actually had, but the book was written in a style that the scientists, at least, were equipped to understand. The *Principia* is an austere book, written in Latin and using the geometrical methods of Apollonius which Newton made obsolete with his invention of fluxions. It was, however, probably less austere to its day than even the English translation is today, for Latin was still the language of science in 1687 and the mathematical tools of geometry had been known to generations of scientists who had yet to learn the fluxions. Because of the substitution of calculus for geometrical methods of analysis, scientists today are almost in the position of the learned nonscientists of the late 17th century and we can sympathize with men who, like Dr. Richard Bentley, were told that they must read upwards of forty books, mostly on geometry, for the "shortest and most proper method for such an end" as to understand the *Principia*.[12] Bentley, it is true, wrote to Newton and got a shorter list of books, instructions that for a "first perusal" it was "enough if you understand the Propositions with some of the Demonstrations which are easier than the rest,"[13] and, as we have seen in the previous section, some letters of specific explanation. This was a course that most nonscientists were not prepared to follow. John Locke wrote to Huygens to find out the soundness of the mathematical demonstrations and, "being told that he might depend upon their certainty; he took them for granted, and carefully examined the Reasonings and Corollaries drawn from them, became Master of all the Physics and was fully convinc'd of all the great Discoveries contained in that Book."[14] For most people, however, knowledge of what the *Principia* contained was acquired through popularizations and simplified extracts from it. Newton, himself, had originally intended to write

[12] Letter of John Craige to Bentley printed in Brewster, *Memoirs*, vol. 1, p. 340, and appendix, pp. 460 ff.

[13] *Ibid*, p. 464.

[14] Desaguliers, *Course of Experimental Philosophy*, 3rd ed. (London, 1763), vol. 1, p. viii.

the third book, "De Systemate Mundi," in a popular style "that it might be read by the many," but had changed his mind.[15] This left a gap which was rapidly filled by numerous authors such as Voltaire, Desaguliers, Pemberton, and others, who wrote books specifically intended, as Pemberton says, "to convey to such, as are not used to mathematical reasoning, some idea of the philosophy of a person, who has acquired an universal reputation, and rendered our nation famous for these speculations in the learned world." [16]

One of the most interesting of these popularizations was that prepared by Halley for James II. The publication of the *Principia* was considered so important that a special meeting was appointed for the purpose of presenting a copy of it to the King.[17] Halley accompanied the presentation with a paper that contained an outline of the book and gave a special explanation of the doctrine of tides. This paper was printed separately and then later reprinted in the *Philosophical Transactions* with the beginning and end omitted. These omissions, not included in the section reproduced below, read as follows:

To King James II.   1687
　　May it please Your most Excellent Majesty.

I could not have presumed to approach Your Majesties Royall presence with a Book of this Nature, had I not been assured, that when the weighty affaires of Your Government permit it; Your Majesty has frequently shown Yourself enclined to favour Mechanicall and Philosophicall discoveries: And I may be bold to say, that if ever Book was worthy the favourable acceptance of a Prince, this, wherein so many and so great discoveries concerning the constitution of the Visible World are made out, and put past dispute, must needs be gratefull to Your Majestie; Being especially the labours of a worthy subject of your own, and a member of the Royall Society founded by Your late Royall

---

[15] Cajori edition of the *Principia*, p. 397. After Newton's death, there was printed *The System of the World demonstrated in an easy and popular manner by the illustrious Sir Isaac Newton* which is included in the Cajori edition and which is described by Rigaud, *Historical Essay*, p. 78, as a translation from the original Latin of the first draft of what formed the third book.

[16] H. Pemberton, *A View of Sir Isaac Newton's Philosophy* (London, 1728), preface.

[17] Newton personally presented a copy of the second edition to Queen Anne in 1713.

Brother for the advancement of Naturall knowledge, and which now flourishes under your Majesties most Gracious Protection.

But being sencible of the little leisure which care of the Publick leaves to Princes, I believed it necessary to present with the Book a short Extract of the matters contained, together with a Specimen thereof, in the genuine Solution of the Cause of the Tides in the Ocean. A thing frequently attempted But till now without success. Whereby Your Majestie may Judge of the rest of the Performances of the Author.

The body of the letter is reproduced in facsimile below.

If by reason of the difficulty of the matter there be anything herein not sufficiently Explained, or if there be any materiall thing observable in the Tides that I have omitted wherein Your Majestie shall desire to be satisfied, I doubt not but if Your Majesty shall please to suffer me to be admitted to the honour of Your Presence, I may be able to give such an account thereof as may be to Your Majesties full content:

I am Great Sir, Your Majesties most Dutifull & obedient Subject

EDMOND HALLEY[18]

Despite the courtly language, there is reason to doubt that James did, or could, take an interest in the *Principia*. Far from having frequently shown himself "enclined to favour Mechanicall and Philosophicall discoveries," James gave little evidence of being interested in science. Although he had become a Fellow of the Royal Society (as Duke of York) on the same occasion that his brother Charles II had signed the Charter book as Patron, there is no indication that he ever attended another meeting of the Society or emulated Charles or his uncle, Prince Rupert, in performing private experiments. One may reasonably suppose that it was the expected lack of understanding, rather than any tribute to interest, that prompted this choice of extract. The only technical interest of James was the Navy, which most likely explains the choice of tides as the subject of Halley's discourse.

[18] Quoted in E. F. MacPike, *Correspondence and Papers of Edmond Halley* (Oxford, 1932), p. 85. I have spelled out the abbreviations. In the Pepysian library, Magdalene College, Cambridge, one may find the diarist's own copy of the first edition of the *Principia;* bound with it is an example of the first printing of Halley's letter, described by A. N. L. Munby, *op. cit.,* p. 33 (with a facsimile of one page of this letter).

[291]

II. *Philofophiæ Naturalis Principia Mathematica, Au-*
tore If. Newton Trin. Coll. Cantab. *Soc. Mathe-*
feos Profeffore Lucafiano, *& Societatis Regalis*
Sodali. 4to. Londini. *Proftat apud plures Biblio-*
polas.

THis incomparable Author having at length been pre-
vailed upon to appear in publick, has in this Treatife given a moft notable inftance of the extent of the powers of the Mind; and has at once fhewn what are the
Principles of Natural Philofophy, and fo far derived from
them their confequences, that he feems to have exhaufted
his Argument, and left little to be done by thofe that fhall
fucceed him.   His great skill in the old and new Geometry, helped by his own improvements of the latter, (I
mean his method of *infinite Series*) has enabled him to
mafter thofe Problems, which for their difficulty would
have ftill lain unrefolved, had one lefs qualified than himfelf attempted them.

This Treatife is divided into three Books, whereof the
two firft are entituled *de Motu Corporum*, the third *de Sy-*
ftemate Mundi.

The firft begins with definitions of the Terms made ufe
of, and diftinguifhes *Time, Space, Place* and *Motion* into
abfolute and relative, real and apparent, Mathematical and vulgar: fhewing the neceffity of fuch diftinction.   To thefe definitions are fubjoyned, the Laws of
Motion, with feveral Corollaries therefrom ; as concerning
the compofition and refolution of any direct force out of,
or into any oblique forces, (whereby the powers of all
forts of Mechanical Engines are demonftrated :) the Laws

O o   of

[292]

of the reflection of Bodies in Motion after their Collision : and the like.

These neceffary *Præcognita* being delivered, our Author proceeds to confider the Curves generated by the compofition of a direct impreffed motion with a gravitation or tendency towards a Center : and having demonftrated that in all cafes the Areas at the Center, defcribed by a revolving Body, are proportional to the Times; he fhews how from the Curve defcribed, to find the Law or Rule of the decreafe or increafe of the Tendency or Centripetal forces (as he calls it) in differing diftances from the Center. Of this there are feveral examples : as if the Curve defcribed be a Circle paffing through the Center of tendency; then the force or tendency towards that Center is in all points as the fift power or fquared-cube of the diftance therefrom reciprocally. If in the proportional Spiral, reciprocally as the cube of the diftance. If in an Ellipfe about the Center thereof directly as the diftance. If in any of the *Conick* Sections about the *Focus* thereof; then he demonftrates that the *Vis Centripeta*, or tendency towards that *Focus*, is in all places reciprocally as the fquare of the diftance therefrom; and that according to the Velocity of the impreffed Motion, the Curve defcribed is an *Hyperbola* ; if the Body moved be fwift to a certain degree than a *Parabola*; if flower an *Ellipfe* or Circle in one cafe. From this fort of tendency or gravitation it follows likewife that the fquares of the Times of the periodical Revolutions are as the Cubes of the Radii or *tranfverfe Axes* of the *Ellipfes*. All which being found to agree with the *Phenomena* of the Celeftial Motions, as difcovered by the great Sagacity and Diligence of *Kepler*, our Author extends himfelf upon the confequences of this fort of *Vis centripeta*; fhewing how to find the *Conick* Section which a Bodie fhall defcribe when caft with any velocity in a given Line, fuppofing the quantity of the faid force known : and laying down feveral neat conftructions to determine

[293]

termine the Orbs,either from the *Focus* given and two points or Tangents; or without it by five points or Tangents or any number of Points and Tangents making together five. Then he shews how from the Time given to find the Point in a given Orb answering thereto; which he performs accurately in the *Parabola,*and by concise approximations comes as near as he pleases in the *Ellipse* and *Hyperbola:* all which are Problems of the highest concern in Astronomy. Next he lays down the Rules of the perpendicular descent of Bodies towards the Center, particularly in the case where the tendency thereto is reciprocally as the square of the distance; and generally in all other cases, supposing a general quadrature of Curve lines: upon which supposition likewise he delivers a general method of discovering the Orbs described by a Body moving in such a tendency towards a Center, increasing or decreasing in any given relation to the distance from the Center; and then with great subtilty he determines in all cases the Motion of the *Apsides* (or of the Points of greatest distance from the Center in all these *Curves,* in such Orbs as are nearly Circular. Shewing the *Apsides* fixt, if the tendency be reciprocally as the square of the distance; direct in Motion in any *Ratio* between the Square and the Cube and retrograde; if under the Square : which Motion he determines exactly from the Rule of the increase or decrease of the *Vis Centripeta.*

Next the Motion of bodies in given Surfaces is considered,as likewise the Oscillatory Motion of Pendules, where is shewn how to make a *Pendulum* Vibrate always in equal times, tho' the center or point of tendency be never so near ; to which, the Demonstration of Mr. *Hugens de Cycloide* is but a *Corollary.* And in another Proposition is shewn the Velocity in each Point, and the time spent in each part of the Arch described by the Vibrating Body. After this the Effects of two or more Bodies, towards each of which there is a tendency, is considered ; and 'tis made out that two Bodies, so drawing or attracting each other, describe

[294]

about the common center of Gravity, Curve Lines, like to those they seem to describe about one another. And of three Bodies, attracting each other, reciprocally as the Square of the distance between their Centers, the various Consequences are considered and laid down, in several *Corollarys* of great use in explicating the *Phenomena* of the *Moons* Motions, the Flux and Reflux of the Sea, the Precession of the *Equinoctial* Points; and the like.

This done our Author with his usual Acuteness proceeds to examine into the Causes of this Tendency or centripetal Force, which from undoubted Arguments is shown to be in all the great Bodies of the Universe. Here he finds that if a Sphere be composed of an infinity of Atoms, each of which have a *Conatus accedendi ad invicem*, which decreases in duplicate Proportion of the Distance between them ; then the whole *Congeries* shall have the like tendency towards its Center, decreasing, in Spaces without it, in duplicate Proportion of the Distances from the Center; and decreasing, within its Surface, as the distance from the Center directly ; so as to be greatest on the Surface, and nothing at the Center : and tho' this might suffice, yet to compleat the Argument, there is laid down a Method to determine the forces of Globes composed of Particles whose Tendencies to each other do decrease in any other *Ratio* of the Distances : Which Speculation is carryed on likewise to other Bodies not Spherical, whether finite or indeterminate. Lastly is proposed a Method of explaining the Refractions and Reflections of transparent Bodies from the same Principles; and several Problems solved of the greatest Concern in the Art of *Dioptricks.*

Hitherto our Author has considered the Effects of compound Motions *in Mediis non resistentibus,* or wherein a Body once in Motion would move equably in a direct Line, if not diverted by a supervening Attraction or tendency toward some other Body. Here is demonstrated what
would

[295]

would be the confequence of a refiftence from a *Medium*,
either in the fimple or duplicate *Ratio* of the Velocity, or
elfe between both: and to compleat this Argument is laid
down a general Method of determining the denfity of the
Medium in all places, which, with a uniform Gravity tending perpendicularly to the plain of the *Horizon*, fhall
make a *Project* move in any curve Line affigned ; which
is the 10*th. Prop. Lib.* II.   Then the circular Motion of
Bodies in refifting *Media* is determined, and 'tis fhown
under what Laws of decreafe of Denfity, the Circle will
become a proportional Spiral.   Next the denfity and compreffion of Fluids is confidered, and the Doctrine of *Hydroftaticks* demonftrated ; and here 'tis propofed to the
Contemplation of Natural Philofophers, whether the furprizing *Phenomena* of the Elafticity of the Air and fome o-
ther Fluids may not arife from their being compofed of
Particles which flie each other ; which being rather a
Phyfical than Mathematical Inquiry, our Author forbears
to Difcufs.

Next the Oppofition of the *Medium* and its Effects on
the Vibrations of the *Pendulum* is confidered, which is
followed by an Inquiry into the Rules of the Oppofition
to Bodies, as their Bulk, Shape, or Denfity may be vary-
ed : Here with great exactnefs is an Account given of feveral Experiments tried with *Pendula,* in order to verify the
aforegoing Speculation, and to determine the quantity
of the Airs Oppofition to Bodies moving in it.

From hence is proceeded to the undulation of Fluids,
the Laws whereof are here laid down, and by them the
Motion and Propagation of Light and Sound are explained.   The laft *Section* of this Book is concerning the Circular Motion of Fluids, wherein the Nature of their *Vortical* Motions is confidered, and from thence the *Cartefian*
Doctrine of the *Vortices* of the Celeftial Matter carrying
with them the Planets about the *Sun,* is proved to be
alltogether impoffible.

The

[296]

The III. and laft Book is entituled *de Syftemate Mundi*, wherein the Demonftrations of the two former Books are applyed to the Explication of the principal *Phenomena* of Nature : Here the verity of the *Hypothefis* of *Kepler* is demonftrated ; and a full Refolution given to all the difficulties that occur in the *Aftronomical* Science ; they being nothing elfe but the neceffary confequences of the *Sun, Earth, Moon,* and *Planets,* having all of them a gravitation or tendency towards their Centers proportionate to the Quantity of Matter in each of them, and whole Force abates in duplicate proportion of the Diftance reciprocally. Here likewife are indifputably folved the Appearances of the Tides, or Flux and Reflux of the Sea ; and the Spheroidical Figure of the *Earth* and *Jupiter* determined, (from which the preceffion of the Equinoxes, or rotation of the Earths Axis is made out,) together with the retroceffion of the *Moons* Nodes, the Quantity and inequalities of whofe Motion are here exactly ftated *a priore* : Laftly the Theory of the Motion of Comets is attempted with fuch fuccefs, that in an Example of the great Comet which appeared in 168$\frac{4}{1}$, the Motion thereof is computed as exactly as we can pretend to give the places of the primary Planets; and a general Method is here laid down to ftate and determine the *Trajectoriæ* of Comets, by an eafy Geometrical Conftruction; upon fuppofition that thofe Curves are *Parabolick,* or fo near it that the *Parabola* may ferve without fenfible Error ; tho' it be more probable, faith our Author, that thefe Orbs are *Elliptical,* and that after long periods Comets may return again. But fuch *Ellipfes* are by Reafon of the immenfe diftance of the *Foci,* and fmallnefs of the *Latus Rectum,* in the Parts near the Sun where Comets appear, not eafily diftinguifhed from the Curve of the *Parabola* : as is proved by the Example produced.

The whole Book is interfperfed with *Lemma's* of General ufe in *Geometry,* and feveral new Methods applyed, which

[297]

which are well worth the confidering; and it may be juftly faid, that fo many and fo Valuable *Philofophical Truths*, as are herein difcovered and put paft Difpute, were never yet owing to the Capacity and Induftry of any one Man.

ADVERTISEMENT;

Whereas the Publication of thefe Tranfactions *has for fome Months laft paft been interrupted* ; *The Reader is defired to take notice that the care of the Edition of this Book of Mr.* Newton *having lain wholly upon the Publifher (wherein he conceives he hath been more ferviceable to the Commonwealth of Learning) and for fome other preffing reafons, they could not be got ready in due time* ; *but now they will again be continued as formerly, and come out regularly, either of three fheets, or five with a Cutt* ; *according as Materials fhall occur.*

L O N D O N,

Printed by *J. Streater*, and are to be fold by *Samuel Smith* at the *Princes Arms* in St. *Paul's* Church-yard.

(445)

II. The true Theory of the Tides, extracted from ·hat admired Treatise of Mr. Isaac Newton, Intituled, Philosophiæ Naturalis Principia Mathematica; being a Discourse presented with that Book to the late King James, by Mr. Edmund Halley.

IT may, perhaps, seem strange, that this Paper, being no other than a partile Account of a Book long since published, and whereof a fuller Extract was given in Numb. 187. of these Transactions, should again appear here; but the Desires of several honourable Persons, which could not be withstood, have obliged us to insert it here, for the sake of such, who being less knowing in Mathematical Matters; and therefore, not daring to adventure on the Author himself, are notwithstanding, very curious to be informed of the Causes of Things; particularly of so general and extraordinary Phænomena, as are those of the Tides.   Now this Paper having been drawn up for the late King James's Use, (in whose Reign the Book was published) and having given good Satisfaction to those that got Copies of it; it is hoped the Savans of the higher Form will indulge us this liberty we take to gratifie their Inferiours in point of Science; and not be offended, that we here insist more largely upon Mr. Newton's Theory of the Tides, which, how plain and easie soever we find, is very little understood by the common Reader.

The sole Principle upon which this Author proceeds to explain most of the great and surprising Appearances of Nature, is no other than that of *Gravity*, whereby in the Earth all Bodies have a tendency towards its Centre;

X x x   as

(445)

as is moſt evident : and from undoubted Arguments its proved, that there is ſuch a Gravitation towards the Centre of the Sun, Moon, and all the Planets.

From this Principle, as a neceſſary Conſequence, follows the Sphærical Figure of the Earth and Sea, and of all the other Cæleſtial Bodies : and tho' the tenacity and firmneſs of the Solid Parts, ſupport the Inequalities of the Land above the Level; yet the Fluids, preſſing equally and eaſily yielding to each other, ſoon reſtore the *Æquilibrium*, if diſturbed, and maintain the exact Figure of the Globe.

Now this force of Deſcent of Bodies towards the Center, is not in all places alike, but is ſtill leſs and leſs, as the diſtance of the Center encreaſes : and in this Book it is demonſtrated,that this Force decreaſes as the Square of the diſtance increaſes; that is, the weight of Bodies and the force of their Fall is leſs, in parts more removed from the Center, in the proportion of the Squares of the Diſtance. So as for Example, a Ton weight on the Surface of the Earth, if it were raiſed to the height of 4000 Miles, which I ſuppoſe the ſemidiameter of the Earth, would weigh but ¼ of a Ton, or 5 Hundred weight : if to 12000 Miles, or 3 ſemidiameters from the Surface, that is 4 from the Center, it would weigh but 1/16 part of the Weight on the Surface, or a Hundred and Quarter: So that it would be as eaſie for the Strength of a Man at that height to carry a Ton weight, as here on the Surface a 100 ℔. And in the ſame Proportion does the Velocities of the fall of Bodies decreaſe: For whereas on the Surface of the Earth all things fall 16 Foot in a ſecond, at one ſemidiameter above this Fall is but 4 Foot; and at 3 ſemidiameters, or 4 from the Centre, it is but 1/16 of the Fall at the Surface, or but one Foot in a ſecond : And at greater Diſtances both Weight and Fall become very

ſmall,

(447)

fmall, but yet at all given Diftances is ftill fome thing, tho' the Effect become infenfible. At the diftance of the Moon (which I will fuppofe 60 Semidiameters of the Earth) 3600 Pounds weigh but one Pound, and the fall of Bodies is but $\frac{15}{3600}$ of a Foot in a fecond, or 16 Foot in a minute; that is, a Body fo far off defcends in a Minute no more than the fame at the Surface of the Earth would do in a Second of Time.

As was faid before, the fame force decreafing after the fame manner is evidently found in the Sun, Moon, and all the Planets; but more efpecially in the Sun, whofe Force is prodigious; becoming fenfible even in the immenfe diftance of *Saturn:* This gives room to fufpect, that the force of Gravity is in the Celeftial Globes proportional to the quantity of Matter in each of them : And the Sun being at leaft ten Thoufand times as big as the Earth, its Gravitation or attracting Force, is found to be at leaft ten Thoufand times as much as that of the Earth, acting on Bodies at the fame diftances.

This Law of the decreafe of Gravity being demonftratively proved, and put paft contradiction; the Author with great Sagacity, inquires into the neceffary Confequences of this Suppofition; whereby he finds the genuine Caufe of the feveral Appearances in the Theory of the Moon and Planets, and difcovers the hitherto unknown Laws of the Motion of Comets, and of the Ebbing and Flowing of the Sea. Each of which are Subjects that have hitherto taken up much larger Volumes; but Truth being uniform, and always the fame, it is admirable to obferve how eafily we are enabled to make out very abftrufe *and difficult Matters,* when once true and genuine Principles are obtained: And on the other hand it may be wondred, that, notwithftanding the great facility of truth, and the perplexity and nonconfequences that always attend erroneous Suppofitions, thefe

X x x 2   great

(448)

great Difcoveries fhould have efcaped the acute Dif-
quifitions of the beft Philofophical Heads of all paft
Ages, and be referved to thefe our Times. But that
wonder will foon ceafe, if it be confidered how great
Improvements Geometry has received in our Memory,
and particularly from the profound Difcoveries of our
incomparable Author.

The Theory of the Motion of the primary *Planets*
is here fhewn to be nothing elfe, but the contemplation
of the Curve Lines which Bodies caft with a given Velocity, in a given Direction, and at the fame time
drawn towards the Sun by its gravitating Power, would
defcribe. Or, which is all one, that the Orbs of the
Planets are fuch Curve Lines as a Shot from a Gun defcribes in the Air, being caft according to the direction
of the Piece, but bent into a crooked Line by the fu-
pervening Tendency towards the Earths Centre: And
the Planets being fuppofed to be projected with a given
Force, and attracted towards the Sun, after the aforefaid manner, are here proved to defcribe fuch Figures,
as anfwer punctually to all that the Induftry of this
and the laft Age has obferved in the Planetary Motions.
So that it appears, that there is no need of folid Orbs
and Intelligences, as the Ancients imagined, nor yet of
Vortices or Whirlpools of the Celeftial Matter, as *Des
Cartes* fuppofes; but the whole Affair is fimply and
mechanically performed, upon the fole Suppofition of
a Gravitation towards theSun ; which cannot be denied.

The Motion of *Comets* is here fhewn to be compounded of the fame Elements, and not to differ from Planets, but in their greater fwiftnefs, whereby overpow-
ering the Gravity that fhould hold them to the Sun, as
it doth the Planets, they flie off again, and diftance
themfelves from the Sun and Earth, fo that they foon
are out of our fight. And the imperfect Accounts and
Obfer-

(459)

Obſervations Antiquity has left us, are not ſufficient to
determine whether the ſame Comet ever return again.
But this Author has ſhewn how Geometrically to determine the Orb of a Comet from Obſervations, and to
find his diſtance from the Earth and Sun, which was never before done.

The third thing here done is the Theory of the
Moon, all the Inequalities of whoſe Motion are proved
to ariſe from the ſame Principles, only here the effect of
two Centers operating on, or attracting a projected Body comes to be conſidered ; for the Moon, tho' principally attracted by the Earth, and moving round it, does,
together with the Earth, move round the Sun once a
Year, and is according as ſhe is, nearer or farther from
the Sun, drawn by him more or leſs than the Center of
the Earth, about which ſhe moves ; whence ariſe ſeveral Irregularities in her Motion, of all which, the Author
in this Book, with no leſs Subtility than Induſtry, has
given a full Account.   And tho' by reaſon of the great
Complication of the Problem, he has not yet been able
to make it purely Geometrical, 'tis to be hoped, that in
ſome farther Eſſay he may ſurmount the difficulty : and
having perfected the Theory of the Moon, the long
deſired diſcovery of the Longitude (which at Sea is only practicable this way) may at length be brought to
light, to the great Honour of your Majeſty and Advantage of your Subjects.

All the ſurprizing Phenomena of the Flux and Reflux
of the Sea, are in like manner ſhewn to proceed from
the ſame Principle ; which I deſign more largely to inſiſt
on, ſince the Matter of Fact is in this caſe much better
known to your Majeſty than in the foregoing.

If the Earth were alone, that is to ſay, not affected
by the Actions of the Sun and Moon, it is not to be
doubted, but the Ocean, being equally preſſed by the
                                                    force

(450)

force of Gravity towards the Center, would continue
in a perfect ftagnation, always at the fame height, without ever Ebbing or Flowing ; but it being here demonftrated, that the Sun and Moon have a like Principle
of Gravitation towards their Centers, and that the
Earth is within the Activity of their Attractions, it
will plainly follow, that the Equality of the preffure of
Gravity towards the Center will thereby be difturbed ;
and tho' the fmallnefs of thefe Forces, in refpect of the
Gravitation towards the Earths Center, renders them altogether imperceptible by any Experiments we can de-
vife, yet the Ocean being fluid and yielding to the leaft
force, by its rifing fhews where it is lefs preft, and where
it is more preft by its finking.

Now if we fuppofe the force of the Moons attraction
to decreafe as the Square of the Diftance from its Center
increafes (as in the Earth and other Celeftial Bodies) we
fhall find,that where the Moon is perpendicularly either
above or below the Horizon, either in Zenith or Nadir,
there the force of Gravity is moft of all diminifhed, and
confequently that there the Ocean muft neceffarily fwell
by the coming in of the Water from thofe parts where
the Preffure is greateft, viz. in thofe places where the
Moon is near the Horizon : but that this may be the
better underftood, I thought it needful to add the following Figure, where *M* is the Moon, *E* the Earth, *C*
its Centre, and *Z* the place where the Moon is in the
Zenith, *N* where in the Nadir.

Now

(451)

Now by the Hypothefis it is evident, that the Water
in Z, being nearer, is more drawn by the Moon, than
the Center of the Earth C, and that again more tha
the Water in N, wherefore the Water in Z has a tendency towards the Moon, contrary to that of Gravity,
being equal to the Excefs of the Gravitation in Z, above
that in C : And in the other cafe, the Water in N, tending lefs towards the Moon than the Center C, will be
lefs preffed, by as much as is the difference of the Gravitations towards the Moon in C and N.   This rightly underftood, it follows plainly, that the Sea, which otherwife would be Spherical, upon the Preffure of the
Moon, muft form it felf into a Spheroidal or Oval Figure, whofe longeft Diameter is where the Moon is
Vertical, and fhorteft where fhe is in the Horizon; and
that the Moon fhifting her Pofition as fhe turns round
the Earth once a day, this Oval of Water fhifts with
her, occafioning thereby the two Floods and Ebbs obfervable in each 25 Hours.

And this may fuffice as to the general Caufe of the
Tides ; it remains now to fhew how naturally this Motion accounts for all the Particulars that has been obferved about them ; fo that there can be no room left to
doubt, but that this is the true caufe thereof.

The Spring Tides upon the new and full Moons, and
Neap Tides on the Quarters, are occafioned by the attractive Force of the Sun in the New and Full, confpi-
ring with the Attraction of the Moon, and producing
a Tide by their united Forces : Whereas in the Quarters, the Sun raifes the Water where the Moon depref-
fes it, and the contrary ; fo as the Tides are made only by the difference of their Attractions. That the force of
the Sun is no greater in this cafe, proceeds from the very
fmall Proportion the Semidiameter of the Earth bears to
the vaft diftance of the Sun.

It

(452)

It is alſo obſerved, that *cæteris paribus*, the Æquinoctial Spring Tides in *March* and *September*, or near
them, are the Higheſt, and the Neap Tides the Loweſt;
which proceeds from the greater Agitation of the Waters, when the fluid *Sphæroid* reſolves about a great
Circle of the Earth, than when it turns about in a leſſer
Circle; it being plain, that if the Moon were conſtituted in the Pole and there ſtood, that the Sphæroid would
have a fixt Poſition, and that it would be always high
Water under the Poles, and low Water every where under the Æquinoctial:. and therefore the nearer the Moon
approaches the Poles, the leſs is the agitation of the O-
cean, which is of all the greateſt, when the Moon is
in the Æquinoctial, or fartheſt diſtant from the Poles.
Whence the Sun and Moon, being either conjoyned or
oppoſite in the Æquinoctial, produce the greateſt Spring
Tides; and the ſubſequent Neap Tides, being produced
by the Tropical Moon in the Quarters, are always the
leaſt Tides; whereas in *June* and *December*, the Spring
Tides are made by the Tropical Sun and Moon, and
therefore leſs vigorous; and the Neap Tides by the Æ-
quinoctial Moon, which therefore are the ſtronger:
Hence it happens, that the difference between the Spring
and Neap Tides in theſe Months, is much leſs conſiderable than in *March* and *September*. And the reaſon
why the very higheſt Spring Tides are found to be rather before the Vernal and after the Antumnal Equinox,
viz. in *February* and *October*, than preciſely upon them,
is, becauſe the Sun is nearer the Earth in the Winter
Months, and ſo comes to have a greater Effect in producing the Tides.

   Hitherto we have conſidered ſuch Affections of the
Tides as are Univerſal, without relation to particular Ca-
ſes; what follows from the differing Latitudes of places,
will be eaſily underſtood by the following Figure.

Let

(453)

Let *A p E P* be the Earth covered over with very
deep Waters, *C* its Center, *P, p,* its Poles, *A E* the
Æquinoctial, *F f* the parallel of Latitude of a place,
D d another Parallel at equal diftance on the other fide
of the Æquinoctial, *H h* the two Points where the
Moon is vertical, and let *K k* be the great Circle, where-
in the Moon appears Horizontal. It is evident, that a
Spheroid defcribed upon *H h*, and *K k* fhall nearly repre-

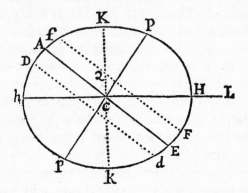

fent the Figure of the Sea, and *C f, C D, C F, C d* fhall
be the hights of the Sea in the places *f, D, F, d,* in all
which it is High-water: and feeing that in twelve Hours
time, by the diurnal Rotation of the Earth, the point
F is transferred to *f,* and *d* to *D :* the hight of the Sea
C F will be that of the High-water when the Moon is
prefent, and *C f* that of the other High water, when
the Moon is under the Earth : which in the cafe of this
Figure is lefs than the former *C F.* And in the oppofite Parallel *D d* the contrary happens. The Rifing of
the Water being always alternately greater and lefs in
each place, when it is produced by the Moon declining
fenfibly from the Æquinoctial ; that being the greateft
of the two High-waters in each diurnal Revolution of
Y y y   the

(454)

the Moon, wherein she approaches neareft either to the
Zenith or Nadir of the place : whence it is that the
Moon in the Northern Signs, in this part of the World,
makes the greateft Tides when above the Earth, and in
Southern Signs, when under the Earth; the Effect being always the greateft where the Moon is fartheft from
the Horizon, either above or below it. And this alternate increafe and decreafe of the Tides has been obferved to hold true on the Coaft of *England*, at *Briftol* by
Capt. *Sturmy*, and at *Plymouth* by Mr. *Coleprefe*.

But the Motions hitherto mentioned are fomewhat altered by the Libration of the Water, whereby, tho'
the Action of the *Luminaries* fhould ceafe, the Flux
and Reflux of the Sea would for fome time continue :
This Confervation of the impreffed Motion diminifhes
the differences that otherwife would be between two
confequent Tides, and is the reafon why the higheft
Spring Tides are not precifely on the new and full
Moons, nor the Neaps on the Quarters; but generally they are the third Tides after them, and fometimes
later.

All thefe things would regularly come to pafs, if the
whole Earth were covered with Sea very deep; but by
reafon of the fhoalnefs of fome places, and the narrownefs of the Streights, by which the Tides are in many
cafes propagated, there arifes a great diverfity in the Effect, and not to be accounted for, without an exact
Knowledge of all the Circumftances of the Places, as
of the Pofition of the Land, and the Breadth and Depth
of the Channels by which the Tide flows ; for a very
flow and imperceptible Motion of the whole Body of
the Water, where it is (for example) 2 Miles deep,
will fuffice to raife its Surface 10 or 12 Feet in a Tides
time ; whereas, if the fame quantity of Water were to
be conveyed upon a Channel of 40 Fathoms deep, it
would

(455)

would require a very great Stream to effect it, in fo
large Inlets as are the Channel of *England* and the *Ger-
man* Ocean ; whence the Tide is found to fet ftrongeft
in thofe places where the Sea grows narroweft ; the fame
quantity of Water being to pafs through a fmaller Paffage: This is moft evident in the *Streights*, between
Portland and *Cape de Hague* in *Normandy*, where the
Tide runs like a Sluce ; and would be yet more between
Dover and *Calis*, if the Tide coming about the Ifland
from the North did not check it.   And this force being
once impreffed upon the Water, continues to carry it
about the level of the ordinary height in the Ocean,
particularly where the Water meets a direct Obftacle, as
it is at St. *Malo's* ; and where it enters into a long Channel, which running far into the Land grows very ftreight
at its Extremity ; as it is in the *Severn-Sea* at *Chepftow*
and *Briftol*.

   This fhoalnefs of the Sea and the intercurrent Continents are the reafon, that in the open Ocean the time
of High-water is not at the Moons appulfe to the Meri-
dian, but always fome Hours after it ; as it is obferved
upon all the Weft-Coaft of *Europe* and *Africa*, from *Ireland* to the *Cape of Good-Hope* : In all which a S. W.
Moon makes High-water, and the fame is reported to
be on the Weft fide of *America*.   But it would be endlefs to account all the particular Solutions, which are
eafie Corollaries of this *Hypothefis* ; as why the *Lakes*,
fuch as the *Cafpian Sea*, and *Mediterranian Seas*, fuch as
the *Black Sea*, the *Streights* and *Baltick*, have no fenfible Tides: For *Lakes* having no Communication with
the Ocean, can neither increafe nor diminifh their Water, whereby to rife and fall ; and Seas that communicate by fuch narrow Inlets, and are of fo immenfe an
Extent, cannot in a few Hours time receive or empty Water enough to raife or fink their Surface any thing fenfibly.

(456)

Laſtly, to demonſtrate the excellency of this Doĉtrine, the Example of the Tides in the Port of *Tunking* in *Chi-na*, which are ſo extraordinary, and differing from all others we have yet heard of, may ſuffice. In this Port there is but one Flood and Ebb in 24 Hours ; and twice in each Month, *viz.* when the Moon is near the Æqui-noĉtial there is no Tide at all, but the Water is ſtagnant ; but with the Moons declination there begins a Tide, which is greateſt when ſhe is in the Tropical Signs: only with this difference,that when the Moon is to the North-ward of the Æquinoĉtial, it Flows when ſhe is above the Earth, and Ebbs when ſhe is under, ſo as to make High-water at Moons-ſetting, and Low-water at Moons-riſing: But on the contrary, the Moon being to the Southward, makes High-water at riſing and Low-water at ſetting ; it Ebbing all the time ſhe is above the Hori-zon. As may be ſeen more at large in the *Philoſophical Tranſaĉtion*, Num. 162.

The Cauſe of this odd Appearance is propoſed by *Mr. Newton*, to be from the concurrence of two Tides ; the one propagated in ſix Hours out of the great *South-Sea* along the Coaſt of *China* ; the other out of the *Indian-Sea*, from between the Iſlands in twelve Hours, along the Coaſt of *Malacca* and *Cambodia*. The one of theſe Tides, being produced in North-Latitude, is, as has been ſaid, greater, when the Moon being to the North of the Equator is above the Earth, and leſs when ſhe is under the Earth. The other of them, which is propagated from the *Indian-Sea*, being raiſed in South Latitude, is greater when the Moon declining to the South is above the Earth, and leſs when ſhe is under the Earth: So that of theſe Tides alternately greater and leſſer, there comes always ſucceſſively two of the great-er and two of the leſſer together every day ; and the High-water falls always between the times of the arri-

val

(457)

val of the two greater Floods ; and the Low-water be
tween the arrival of the two leſſer Floods.   And the
Moon coming to the Æquinoctial, and the alternate
Floods becoming equal, the Tide ceaſes and the Water
ſtagnates : but when ſhe has paſſed to the other ſide of
the Equator, thoſe Floods which in the former Order
were the leaſt, now becoming the greateſt, that that before was the time of High-water now becomes the Low-
water, and the Converſe.   So that the whole appearance of theſe ſtrange Tides, is without any forcing naturally deduced from theſe Principles, and is a great Argument of the certainty of the whole *Theory*.

VI.

The First Biography of Newton

Fontenelle and Newton

CHARLES COULSTON GILLISPIE

There is a certain piquancy in the chance that Sir Isaac Newton's
first biographer should have been a Frenchman and a Cartesian.
So it happened, however, in consequence of Newton's position as
associé étranger of the *Académie Royale des Sciences*. On the death of a
member, the custom of that body is to commemorate his life and
accomplishments in an essay composed by the permanent secretary. When Newton died in 1727, this post was occupied, as it had
been for thirty years, by Bernard le Bovier de Fontenelle, who was
then at the height of the career that made him the intermediary
between the science of the 17th century and the ideology of the
Enlightenment. Immediately translated, his *éloge* became the first
biography to appear in England. This is the document that is here
reproduced, and, in order to place it in its historical context, it may
be well to enter into a little introductory detail on the ambiguity
of Newton's early relations with his French colleagues, to indicate
the place of the *éloge* in Newtonian biography, and to point out
certain casts given to the exposition by Fontenelle's inability to accept, or perhaps to appreciate, Newton's conception of what it is
that science explains.

427

One sometimes reads that Newton was the first foreigner elected to the *Académie des Sciences* upon its reorganization in 1699, and the inference is that by this gesture the French were magnanimously recognizing the magnitude of his challenge to Descartes. Neither the fact nor the implication is correct. When the Academy began operating under its new charter, it already included three foreign members, Leibniz, Tschirnhaus, and Guglielmini, and it filled the five additional vacancies authorized in the following order: Hartsoeker, the brothers Bernoulli, Roemer, and Newton.[1] Nor, although *Naturalis Philosophiae Principia Mathematica* had been in print since 1687, was the Academy yet aware that this book posed a fundamental challenge to the science known to its members, or that they were bringing into their company the founder of classical physical science, in the consciousness of which the world was to live ever after. In choosing Newton eighth on the list, the Academy thought itself to be electing simply a mathematician of extraordinary geometrical skill, and the author of important experiments (and a very questionable theory) bearing on the nature of light.

Professor Cohen has pointed out that it was through the *Opticks,* not the *Principia,* that Newton exerted his influence on the imagination of his 18th-century admirers.[2] The optical work attracted attention from the outset, even before the *Opticks* itself was published in 1704. In the volumes that record the proceedings of the Academy from 1666, the year of its foundation, to 1699, that of Newton's election, the only reference to him is a letter of 1672 from Huygens on the advantages of his reflecting telescope.[3] In 1688 the *Journal des Savants* noticed the *Principia* in three paragraphs, describing the work as "une Mecanique la plus parfaite qu'on puisse imaginer," but pointing out (somewhat misleadingly) that Newton himself says of his proofs "qu'il n'a pas consideré leurs principes en Physicien, mais en simple Géometre," and urging him to "nous donner une Physique aussi exacte qu'est la Me-

---

[1] See, *ante,* p. 12; also, *Les membres* et *les correspondants de l'Académie royale des sciences (1666–1793)* (Paris, 1931); and on the reorganization, Alfred Maury, *L'Ancienne Académie des Sciences* (Paris, 1864), pp. 40–45.

[2] I. B. Cohen, preface to Newton's *Opticks* (New York, 1952).

[3] *Mémoires de l'Académie Royale des Sciences depuis 1666 jusqu'à 1699,* vol. 10 (1730), pp. 505–507. It should perhaps be explained that the volumes covering this period were published through the efforts of Fontenelle long after the events.

canique" by substituting "de vrais mouvemens en la place de ceux qu'il a supposez."[4] Thereafter, Newton was not again discussed in the *Journal* until 1703, when a passing reference appears in an article drawn from Jean Bernoulli's *Recherche de Catoptrique et Dioptrique* of 1701. Newton is introduced casually and only in order to be dismissed, but the turn of argument is interesting, for, although it refers to an optical passage of the *Principia*, it too is all unwittingly prophetic of the larger issues in the offing. To certain considerations on refrangibility which follow from the views of one Herigone (and indeed of Descartes), the author objects that in a homogeneous medium the relative obliquity of rays is meaningless except with reference to a second medium, which cannot be supposed to affect the path of the ray before ever it arrives,

à moins qu'avec le subtil M. Newton, (*Princ. Math. Phil. Nat. pag.* 231.) on ne veüille mettre dans le second milieu quelque vertu attractive qui agisse sur les rayons lors qu'ils sont encore dans le premier milieu, & qui les attire plus fortement les uns que les autres. C'est en effet par là que M. Newton explique la nature de la reflexion, & de la refraction: mais son explication est plus ingenieuse qu'elle n'est vraye; car il ne nous apprend point ce que c'est que cette vertu attractive, ni d'où elle vient: il la suppose seulement. J'avoüe que si on la lui accorde, l'explication qu'il donne est forte élegante, & peut contenter un Mathematicien.[5]

In fact, Newton had addressed himself mathematically to reality, and not just abstractly to mathematics. And that he had undertaken a radical approach to the great question of how the world is made was borne in on his French colleagues less by perusal of the *Principia*, that intractable book, than by attending to the discussions raised by philosophers who did perceive how deep the

[4] *Journal des Savants 16*, 237–238 (1688). The survey of this important journal for French reaction to Newton is greatly facilitated by the availability of Jacqueline de La Harpe, "Le Journal des Savants et l'Angleterre, 1702–1789," *University of California Publications in Modern Philology*, XX (1937–1941), pp. 289–520, especially pp. 319–323, 358–363. This meticulous and useful monograph is marred only by a note that cites as the first treatment of the *Principia* in the *Journal* an *extrait* of 1682.

[5] *Journal des Savants 31*, 1002 (1703). I can find no discussion of the principle of gravity before the review of the second edition of the *Principia* (*Journal des Savànts*, June 1715, Pt. I, 667–674). Even here the principle of attraction is simply set off against the theory of vortices in a literal and superficial fashion.

issues went: Malebranche, the final edition of whose *Recherches de la vérité* appeared in 1712; Leibniz, who attacked the theory of gravity in 1710 and the publication of whose ensuing correspondence with Clarke was the most important single event in bringing home the problem; Roger Cotes and Newton himself, whose preface and General Scholium to the second edition of the *Principia* in 1712 joined issue with continental philosophy.[6] As everyone knows, the acceptance of Newton's principles in France had to await his death—and Voltaire.[7] But even the full awareness of Newton was delayed until the period, after 1710 or thereabouts, when he had long since withdrawn from the arena of science, if not of controversy.

Nor were his relations ever close with France. There were a few letters from Fontenelle thanking Newton for copies of certain books, and a few complaints by Newton of the credit allowed to Leibniz on the invention of the calculus in the *éloges* of Leibniz and L'Hôpital.[8] There was some discussion in the Academy, mathemati-

[6] Although Malebranche (who admired the *Opticks*) does not allude directly to the *Principia,* the discussion of gravity and the adaptation of Villemot's theory of spherical vortices were directed against Newton; see *Recherche de la verité,* ed. Francisque Bouillier, 2 vols. (Paris, 1880), Ph. Villemot, *Nouveau système, ou nouvelle explication du mouvement des planètes* (Lyon, 1707), and, for a discussion of these works, P. Mouy, *Le Développement de la physique cartésienne* (Paris, 1934), pp. 271, 310–314. In the opinion of the latest student of Fontenelle's science, this last edition of Malebranche was the point of departure of Fontenelle's comprehensive and thought-out opposition to Newton; see F. Grégoire, *Fontenelle, une "philosophie" désabusée* (Nancy, 1947), p. 130. A translation of the text of the Leibniz-Clarke correspondence has just been republished in a critical edition, H. G. Alexander, ed., *The Leibniz-Clarke Correspondence* (Manchester, 1956), with a most useful analytical introduction. Though far from satisfactory, the most accessible edition of the *Principia,* containing the Cotes preface and the General Scholium, is that by Florian Cajori, *Sir Isaac Newton's Mathematical Principles of Natural Philosophy* (Berkeley, 1934), based on Andrew Motte's translation of the 3rd edition (1729). A facsimile reproduction of the first edition has recently been published by William Dawson (London, 1955). Mention, too, must be made of the work which prints (unfairly) selected documents in the *Streit* with Leibniz over the invention of the calculus, from which controversy the larger argument emerged, *Commercium epistolicum D. Johannis Collins et aliorum de analysi promota* (London, 1712) and of the compilation which was very influential in bringing the whole issue before French readers, P. des Maizeaux, *Recueil de diverses pièces sur la philosophie . . . par Messieurs Leibniz, Clarke, Newton, et autres auteurs celèbres (Amsterdam, 1720).*

[7] Pierre Brunet, *L'Introduction des théories de Newton en France* (Paris, 1931).

[8] Fontenelle was pleased and touched by the kindly reference to his own work

cal rather than physical, of "forces centrales." [9] In 1715 certain optical experiments were demonstrated by Desaguliers in London in the presence of the Chevalier de Bouville and other members of the Academy. Many of them were verified in Paris by Père Sebastien in the presence of the Cardinal de Polignac, Varignon, and Fontenelle.[10] And it appears that the image of Newton which Fontenelle develops in the *éloge,* compounded of admiration for his talent and rejection of his principles, was not fully formed until the fifteen years or so before Newton's death. The *éloge* stands, then, at the middle stage in that passage from incomprehension through rejection to idealization that was the route by which Newton penetrated and ultimately transformed scientific understanding in France.

A persistent current of interest in Fontenelle himself runs through the scholarly literature—persistent, but a little thin, for the one point on which all his interpreters agree is that he cuts at best a minor figure, if a witty one. Thus, Laborde-Milaà makes him the *philosophe* who transformed Cartesianism into positivism,[11] while Louis Maigron presents a comprehensive picture of the transformation of Sainte-Beuve's "bel esprit . . . au gout détestable" [12] into the *accoucheur* of ideas who brought science to bed of the Enlightenment.[13] Carré discovers in him a sort of preincarnation of Voltaire, without the fire and passion that informed the life and work of Voltaire.[14] Cosentini, in turn, offers us Fontenelle as a lesser master of the art of philosophic dialogue,[15] and Shackleton gives us a

that the translator of the *Opticks,* one Coste, included in the preface and which Fontenelle took as coming from Newton himself; see G. Bonno, "Deux lettres inédites de Fontenelle à Newton," *Modern Language Notes 44,* 188–190 (1939); David Brewster, *Memoirs of the Life, Writings, and Discoveries of Sir Isaac Newton,* 2 vols. (Edinburgh, 1855), II, 290–295, 494–500.

[9] The suggestion of Robert Shackleton that Fontenelle's treatment of this question may be taken as the beginning of his systematic anti-Newtonianism is to be treated with reserve. See Shackleton's introduction to his edition of Fontenelle, *Entretiens sur la pluralité des mondes* (Oxford, 1955), pp. 20–28.

[10] *Journal des Savants 67,* 546 (1720), in a review of the French translation of the *Opticks* (Amsterdam, 1720).

[11] A. Laborde-Milaà, *Fontenelle* (Paris, 1905).

[12] C. A. Sainte-Beuve, *Causeries du Lundi* (Paris, n. d.), III, 314–335.

[13] Louis Maigron, *Fontenelle, l'homme, l'oeuvre, l'influence* (Paris, 1906).

[14] J. R. Carré, *La Philosophie de Fontenelle, ou la sourire de la raison* (Paris, 1932).

[15] John W. Cosentini, *Fontenelle's Art of Dialogue* (New York, 1952).

Fontenelle *savant* and dignifies the *Entretiens,* which made his reputation, with all the apparatus of an elaborate variorum edition.[16]
Grégoire, finally, finds that the career of the permanent secretary
of the Academy was a mask to philosophic disenchantment and
his commitment to science a role played but not believed by a
secret nihilist.[17] This is not the place to choose between these Fon-
tenelles, or to add another to the list. But it may perhaps be per-
missible to suggest that the sardonic manner, the tendency to
denigrate his own commitments, which give rise to such varying
interpretations may have been in part the expression of uneasy
consciousness that he remained an amateur, a science reporter and
not a *savant.* The *Éloge* of Malebranche includes a remark discon-
certing to the intellectual historian. "On peut savoir," writes Fontenelle, "l'histoire des pensées des hommes sans penser." [18] And whatever else he was, Fontenelle was a historian of ideas.

He was also a humanist of science, and his best efforts were devoted to the men of science, to his colleagues. His *éloges* remain his
finest work.[19] Here his distinctive qualities appear to best advantage: the personal dispassionateness, the respect for knowledge, the
real if not always discriminating comprehension of scientific accomplishments, the faith he expressed (whether or not he felt it) in
the civilizing mission of science, the talent for lucid exposition if
not for profound discussion (he was never profound). He disliked
the term *éloge* since he conceived these essays not as eulogies, but
as historical sketches supplementing the account of the work of the
year which he prepared for each volume of the *Histoire et mémoires*

[16] See above, note 9. Shackleton also prints the *Digression sur les anciens et les
modernes* in this useful volume.

[17] Grégoire, *Fontenelle;* see especially his summaries, pp. 270–271 and 465–466.
This work contains the best discussion of Fontenelle's science, and of his attitude
to Newtonianism; see especially pp. 119–184.

[18] Fontenelle, *Oeuvres,* 8 vols. (Paris, 1790–1792), VI, 416.

[19] First published in the current volumes of the *Histoire de l'Académie,* they were
collected in volumes VI and VII of the edition of the *Oeuvres* cited in note 18, and
selections have been several times reprinted. An English translation of the early
éloges was published in 1717, under the title *The Lives of the French, Italian and Ger-
man Philosophers,* which contains, too, a selection from "some of the most curious
Relations of Philosophical Matters," in offering which the translator (John Cham-
berlayne) has "affected to join the *Utile* with the *Dulce,* according to the Poet's
Advice."

de l'Académie.[20] The vein is ceremonial and impartial, elegant and concise, objective and decently respectful—combinations achieved more readily by the French mind and language than the English.

For a long time the *éloge* of Newton served as the cornerstone of Newtonian biography, and not only in the sense that it was the first. Though somewhat obscured by translation, the trail of Fontenelle's phrases can be followed through successive accounts of Newton's life well into the nineteenth century. Even the structure of Fontenelle's essay proved remarkably durable. Here appear the essential features of posterity's image of Newton. Here Newton and Descartes are set over against each other as the prototypes of the inductive and deductive philosophers, though of the many commentators who elaborated this comparison, none hit upon so happy a thought as Fontenelle in balancing their merits. Here, too, occur, among other things, the story of the youthful Newton's inattention to business and absorption in his studies; the description of how mathematics came to him at a glance (only the nineteenth century turned him also into a mechanical prodigy); the portrait of the insatiable investigator, whose "accurate and importunate" manner of research is an object lesson to all who would interrogate nature; the account of his entry into public affairs to defend the university from James II and of his later practical life at the Mint and the Royal Society; the attributing of his reluctance to publish his discoveries to his loathing for controversy; the tale of his solution of Bernoulli's problem at the end of a tiring day; and the delineation of his outstanding personal characteristics—manners, modesty, kindliness, generosity, and appearance (unfortunately Fontenelle was misinformed about Newton's appearance, and there were in fact unhappy episodes in his life in which the qualities appropriate to the role of selfless and retiring searcher into nature were honored in the breach).

One crucial episode, featured in all later biographies, does not appear in the *éloge*. In 1727, Fontenelle did not know of that most famous meditation in the history of science, the train of thought about the force retaining the moon in her orbit, which had come to Newton as he sat at home in the garden in the plague year of

[20] Francisque Bouillier, in the introduction to his edition of the *Eloges* (Paris, 1883), pp. xxiii ff.

1666 and had led him to his theory of gravitation. The first account of this event was published in the preface to Henry Pemberton's *View of Sir Isaac Newton's Philosophy* (1728). In the article on Newton printed in 1738 in the *General Dictionary,* Pemberton's information was incorporated into that found in the *éloge,* in the first appearance of what became the standard narrative of Newton's personal history.[21] The same article gave a rather more detailed and documented treatment of Newton's thought than had Fontenelle, and for this purpose the author published a selection from the scientific papers and correspondence. In 1760, the *Biographia Britannica* printed an even larger selection.[22] Neither of these articles, however, altered the picture derived from Fontenelle and Pemberton. Nor did the other accounts that appeared here and there throughout the eighteenth century.[23]

The first work really to supersede Fontenelle was Sir David Brew-

[21] The *General Dictionary,* 10 vols. (1734–1741), was the English translation and adaptation of Bayle's *Dictionary,* based on the latest Paris edition, and "interspersed with several thousand lives never before published. The whole containing the history of the most illustrious persons of all ages and nations, particularly those of Great Britain and Ireland . . ." Newton's life was one of the additions.

It will be noticed that the famous story of the apple does not appear in the *éloge.* Neither is it mentioned in Pemberton. Fontenelle knew of it, from the biographical information sent him by John Conduitt (see below, n. 30), who, however, says only that "He first thought of his system of gravity . . . by observing an apple fall from a tree," and does not describe the train of thought to which it led. Not knowing this, Fontenelle would not have seen the point, and it was left to Voltaire to work this anecdote into the biographical corpus. For the authenticity of the story, see Jean Pelseneer, "La Pomme de Newton," *Ciel et Terre* (1937), 1–4, and G. R. de Beer and Douglas McKie, "Newton's Apple" and "Newton's Apple —an Addendum," *Notes and Records of the Royal Society 9,* 46–54, 333–335 (1951–52). The authors omit only to point out that it was not until the article by Benjamin Martin (below, n. 23) that what Voltaire referred to as "fruits" were generally identified as apples. The story of a single apple was apparently not canonical until the 19th century.

[22] To the material from Fontenelle, Pemberton, and the scientific correspondence itself, this article added a few anecdotes drawn from Whiston's reminiscences, available only since 1749: *Memoirs of the Life and Writings of Mr. William Whiston,* 2 vols. (London, 1749). Here appears for the first time the explanation that in 1666 Newton supposed the discrepancy between the theoretical and the observed positions of the moon, which caused him to set aside his work on gravity, to be the consequence of the disturbing influence of the Cartesian vortex.

[23] For example, *Universal Magazine 3,* 289–300 (1748); Benjamin Martin, *Biographia Philosophica* (London, 1764), pp. 361–376; Paolo Frisi, *Elogio del Cavaliere I. Newton* (Milan, 1778).

ster's *Life of Sir Isaac Newton*.[24] Suggestions had been advanced by Biot that Newton had suffered a period of mental derangement, that, though he recovered his sanity, he never regained his scientific powers, and that his religious writings were the products of intellectual decay.[25] These theories shocked Brewster into producing the first full-length biography. It was a work of national and scientific piety, which displayed Newton, in Brewster's own phrase, as the "high priest," not to say the Sir Galahad, of science. The tendency, well developed even before Brewster, to make Newton's life an edifying object lesson, reached its nadir in an anonymous work published in 1860, *The Triumphs of Perseverance and Enterprise,* "written with the view to inspire the youthful reader with a glow of emulation, and to induce him to toil and advance in the peaceful achievements of science and benevolence, remembering the adage, 'Whatever man has done, man may do.'" This sort of thing produced a reaction, of course,[26] and now the wheel has come full circle, turning through disputes about Newton's character and theories about his mental processes, until J. W. N. Sullivan advances as the key to his life the proposition that, the greatest of scientists, he thought science unimportant,[27] and Lord Keynes, with Bloomsbury perversity, describes him as the last of the magicians.[28] It has, indeed, been Newton's fate that other people have always projected their philosophies or theologies of science upon him in explanation of his achievements. It is refreshing, therefore, to turn back to the plainer

[24] London, 1831. In 1855 appeared a second and enlarged edition, which printed a few selections from Newton's correspondence; see note 8, above.

[25] Biot wrote the article "Newton" (1821) in the Michaud *Biographie universelle,* vol. 30, pp. 367–404; see especially pp. 390–391, 402. A selection of Newton's theological writings has recently been published, Herbert MacLachlan, ed., *Sir Isaac Newton's Theological Manuscripts* (Liverpool, 1950). In 1829 Henry (later Lord) Brougham published what was essentially a translation of the Biot article, *Life of Sir Isaac Newton* (London, 1829), which appeared in the Library of Useful Knowledge series and appears to have been the immediate occasion of Brewster's work. For Biot's criticism of the Brewster *Memoirs* (see preceding note), see *Journal des Savants,* Oct. and Nov. 1855, 589–606, 662–677.

[26] See particularly Augustus de Morgan, *Essays on the Life and Work of Newton* (Chicago, 1914). The first of these essays appeared in *The Cabinet Portrait Gallery of British Worthies* (London, 1846).

[27] *Isaac Newton* (London, 1938).

[28] "Newton, the Man," *Newton Tercentenary Celebrations, 15–19 July 1946,* published by The Royal Society (Cambridge, 1947), 27–34.

account of Fontenelle, embellished only with literary grace, where, if the mystery of Newton's genius is not dispelled, neither is it deepened. [29]

Fontenelle drew his discussion of Newton's scientific accomplishments from his own knowledge; for the biographical facts, however, he relied entirely on notes sent him by John Conduitt, who had married Newton's niece.[30] Unfortunately, Conduitt was most dissatisfied with the use Fontenelle made of the information. "I fear," wrote Conduitt of Fontenelle after the *éloge* was published, "he had neither abilities nor inclination to do justice to that great man, who has eclipsed the glory of their hero, Descartes." [31] There were no real grounds for these complaints, but Fontenelle had, in fact, omitted several points included by Conduitt, among them a number of derogatory remarks about Descartes's hypotheses and the statement that Newton originally undertook the study of mathematics to discover whether there was anything in judicial astrology. He ignored Conduitt's request that he recall the passages in his *éloges* of l'Hôpital and Leibniz which allowed Leibniz a portion of the credit for developing the calculus. He passed lightly and tactfully over Newton's ventures into history, chronology, and divinity, about which Conduitt had given him a considerable amount of information. And though he compares England favorably to France in regard to the respect which society accorded to men of science, it is also clear from his reserve that he regarded the contemporary apotheosis of Newton as excessive, and not only in contrast to the neglect encountered by Descartes in his last years. To a temperament like Fontenelle's, apotheosis was a repellent process, no matter whom it involved.

Fontenelle always remained faithful to the cosmology he had

[29] For a complete guide to the biographical literature, see G. J. Gray, *A Bibliography . . . of Sir Isaac Newton* (2nd ed., Cambridge, 1907), together with *A Descriptive Catalogue of the Grace K. Babson Collection of the Works of Sir Isaac Newton* (New York, 1950) and its *Supplement* (Babson Institute, 1955), corrected in a few particulars in the *compte-rendu* by G. F. Shirras, *Archives internationales d'histoire des sciences 29*, 949–953 (1950). The most comprehensive biography is that by Louis T. More, *Isaac Newton* (New York and London, 1934).

[30] These notes were published in Edmund Turnor, *Collections for the History of the Town and Soke of Grantham* (London, 1806).

[31] *Dictionary of National Biography*, article "John Conduitt."

learned and expounded as a young man. His last book, *Théorie des tourbillons cartésiens* (1752), was also one of the last general defenses of the system to see print. But though his life embraced almost the full span of Cartesian science, he must not be regarded as the moribund champion of some fossilized doctrine. Cartesianism was a living body of thought about nature. On the basis of the principles laid down by Descartes, there developed a real physics—indeed *too real* because too literal.[32] Nor was Descartes exempt from the spirit of criticism he enjoined. Already by 1700, there were several schools. Malebranche had created a Catholic Cartesianism, to which was opposed the skeptical Cartesianism represented by Fontenelle. Yet it was from Malebranche that Fontenelle took the doctrine of spherical vortices to oppose to the Newtonian theory of gravity.

The web of resistance to Newton was, in fact, complex. Some strands ran parallel and others counter to each other. In the *éloge* there is apparent the influence, not just of Descartes and Malebranche, but of Huygens and of Leibniz. For Huygens, the true physicist, the decisive objection was concrete. What was inadmissible in Newtonianism was primarily the idea of a universal attraction subsisting between all the particles of the world as an inherent property of matter "parce qu'une telle hypothèse nous éloignerait fort des principes mathématiques ou mécaniques." [33] But for Leibniz and the general run of Cartesians the problem arose from differing conceptions of what science does.[34] In the Cartesian view, for all its hostility to scholasticism, science moves through nature from definition to explanation; in that of Leibniz it moves rather from

[32] See the excellent book by Paul Mouy, cited in note 6.

[33] Nor did Huygens think that Newton could have seriously meant that gravity is an essential property of matter. See "Théorie de la pesanteur," *Oeuvres complètes de Christiaan Huygens* (The Hague, 1944), XXI, 474; quoted too by Mouy, pp. 260–261, in his discussion of Huygens and Newton.

[34] This whole question has been treated by many writers, of course, and from many points of view. For the Cartesian side, see (in addition to Mouy and Grégoire, note 6), Francisque Bouillier, *Histoire de la philosophie cartésienne*, 2 vols. (Paris and Lyon, 1854). For the differences between Newton and Leibniz, see Alexander, *The Leibniz-Clarke Correspondence*, with the editor's introduction; Ernst Cassirer, *Leibniz' System in seinem wissenchaftlichen Grundlagen* (Marburg, 1902), esp. pp. 245–282; Josef Durdik, *Leibniz und Newton* (Halle, 1869); F. S. C. Northrop, "Leibniz's Theory of Space," *Journal of the History of Ideas 7*, 422–446 (1946); and an interesting unpublished doctoral dissertation in the library of Princeton Uni-

principles to values; and in that of Newtonians from descriptions to abstract generalizations. Strictly speaking, therefore, Newtonian science could never get outside itself, and might in a sense be said to be a tautology, or at least to accomplish nothing of interest or value.

More immediately, the theory of gravity was unacceptable to Cartesians because of their commitment to a mechanistic universe. For Leibniz, though a strict mechanist in practice, the planetary theory was excluded rather by his commitment to a finalism unreconcilable with Newton's way of taking the phenomena as given, as the data of thought. Disagreements were profound on the fundamental question of space. Descartes having unified his science by identifying space and matter, it remained for them to be properly distinguished: unsuccessfully by Leibniz, who turned space from a substance into a relation (that of simultaneous events), after which he sought to unite his system metaphysically by the principle of preëstablished harmony; successfully by Newton's bolder stroke of emptying space to turn it into the physical expression of an abstract geometry (and an attribute of God), after which he did unite his system around the principle of gravity.[35] Fontenelle, for his part, rejected the very different providentialisms of Malebranche, of Leibniz—and of Newton. But for Leibniz (seeing more deeply, showing more insight into the rationalizing powers of the calculus), what was abhorrent in Newtonianism was not its providentialism, but the exact contrary, its tendency to lead in the direction already marked by Hobbes, a self-sufficient materialism destructive of natural religion. One important matter found Newtonians and Cartesians standing together. Both rejected finalism in scientific explanation, and, in the controversy over vis viva, both held as against Leibniz that the

versity, Nicholas Rescher, "Leibniz' Cosmology: A Reinterpretation of the Philosophy of Leibniz in the Light of his Physical Theories" (1951). For Fontenelle's respect for Leibniz, see his *Eloge de Leibniz, Oeuvres,* VI, 450–505. The best guides to Newton's principles are Alexandre Koyré, "The Significance of the Newtonian Synthesis," *Archives internationales d'histoire des sciences 29,* 291–311 (1950), and F. Rosenberger, *I. Newton und seine physikalischen Prinzipien* (Leipzig, 1895).

[35] I owe this way of seeing it to Koyré, "The Significance of the Newtonian Synthesis." On space as a divine attribute, see Alexander, *Leibniz-Clarke Correspondence,* pp. xiv, 47 (Clarke's Fourth Reply to Leibniz).

quantity conserved in a dynamical situation is momentum and not kinetic energy.[36]

On the whole, the confrontation of Newton with Leibniz was philosophically more interesting and deeper; that of Newton with Descartes was historically more influential and more obvious—in some respects, indeed, this latter was the kind of opposition which in mathematics is expressed by a change of sign from plus to minus. But on specific points about the actual working of the real world, the influences of Leibniz and Descartes came together in the way reflected in the *caveats* and passing emphases in Fontenelle's *éloge* which imply his own disbelief that Newton's was a satisfactory picture of what happens.

For example, Newton's adherents did not, like Fontenelle, describe the *Principia* as resting equally on two leading theories, one concerned with the force of attraction exerted by bodies, the other with the resistance offered by fluid mediums to motion. Expositions by Newtonians generally emphasized the former, the positive, constructive side of Newton's work, rather than the latter which, though it is indeed the subject of much of Book II, served rather the negative purpose of disproving the existence of Cartesian vortices.[37] Further on, at the close of his discussion, Fontenelle complained in passing that Newton never makes clear what causes gravity itself, wherein it consists, or how action at a distance is mechanically possible. Now this was the crucial objection which united all the opponents of Newton. To call gravity a force of attraction was no clarification. Attraction had not even the elementary merit of working properly. From time to time Newton's cosmos got out of order, and Providence had to step in to repair it. Nor was the idea comprehensible, and in place of attraction Fontenelle suggested the term "impulse" as more appropriate. In Cartesian mechanics, force was transmitted in good, concrete, di-

---

[36] There is a good account of this well-known issue in Martial Gueroult, *Dynamique et métaphysique leibniziennes* (Paris, 1934).

[37] See, for example, Henry Pemberton, *A View of Sir Isaac Newton's Philosophy* (London, 1728); Colin Maclaurin, *Account of Sir Isaac Newton's Philosophical Discoveries* (London, 1748); Voltaire, *Elémens de la philosophie de Newton* (Amsterdam, 1738). For a useful guide, see W. W. Rouse Ball, *An Essay on Newton's Principia* (London, 1893).

rect ways: by impact, by pressure, by the frictional drag of swirl-
ing vortices of cosmic stuff, none the less real for being subtle,
which carried the planets around in their courses. (Fontenelle, it
will be noticed, included no discussion of the laws of motion or of
Newtonian mechanics.) To describe the fall of an apple or the motion of the moon and the tides not as a definite push by something
against something else, but as the pull of an intangible force, itself
inexplicable, was to offer not an explanation, but, like the scho-
lastics, a mystification, a word in place of a fact. And as gravity
seemed simply an occult force or a perpetual miracle, so the Newtonian idea of an empty space across which it flings its influence
seemed a reversion to the mysterious void that had only recently
been filled up by the Cartesian plenum. So nebulous was the whole
conception that, in the 1730's, Fontenelle saw the theory of gravity
as a passing fancy, of some value perhaps for having posed certain
criticisms which inspired improvements in the system of vortices at
the hands of Privat de Moliéres.

Fontenelle did admire the matchless mathematical virtuosity displayed in the *Principia*. The trouble was not in the mathematics,
but that, taken as an explanation of the universe, the system failed
—or rather that it was no explanation at all since no cause could
be assigned for its central principle, the principle of attraction, and
since it substituted for a concrete, working, mechanical picture a
set of mathematical and geometrical abstractions. At issue, in fact,
was the question, as old as Aristotle, whether mathematics and
nature really fit. Newton (writes Fontenelle) "s'est mis dans le
Vuide, à des forces mouvantes connuës & Méchaniques il a substitué
une force inconnuë & Métaphisique, une Attraction, dont on ne
peut prêvoir les effets, mais que l'on suppose telle que certains
faits établis la demandent, & qui par conséquent satisfait toujours
précisément à tout. M. l'Abbé de Moliéres lui reproche même
assés finement cette extrême précision, les principes Phisiques n'en
ont pas tant, lorsqu'on vient à les appliquer aux Phénomenes." [38]
The trouble with Newton's mathematical approach was that the fit
with phenomena is impossibly tight. It squeezes out reality, where
things rub against each other physically in a looser, a more com-

[38] *Histoire de l'Academie Royale des Sciences* (1733), p. 94.

prehensible meshing with ordinary experience, and where there is always something left over from an explanation in case it is needed. Much earlier, Fontenelle had remarked approvingly of Malebranche's numberless "petits tourbillons" that their being applicable to the explanation of so many phenomena—light, heat, sound, electricity, weight, whatnot—created a strong presumption in their favor. "Voilà un grand fonds de force pour tous les besoins de la physique"—even those not yet foreseen.[39] For Fontenelle, a theory that comes out precisely *even*, so to say, simply *circles* (whether through reality or not) right back to its starting place.

It may at first seem odd that the Cartesians, whose very definition of matter was mathematical, should have accused the Newtonians of excessive abstraction. But the penalty attached to over-mathematicizing nature in the fashion of Descartes was precisely that the process simultaneously coarsened and adulterated mathematics by confusing its province with that of mechanics and its procedures with common sense. In retrospect, of course, it is apparent that the two arguments never really met, that the two sides were talking about different things. The Newtonians—at least when answering Cartesian critics—claimed only that Newton discovered a relation; the Cartesians accused him of not having found a cause. To the Cartesian complaint that, the cause of attraction being unexplained, the force of gravity was a figment of Newton's mind, an Aristotelian tendency, the Newtonians retorted that, explicable or not, the relation subsisted in phenomena, and that it was Descartes who had imagined, not a force to be sure, but a substance and a motion to explain mechanically what no one could yet understand, the ultimate cause that lies behind the laws of nature, laws which themselves are to be taken only as descriptive generalizations of appearances and not as causes, which derive (it may be) from God whose ways it would be as impious as impossible to prescribe.[40]

Since Newton actually did not provide what Fontenelle required, a system which accounted at once for the behavior and the cause

[39] Fontenelle, "Eloge de Malebranche," *Oeuvres,* VI, 422.

[40] See the General Scholium to the *Principia,* 2nd ed. This, together with other relevant passages from Newton's writings, is printed as an appendix in Alexander, *Leibniz-Clarke Correspondence,* pp. 143–183.

of phenomena, which saw nature steadily and saw it whole, it is
not surprising that, like most Cartesians, he remained unconvinced.
There is, perhaps, a certain irony in the circumstance that Newton's theory, which countless intellectual historians have described
as responsible for the 18th-century picture of a soulless, determi-
nistic world machine, should have been rejected at the time on the
ground that it was overly abstract and insufficiently mechanical
and that it called the hand of Providence into the workings of the
world. And on reflection, it may, after all, seem appropriate that
Newton's first biographer was a Cartesian and a Frenchman. For,
if the English deified Newton, the French rationalized him. Belief
in the self-sufficiency of natural order, expressed by the materialist
philosophes who followed Fontenelle, must be attributed not to the
legacy of Newton, but to that of Descartes[41]—tempered less by
Newton than by Hobbes. The perfectly synchronized world machine that is supposed to have sprung out of Newton's brain to
place itself at the service of the Enlightenment was actually a
fairly uncertain mechanism until, well after the Enlightenment was
past its zenith, it was tidied up mathematically by Laplace—inspired (it might be argued) by the Cartesian spirit which insists on
order and unity. And, on the other hand, the adoption of Newtonianism and the challenge presented by its irregularities were
among the chief influences that carried the rational genius of
France to the leadership of the world of science in the late 18th
century.

The number of editions of the *éloge* published in London con-
firms the admiration of the English public for Newton at the time
of his death. In addition to the Tonson edition reproduced here,
there were at least three others, two of which were different translations. Even in Paris, Newton's death appears to have aroused
considerable interest. The *éloge* of Newton was one of the few that
Fontenelle published separately, and besides that edition (1728),
there was also a single-sheet folio *abrégé* of the same year.

---

[41] See the stimulating book by Aram Vartanian, *Diderot and Descartes* (Princeton,
1953), where this point is argued with much force—perhaps with too much force,
seeing that Mr. Vartanian takes no account of the influence of the associationist
psychology on conceptions of scientific explanation from Locke and Condillac
through the taxonomists and chemists of the latter part of the century to the
idéologues.

The style of the original is graceful, urbane, and good-humored, with here and there a hint of reserve. These qualities are largely lost in the translation, which is frequently clumsy and nowhere better than adequate. In the 18th century as now, "Etranger" meant foreigner rather than stranger (see the last paragraph), and there must have been a better expression for "Grandeur de la surface" than "Magnitude of the Superficies." But the most curious feature of the *éloge* appears also in the original, and that is that Fontenelle should have concluded in good Victorian style by holding up Leibniz and Newton to admiration as exemplars of thrift!

T H E

E L O G I U M

O F

Sir *ISAAC NEWTON:*

B Y

Monſieur *FONTENELLE,*

Perpetual Secretary of the Royal Academy of Sciences at *Paris.*

L O N D O N:

Printed for J. Tonson in the *Strand,* and J. Osborn and T. Longman in *Pater-noſter Row.*

MDCCXXVIII.

[3]

THE
ELOGIUM
O F
Sir *ISAAC NEWTON,*
B Y
Monſieur *FONTENELLE.*

SIR Iſaac Newton, who was born at Woolſtrope in the county of Lincoln, on Chriſtmas day in the year 1642, deſcended from the elder branch of the family of Sir John Newton Baronet. The Manor of Woolſtrope had been in his Family near 200 years. The Newtons came thither from Weſtby in the ſame County, but originally from Newton in Lancaſhire. Sir Iſaac's Mother, whoſe maiden name was Hannah Aſcough, was likewiſe of an ancient family; ſhe married again after his Father's death.

When her Son was twelve years old ſhe put him to the Free-ſchool at Grantham; from whence ſhe

A 2   removed

[4]

removed him some years after, that he might be ac-
cuftomed betimes to look into his affairs, and to manage them himfelf. But fhe found him fo carelefs of
fuch Bufinefs, and fo taken up with his books, that fhe
fent him again to Grantham, that he might be at liberty to follow his inclinations; which he farther in-
dulged by going to Trinity college in Cambridge, where
he was admitted in 1660, being then eighteen years
of age.

In learning Mathematicks he did not ftudy Euclid,
who feemed to him too plain and too fimple, and not
worthy of taking up his time; he underftood him almoft before he read him, and a caft of his eye upon the
contents of the Theorems was fufficient to make him
mafter of them. He advanced at once to the Geometry of Des Cartes, Kepler's Opticks, &c. fo that we
may apply to him what Lucan faid of the Nile, whofe
head was not known by the Ancients,

Arcanum Natura caput non prodidit ulli,
Nec licuit populis parvum te, Nile, videre. Lucan. l. x.

Nature conceals thy infant Stream with care,
Nor lets thee, but in Majefty appear.

It is certain that Sir Ifaac had made his great Difcoveries in Geometry, and laid the foundation of his two
famous pieces the *Principia* and the *Opticks* by the time
that he was twenty four years of age. If thofe
Beings that are fuperior to Man have likewife a
progreffion in Knowledge, they fly whilft we
creep, and leap over thofe *mediums* by which we proceed

[5]

ceed flowly and with difficulty from one Truth to another that has a relation to it.

Nicholas Mercator, who was born in Holftein, but
fpent moft of his time in England, publifhed in 1668
his *Logarithmotechnia*, in which he gave the Quadrature of the Hyperbola by an infinite Series. This
was the firft appearance, in the learned world, of a Series
of this fort, drawn from the particular nature of the Curve,
and that in a manner very new and abftracted. The
famous Dr. Barrow, then at Cambridge, where Mr.
Newton, who was about 26 years of age, refided, re-
collected that he had met with the fame thing in the
writings of that young gentleman, and there not confined to
the Hyperbola only, but extended by general forms to all
forts of Curves, even fuch as are mechanical, to their
quadratures, their rectifications and their centers of Gravity, to the folids formed by their rotations, and to the
fuperficies of thofe folids; fo that fuppofing their determinations to be poffible, the Series ftopt at a certain
point, or at leaft their fums were given by ftated
rules: But if the abfolute determinations were impoffible,
they could yet be infinitely approximated which is the
happieft and moft refined method of fupplying the defects
of Human knowledge that Man's imagination could poffibly invent. To be mafter of fo fruitful and general a
Theory was a mine of gold to a Geometrician, but it
was a greater glory to have been the difcoverer of fo
furprizing and ingenious a Syftem. So that Sir Ifaac
finding by Mercator's book that he was in the way to
it, and that others might follow in his track, fhould
naturally have been forward to open his treafures, and

fecure

[6]

secure the property, which confifted in making the difcovery.   But he contented himfelf with his treafure
which he had found, without regarding the glory.   He
himfelf fays in a letter of the *Commercium epiftolicum*, *that
he thought Mercator had entirely difcovered the fecret, or that others would difcover it before he was of an
age to write himfelf*.   He without any concern fuffered
that to be taken from him, from which he might propofe to himfelf abundance of glory, and flatter himfelf
with the moft pleafing expectations.   He waited with
patience till he was of a fit age to write, or to make
himfelf known to the world, though he was already
capable of the greateft things.

His manufcript upon Infinite feries was communicated to none but Mr. Collins, and the Lord Broun-
ker, both learned in that way.   And even this had not
been done, but for Dr. Barrow, who would not fuffer
him to indulge his modefty fo much as he defired.

This Manufcript was taken out of the Author's ftudy
in the year 1669, entitled, *The method which I formerly
found out*, &c. and fuppofing this *formerly* to mean no
more than three years, he muft then have difcovered
this admirable Theory of his feries when he was not
twenty four years of age; but what is ftill more, this manufcript contains both the difcovery and method of
Fluxions, or thofe *infinitely fmall quantities*, which have
occafioned fo great a conteft between M. Leibnits and
him, or rather between Germany and England; of
which I have given an account in 1716, in * the
Elogium upon M. Leibnits; and tho' it was in the

Elogium

* p. 109, &c.

[7]

Elogium of M. Leibnits, the impartiality of an Historian was so exactly kept that there now remains
nothing new to be said of Sir Isaac Newton. It was
there particularly observed *that Sir Isaac was undoubtedly the Inventor, that his glory was secure, and that the only
question was, whether M. Leibnits did take this notion from
him.* All England is convinced that he did take it from
him, tho' the Royal Society have not declared so in
their Determination, but only hinted it at most. However
Sir Isaac Newton was certainly the first Discoverer, and
that too by many years. M. Leibnits on the other side
was the first that published the Method, and if he did
take it from Sir Isaac, he at least resembled Prometheus in
the fable, who stole fire from the Gods to impart it
to Mankind.

In 1687 Sir Isaac at length resolved to unveil
himself and shew what he was, and accordingly the
Philosophiæ Naturalis principia Mathematica appeared in
the world. This book, in which the most profound
Geometry serves for a basis to a new system of Philosophy, had not at first all the reputation which it deserved, and which it was afterwards to acquire. As it
is written with great learning, conceived in few
words, and the consequences often arise so sud-
denly from their principles, that the Reader is obliged himself to supply the connection, it required
time for the Publick to become masters of it. Considerable Geometricians could not understand it without great application; and those of a lower class undertook it not, 'till they were excited by the applause
of the most skillful, but at length when the book

I   was

[8]

was fufficiently underftood, all thefe applaufes which it fo flowly acquired broke out on all fides, and united in a general admiration. Every body was ftruck with that Original fpirit that fhines throughout the whole work, that mafterly genius which in the whole compafs of the happieft age was fhared only amongft three or four men picked out from all the moft learned Nations.

There are two Theories which chiefly prevail in the *Principia*, That of the Central power, and that of the Refiftance which mediums make to Motion, both almoft entirely new, and treated of according to the fublime Geometry of the Author. We can never touch upon either of thefe fubjects without having Sir Ifaac before us, without repeating what he has faid, or following his track, and if we endeavour'd to difguife it, what skill could prevent Sir Ifaac Newton's appearing in it?

The relation between the revolutions of the Heavenly bodies and their diftances from the common center of thofe revolutions, found out by Kepler, prevails throughout the whole Celeftial fyftem. If we fuppofe, as it is neceffary, that a certain force hinders thefe great bodies from purfuing, above an inftant, their natural motion in a ftreight line from Weft to Eaft, and continually draws them towards a center; it follows, by Kepler's rule, that this force, which will be central or rather centripetal, will act differently upon the fame body according to its different diftances from that center, and this in the reciprocal proportion of the fquares of thofe diftances; that is, for

inftance,

[9]

inftance, if a body be at twice the diftance from the center of its revolution, the action of the central force upon it will be four times weaker. It appears that Sir Ifaac fet out from hence when he entered upon his phyficks of the world in general: We may likewife fuppofe or imagine that he firft confidered the Moon, becaufe the Earth is the center of her motion.

If the Moon fhould lofe all her impulfe or inclination to move from Weft to Eaft in a ftraight line, and if nothing but the central power remained which forces her towards the center of the Earth, fhe would then only obey that power, only follow its directions, and move in a ftrait line towards that center. The velocity of her motion being known, Sir Ifaac demonftrates from that motion that in the firft minute of her defcent fhe would fall 15 Paris feet: her diftance from the Earth is 60 femi-diameters of the Earth, therefore when the Moon comes to the furface of the Earth, the action of the force which brought her thither will be encreafed as the fquare of 60, that is, it would be 3600 times ftronger; fo that the Moon in her laft minute would fall 3600 times 15 feet.

Now if we fuppofe that the force which would have acted upon the Moon is the fame which we call Gravity in terreftrial bodies, it will follow from the fyftem of Galileo that the Moon, which at the furface of the Earth would have fallen 3600 times 15 feet in a minute, fhould likewife have fallen 15 feet in the firft 60th part, or in the firft fecond of that minute. Now

B   it

[10]

it is known by all experiments, and they only can be
made at fmall diftances from the furface of the Earth, that
heavy bodies fall 15 feet in the firft fecond of their
fall: Therefore as to the velocity of their fall they are
exactly in the fame condition, as if having made the
fame revolution round the Earth that the Moon doth
and at the fame diftance, they fhould happen to fall by
the mere force of their Gravity; and if they are in the
fame condition as the Moon, the Moon is in the
fame condition as they, and is only moved each inftant towards the Earth by the fame Gravity. So exact
an agreement of effects, or rather this perfect identity
can proceed from nothing elfe but the caufes being the
fame.

It is true that in the fyftem of Galileo, which is
here followed, the Gravity is equal, and the central
force of the Moon is not fo, even in the demonftration that has juft been given; but Gravity may well
not difcover its inequality, or rather, it only appears
equal in all our experiments, becaufe the greateft height
from which we can obferve bodies falling is nothing
in comparifon of 1500 leagues, the diftance which
they all are from the center of the Earth.   It is demonftrated that a Canon bullet fhot horizontally defcribes, in the Hypothefis of equal Gravity, a parabolic line, terminated at a certain point, where it
meets with the Earth, but if it was fhot from an height
confiderable enough to make the inequality of the
action of its Gravity perceptible, inftead of a Parabola
it would defcribe an Ellipfis, of which the center of the
Earth

[11]

Earth would be one of the Foci, that is, it would perform exactly what the Moon doth.

If the Moon hath Gravity like terreftrial bodies, if fhe is moved towards the Earth by the fame power, by which they are moved; if, according to Sir Ifaac's expreffion, fhe gravitates towards the Earth, the fame caufe acts upon all the reft of that wonderful concourfe of heavenly bodies ; for all nature is one and the fame, there is every where the fame difpofition, every where Ellipfes will be defcribed by bodies, whofe motions are directed to a body placed in one of their Foci. The Satellites of Jupiter will gravitate towards Jupiter, as the Moon gravitates towards the Earth; the Satellites of Saturn towards Saturn, and all the Planets together towards the Sun.

It is not known in what Gravity confifts. Sir Ifaac Newton himfelf was ignorant of it. If Gravity acts only by impulfe, we may conceive that a block of marble falling, may be pufhed towards the Earth, without the Earth being in any manner pufhed towards it; and in a word all the centers to which the motions caufed by Gravity have relation, may be immoveable. But if it acts by Attraction the Earth cannot draw the block of marble, unlefs the block of marble likewife draw the Earth, why then fhould that attractive power be in fome bodies rather than others? Sir Ifaac always fuppofes the action of Gravity in all bodies to be reciprocal and in proportion only to their bulk; and by that feems to determine Gravity to be really an attraction. He all along makes ufe of this word to

B 2   exprefs

[12]

exprefs the active power of bodies, a power indeed
unknown, and which he does not take upon him to explain; but if it can likewife act by Impulfe, why fhould not
that clearer term have the preference? for it muft be agreed
that it is by no means poffible to make ufe of them
both indifferently, fince they are fo oppofite. The
continual ufe of the word Attraction fupported by
great authority, and perhaps too by the inclination
which Sir Ifaac is thought to have had for the thing itfelf,
at leaft makes the Reader familiar with a notion explod-
ed by the Cartefians, and whofe condemnation had
been ratified by all the reft of the Philofophers; and
we muft now be upon our guard, left we imagine that
there is any reality in it, and fo expofe our felves to
the danger of believing that we comprehend it.

However all bodies according to Sir Ifaac gravitate
towards each other, or attract each other in proportion
to their Bulk : and when they revolve about a common
center, by which confequently they are attracted, and
which they attract, their attractive powers are in the
reciprocal proportion of their diftances from that center, and if all of them together with their common
center revolve round another center common to them,
and to others, this will again produce new proportions,
which will become ftrangely complex. Thus each of
the five Satellites of Saturn gravitate towards the other
four, and the other four gravitate towards it; all the
five gravitate towards Saturn, and Saturn towards them;
all together gravitate towards the Sun, and the Sun a-
gain towards them. What an excellent Geometrician
must

[13]

muſt he have been to ſeparate ſuch a Chaos of relations !
the very undertaking ſeems raſhneſs; and we cannot without aſtoniſhment conceive that from ſo abſtracted a
Theory, compoſed of ſo many ſeparate Theories, all very
difficult to handle, ſuch neceſſary concluſions ſhould ariſe,
and all conformable to the approved axioms of Aſtro-
nomy.

Sometimes theſe concluſions even foretel events,
which the Aſtronomers themſelves had not remarked.
It is aſſerted, and more eſpecially in England, that when
Jupiter and Saturn are neareſt, which is at 165 millions
of leagues diſtance, their motions have no longer the
ſame regularity as in the reſt of their courſe; and the
Syſtem of Sir Iſaac at once accounts for it, which
cannot be done by any other Syſtem. Jupiter and Saturn attract each other with greater force, becauſe they
are nearer; and by this means the regularity of the reſt
of their courſe is very ſenſibly diſordered; nay, they go
farther ſtill, and determine the quantity and the bounds
of this irregularity.

The motion of the Moon is the leaſt regular of any
of the Planets, the moſt exact tables are ſometimes
wrong, and ſhe makes certain excurſions which could not
before be accounted for. Dr. Halley, whoſe profound
skill in mathematicks has not hindered his being a
good Poet, ſays in the Latin verſes prefixt to the *Principia*,

> *Diſcimus hinc tandem qua cauſa argentea phœbe*
> *Paſſibus haud æquis graditur; cur ſubdita nulli*
> *Hactenus Aſtronomo numerorum frena recuſet.*

That

[14]

That the Moon till then never submitted to the bridle of
calculations, nor was ever broke by any Astronomer;
but that at laſt ſhe is ſubdued in this new Syſtem. All
the irregularities of her courſe are there ſhewn to proceed
from a neceſſity by which they are foretold. It is difficult
to imagine that a Syſtem in which they take this form ſhould
be no more than a lucky conjecture; eſpecially if we
conſider this but as a ſmall part of a Theory, which with
the ſame ſucceſs comprehends an infinite number of o-
ther ſolutions. The ebbing and flowing of the Tyde ſo
naturally ſhews it ſelf to proceed from the operation of
the Moon upon the Sea, combined with that of the
Sun, that the admiration which this phenomenon uſed
to raiſe in us ſeems to be leſſened by it.

The ſecond of theſe two great Theories, upon which
the *Principia* chiefly runs, is that of the Reſiſtance of
mediums to motion, which muſt enter into the conſideration of all the chief phenomena of Nature, ſuch as
the motions of the celeſtial bodies, of Light and
Sound. Sir Iſaac, according to his uſual method, lays
his foundations in the moſt ſolid proofs of Geometry, he conſiders all the cauſes from which reſiſtance
can poſſibly ariſe; the denſity of the medium, the
ſwift motion of the body moved, the magnitude of its
ſuperficies, and from thence he at laſt draws concluſions
which deſtroy all the Vortices of Des Cartes, and over-
turn that immenſe celeſtial edifice, which we might
have thought immoveable. If the Planets move round
the Sun in a certain medium whatever it be, in an
ætherial matter which fills up the whole, and which notwithſtanding

[15]

withstanding its being extreamly subtil, will yet cause
resistance as is demonstrated, whence comes it then
that the motions of the Planets are not perpetually,
nay instantly lessened? but besides this, how can Comets
traverse those Vortices freely every way, sometimes
with a tendency absolutely opposite to theirs, without
receiving any sensible alteration in their motions, tho'
of never so long a continuance? whence comes it that
these immense torrents whirling round with almost incredible velocity, do not instantly destroy the particular motion of any body, which is but an atom in comparison of them, and why do they not force it to follow their course? The Celestial Bodies do then move
in a vast vacuum, unless their exhalations and the rays of
Light which together form a thousand different mixtures, should mingle a small quantity of matter with
the almost infinite immaterial spaces. Thus Attraction
and Vacuum banished from Physicks by Des Cartes,
and in all appearance for ever, are now brought back
again by Sir Isaac Newton, armed with a power entirely new, of which they were thought incapable, and
only perhaps a little disguised.

Thefe two great men, whose Systems are so opposite,
resembled each other in several respects, they were both
Genius's of the first rank, both born with superior un-
derstandings, and fitted for the founding of Empires
in Knowledge. Being excellent Geometricians, they
both saw the necessity of introducing Geometry into
Physicks; For both founded their Physicks upon difcoveries in Geometry, which may almost be said of

none

[16]

none but themfelves. But one of them taking a bold
flight, thought at once to reach the Fountain of All
things, and by clear and fundamental ideas to make
himfelf mafter of the firft principles; that he might
have nothing more left to do, but to defcend to
the phenomena of Natures as to neceffary confequences; the other more cautious, or rather more mo-
deft, began by taking hold of the known phenomena
to climb to unknown principles; refolved to admit
them only in fuch manner as they could be produced by a
chain of confequences. The former fets out from what he
clearly underftands, to find out the caufes of what he
fees; the latter fets out from what he fees, in order to
find out the caufe, whether it be clear or obfcure. The
felf-evident principles of the one do not always lead
him to the caufes of the phenomena as they are; and
the phenomena do not always lead the other to principles fufficiently evident. The boundaries which ftop'd
two fuch men in their purfuits through different roads,
were not the boundaries of Their Underftanding, but
of Human underftanding it felf.

While Sir Ifaac was compofing his great work, the
Principia, he had alfo another in hand, as much an original and as new; which, tho' by the title it did not
feem fo genetal, is yet as extenfive by the manner in
which he has treated that particular fubject. *This work*
was his *Opticks, or treatife of Light and Colours*, which
firft appeared in the year 1704, after he had been making the neceffary experiments for thirty years together.

It

[17]

It is no fmall art to make experiments exactly. Every matter of fact which offers it felf to our confideration is complicated with fo many others, which either compound or modify it, that without abundance of skill they cannot be feparated; nay without an extraordinary fagacity, the different elements that enter into the compofition can hardly be gueffed at. The fact therefore to be confidered muft be refolved into the different ones of which it is compofed; and they themfelves are perhaps compofed of others; fo that if we have not chofen the right road, we may fometimes be engaged in endlefs Labyrinths. The Principles and Elements of things feem to have been conceal'd from us by Nature, with as much care as the Caufes, and when we attain to the difcovery of them, it is a fight entirely new and unexpected.

What Sir Ifaac Newton aims at quite through his *Opticks*, is the Anatomy of Light; this expreffion is not too bold fince it is no more than the thing it felf. By his experiments, the fmalleft ray of Light that is convey'd into a dark room, and which cannot be fo fmall, but that it is yet compounded of an infinite number of other rays, is divided and diffected in fuch manner, that the Elementary rays of which it is compofed, are feparated from each other, and difcover themfelves every one tinged with its particular colour, which after this feparation can no more be altered. The firft total ray before the diffection, is white, and this whitenefs arofe from all the particular colours of the Primitive rays. The feparating thefe rays is fo difficult, that when Ma-

C   riotte

[18]

riotte undertook it upon the firft news of Sir Ifaac's experiments, he mifcarried in the attempt, even he who
had fuch a genius for experiments, and had been fo
fuccefsful on many other fubjects.

No primitive coloured rays could be feparated, unlefs they were fuch by their nature, that in paffing
through the fame medium, or through the fame glafs
prifm, they are refracted at different angles, and by
that means feparate when they are received at proper
diftances. This different Refrangibility of rays, red, yellow, green, blue, purple, and all other colours infinite
in number, a property which was never before fufpected, and to which we could hardly be led by conjecture, is the fundamental difcovery of Sir Ifaac
Newton's treatife. The different Refrangibility leads
us to the different Reflexibility. But there is fomething
more; for the rays which fall at the fame angle upon a furface are refracted and reflected alternately, with
a kind of play only diftinguifhable to a quick eye, and
well affifted by the judgment of the Obferver. The
only point, the firft idea of which does not entirely belong to Sir Ifaac Newton, is, that the rays which pafs
near the extremities of a body without touching it, do
fomewhat turn from a ftrait line, which is called Inflection. But the whole together forms a body of Opticks fo perfectly new, that we may henceforward look
upon that fcience as almoft wholly owing to this Author.

That he might not confine himfelf to thefe bare
fpeculations, which are fometimes unjuftly ftyled idle,
he gave us the defign of a Telefcope by reflection,
which

[19]

which was not thoroughly put in execution 'till a long time after. It has here been experienc'd that one of these Telescopes but 2 foot and a half long, had as good an * effect as a tolerable common Telescope of 8 or 9 feet, which is a very extraordinary advantage, and the whole improvement of it will probabily be better known hereafter.

One advantage of this book, equal perhaps to that of the many new discoveries with which it abounds, is that it furnishes us with an excellent model of proceeding in Experimental Philosophy. When we are for prying into Nature, we ought to examine her like Sir Isaac, that is, in as accurate and importunate a manner. Things that almost hide themselves from our enquiries, as being of too abstracted a nature, he knows how to reduce to calculation, tho' such calculations might elude the skill of the best Geometricians, without that Dexterity which was peculiar to himself; and the use which he makes of his Geometry, is as artful as the Geometry it self is sublime.

He did not finish his *Opticks*, because several necessary experiments had been interrupted, and he could not begin them again. The parts of this building, which he left unfinished, could by no means be carried on but by as able hands as those of the first Architect: However he hath put such who are inclined to carry on this work in a proper method, and even chalks out to them a way to proceed from Opticks, to a compleat body of Physicks, under the form of *Doubts*, or *Queries*

C 2   pro-

* N. B. *By accurate tryals made here, a reflecting Telescope of 2 foot and a half, hath been found no ways inferior to one of the common sort, of between 40 and 50 foot long.*

[20]

propofing a great many defigns which will help future
Philofophers, or which at leaft will make a curious hiftory of the Conjectures of a great Philofopher.

Attraction is the governing principle in this fhort
plan of Phyficks; that property which is called the *Hard-
nefs* of bodies, is the mutual attraction of their parts,
which clofes them together, and if they are of fuch a
figure as that whole furfaces are capable of being every
where joined, without leaving any void fpaces, the bodies are then perfectly hard. Of this kind there are
only certain fmall bodies, which are primitive and un-
alterable, and which are the elements of all other bodies. *Fermentations,* or chimical *Effervefcences,* whofe
motion is fo violent, that they may fometimes be compared to ftorms, are the effects of this powerful attraction, which acts upon fmall bodies only at fmall diftances.

He conceives in general, that attraction is the active
principle of every thing in Nature, and the caufe of
all motion. If a certain degree of motion that is once
given to any thing by the hand of God, did afterwards only diftribute it felf according to the laws of
Percuffion, it appears that it would continually decreafe in its motion by contrary Percuffions, without
ever being able to recover itfelf, and the Univerfe
would very foon fall into fuch a ftate of reft, as
would prove the deftruction of the whole. The power
of attraction, which always fubfifts and is not weakned
by being exerted, is a perpetual fpring of action and
life. It may likewife happen that the effects of this
power may at length combine in fuch a manner, as
that

[21]

that the Syftem of the Univerfe may be difordered, and
require, according to Sir Ifaac's expreffion, *a hand to
repair it.*

He declares very freely that he lays down this attraction, only as a caufe which he knows not, and
whofe effects he only confiders, compares and calculates;
and in order to avoid the reproach of reviving the *Occult qualities* of the Schoolmen, he fays, that he efta-
blifhes none but fuch Qualities as are *manifeft* and very
vifible by their phenomena, but that the caufes of thefe
Qualities are indeed *occult,* and that he leaves it to other
Philofophers to fearch into them; but are they not properly caufes which the Schoolmen call *occult qualities;*
fince their effects are plainly feen? befides, could Sir Ifaac
think that others would find out thefe *Occult caufes*
which he could not difcover? with what hopes of fuccefs can any other man fearch after them?

At the end of his Opticks he put two treatifes of
pure Geometry, one concerning the *Quadrature of Curves*
and the other of the *Enumeration of Lines,* which he ftyles
of the *third order;* he hath fince left them out, becaufe the
fubject was too different from that of the Opticks, and
they were printed feparately in 1711, with an *Analyfis by
Infinite equations* and the *Differential method.* It would be
only repetition to fay, that throughout all his works
there appears a refined fort of Geometry that is peculiar
to himfelf.

Being fo taken up with thefe fpeculations, he fhould
naturally feem to have had no inclination to Bufinefs,
and to have been incapable of it; but yet when the

pri-

[22]

priviledges of the Univerſity of Cambridge, where he had been Mathematical Profeſſor from 1669, by Dr. Barrow's reſignation to him, were attackt by King *James* II, in 1687. (in which year he publiſhed the *Principia*) he was very zealous in aſſerting them, and the Univerſity named him one of the Delegates to the *High Commiſſion* court. He was likewiſe one of their Repreſentatives in the Convention-Parliament of 1688, and ſate in it 'till it was diſſolved.

In 1696 the Earl of Hallifax, who was Chancellor of the Exchequer and a great patron to learned men; (for the Engliſh Nobility do not think it a point of honour to ſlight them, but are frequently ſuch themſelves) obtained from King William the office of Warden of the Mint for Sir Iſaac Newton; and in this employment he was very ſerviceable in the great re-coynage at that time. Three years after he was made Maſter and Worker, a place of conſiderable profit which he enjoyed 'till his death.

It may be thought that this place in the Mint was ſuitable to him only becauſe he was an excellent Geometrician and had great skill in Phyſicks; and indeed this buſineſs often requires very difficult Calculations, and a great number of Chimical experiments, of his skilfulneſs in which there are many proofs in his *Table of the Eſſays of foreign Coins* printed at the End of Dr. Arbuthnot's book. But his genius extended likewiſe to matters merely political, and in which there was no mixture of ſpeculative Sciences; for upon the calling of the Parliament in 1701, he was again choſen Repreſentative for the Univerſity of

[23]

of Cambridge. After all, it is perhaps an error to look upon the Sciences and Busineſs as incompatible, eſpecially to Men of a certain turn. Political Affairs, when well underſtood, are naturally reduced to refined Calculations, and have ſo near an affinity, that thoſe who are uſed to ſublime ſpeculations comprehend them with greater facility and more certainty, as ſoon as they are acquainted with the facts and furniſhed with proper materials.

It was Sir Iſaac Newton's peculiar happineſs, to enjoy the reward of his merit in his life-time, quite contrary to Des Cartes, who did not receive any honours 'till after his death. The Engliſh do not reſpect great Genius's the leſs for being born amongſt them; and ſo far are they from endeavouring to depreciate them by malicious criticiſms, ſo far from approving the envy which attacks them, that they all conſpire to raiſe them; and that great degree of Liberty which occaſions their differences in the moſt important points, does not hinder them from uniting in this. They are all very ſenſible how much the glory of the *Underſtanding* ſhould be valued in a State, and whoever can procure it to their Country becomes extremely dear to them. All the learned Men of a Nation, which produces ſo many, placed Sir Iſaac at their head by a kind of unanimous applauſe, they acknowledged him for their Chief and their Maſter: not ſo much as one oppoſer durſt appear, nay they would not even have admitted of a moderate admirer. His Philoſophy hath been adopted throughout England, it prevails in the Royal Society, and in all the excellent

per-

[24]

performances which have come from thence; as if it had been already made facred by the refpect of a long feries of ages. In fhort He was reverenced to fo great a degree that death could not procure him new honours, and he himfelf faw his own *Apotheofis*. Tacitus who has reproach'd the Romans with their extreme indifference for the great men of their Nation, would certainly have given the Englifh the quite contrary Character. In vain would the Romans have excufed themfelves by pretending that great merit was no more than what was common amongft them. Tacitus would have told them that it never was fo, or that we fhould even endeavour to make it fo by the honour we annex to it.

In 1703, Sir Ifaac Newton was chofen Prefident of the Royal Society, and continued fo without any interruption 'till the time of his death, for the fpace of 23 years; a fingular example, and one from which they could fear no ill confequences hereafter. Queen Anne Knighted him in 1705, a title of honour which at leaft ferves to fhew that his name had reached the Throne, to which the moft celebrated names do not always arrive.

He was more known than ever in the court of the late King. The Princefs of Wales, who is now Queen of Great Britain, has fo excellent an underftanding and fo much knowledge that fhe was capable of asking queftions of fo great a Man, and could receive fatisfactory anfwers from none but himfelf. She has often declared publickly that fhe thought it an happinefs to live in his time and to be acquainted with him. In how many other Ages, in how many other Nations might

he

[25]

he have been placed without meeting with such another Princess!

He had composed a treatise of Ancient Chronology, which he had no thoughts of publishing, but that Princess, to whom he imparted some of the chief points, thought them so new, and so full of art, that she desired a summary of the whole Work, which she never would part with, and would be alone in possession of. She still keeps it amongst her choicest treasures. However there escaped a copy of it. A curiosity excited by such a particular piece of Sir Isaac Newton could hardly be hindered from employing the utmost address to come at so great a treasure, and in truth they must have been very severe who would have condemned such a curiosity. This Copy was brought into France, by the person who was so happy as to procure it, and the value which he had for it hindered his being very careful of it; so that it was seen, translated, and at length printed.

The main design of this System of Chronology of Sir Isaac, as appears by the extract we have of it, is to find out by following with abundance of Sagacity some of the tracks, however faint they are, of the most ancient Greek Astronomy, what was the position of the colure of the Equinoxes with respect to the fix'd stars, in the time of Chiron the Centaur. As it is now known that these Stars have a motion in longitude of one degree in 72 years, if it is once known that in Chiron's time the Colure passed through certain fixt Stars, it may be known by taking their distance from those, through which it now passes, how much time hath elapsed from

D   Chiron

[26]

Chiron until our days. Chiron was one of thofe who went along with the Argonauts in their famous expedition; this would therefore fix the Epocha of that expedition, and confequently afterwards that of the Trojan War; two great Events upon which all ancient Chronology depends. Sir Ifaac places them 500 years nearer the Chriftian Æra than they are ufually placed by other Chronologers.

This Syftem has been attackt by two learned Frenchmen; who are blamed in England for not having ftaid for the whole work, and with having been fo hafty in their Criticifm. But is not this their earneftnefs an honour to Sir Ifaac? They feized as foon as poffible the glory of having fuch an adverfary; and they are like to find others in his ftead: For the famous Dr. Halley, chief Aftronomer to the King of Great Britain, has already written in the defence of the Aftronomical part of the Syftem; and his friendfhip for the great man deceafed, as well as his great skill in this Science make him a formidable adverfary. But after all the conteft is not determined; the publick, fuch I mean as are capable of judging of it, and who are but few in number, have not yet done it, and tho' it fhould happen that the ftrongeft arguments were on one fide, and only Sir Ifaac's name on the other, perhaps the World would remain fome time in fufpence, and perhaps too with reafon.

As foon as the Academy of Sciences, by their Regulation in 1699, could chufe foreigners into the number of their affociates, they failed not to make Sir Ifaac Newton one of them. He all along held correfpondence with them, by fending them whatever he publifhed.

This

[27]

This was fome of his former works which he either caufed to be reprinted, or which he now firft publifhed. But after he was employed in the Mint where he had now been for fome time, he no more engaged himfelf in any confiderable new undertaking either in Mathematicks or Philofophy. For tho' his folution of the famous problem of the *Trajectoriæ* propofed to the Englifh by way of challenge by M. Leibnits during his conteft with them, and which was much fought after both for the perplexity and difficulty of it, may be reckon'd a confiderable attempt, it was hardly more than diverfion to Sir Ifaac Newton. He received this problem at four of the clock in the afternoon, at his return from the Mint very much fatigued, and never went to bed 'till he had maftered it.

After having been fo ferviceable to all the learned part of Europe in fpeculative Sciences, he devoted himfelf entirely to the fervice of his country in affairs that were more vifibly and directly advantageous to it, a fenfible pleafure to every good fubject ; but all his leifure time he devoted to the curiofity of his Mind ; he thought no kind of knowledge beneath his confideration, and he knew how to improve himfelf by every thing. After his death there were found amongft his papers feveral writings, upon Antiquity, Hiftory, and even Divinity it felf, which is fo widely different from thofe Sciences, for which he is fo much diftinguifhed. He never fuffered a moment to pafs unemployed, and he never fpent his time after a trifling manner, or with flight attention to what he was about.

D 2   He

[28]

He all along enjoyed a fettled and equal ftate of health untill he was fourfcore years old ; a very effential circumftance of the extraordinary happinefs which he enjoyed. He then began to be afflicted with an Incontinence of Urine, and yet the five years following which preceded his death, he enjoyed long intervals of health, or was tolerably well by means of the regularity of his diet, or by taking that care of himfelf which he had hitherto had no occafion for. He was then forced to rely upon Mr. Conduit, who had married his Neice, to manage his bufinefs at the Mint; which he had not done but that he was very confident that he repofed a truft that was of fo important and delicate a nature, in good hands; and his opinion has been confirmed fince his death by the choice of the King, who has given that Employment to Mr. Conduit. Sir Ifaac Newton did not undergo much pain till the laft twenty days of his life, when it was thought that he certainly had the Stone in his bladder, and that he could not recover. In thefe fits of pain, which were fo violent that drops of fweat fell from his face, he never cried out, nor expreffed the leaft impatience; and as foon as he had a moment's eafe, he fmiled, and fpoke with his ufual cheerfulnefs. Till that time he had always read and writ feveral hours every day. He read the News Papers on Saturday morning the eighteenth of March, and talked a great while with the famous phyfician Dr. Mead, and perfectly enjoyed all his fenfes and his underftanding, but at night he entirely loft all manner of fenfe, and never recovered it again; as if

the

[29]

the Faculties of his Soul were fubject only to be totally
extinguifhed, and not to be leffened by degrees. He died
on the Monday following the twentieth of March, being in his Eighth-fifth year.

His corps was laid in ftate in the Jerufalem Chamber, from whence perfons of the greateft quality and
fometimes crowned heads are carried to their grave. He
was buried in Weftminfter Abby, his pall being held
up by the Lord Chancellor, the Dukes of Montrofe
and Roxburgh, and by the Earls of Pembroke, Suffex
and Macclesfield. By thefe fix peers of England you
may eafily judge how many perfons of diftinction attended his funeral. The Bifhop of Rochefter (as dean
of Weftminfter) performed the fervice, attended by all
the Clergy belonging to the Abby, and the body was
interred juft at the entrance into the choire. We muft
look back to the Ancient Greeks if we would find out
examples of fo extraordinary a veneration for learning.
His family imitate the Grecians as near as poffible by
a monument which they intend to erect for him, and
which will coft a confiderable fum of money; and the
Dean and Chapter of Weftminfter have allowed it to be
put up in a place in the Abby, which hath often been
refufed to Nobility of the firft rank. Both his Country and Family were as remarkable in expreffing their
grateful refpect towards him; as if by voluntary choice
he had made them his.

He was of a middle ftature, fomewhat inclined to
be fat in the latter part of his life; he had a very lively
and piercing eye; his countenance was pleafing and ve-
nerable

[30]

nerable at the same time, especially when he pulled off
his peruke and shewed his white head of hair that was
very thick.   He never made use of spectacles, and lost
but one tooth in all his life. His name is a sufficient ex-
cuse for our giving an account of these minute circumstances.

He was born with a very meek disposition, and an
inclination for quietness.   He could rather have chosen
to have remained in obscurity, than to have the calm of
his life disturbed by those storms of Literature, which
Wit and Learning brings upon those who set too great
a value upon themselves.   We find by one of his letters in the *Commercium Epistolicum*, that his treatise of Opticks being ready for the press, certain unseasonable objections which happened to arise made him lay aside this
design at that time. *I upbraided my self,* says he, *with my
imprudence, in losing such a reality as Quiet in order to
run after a shadow.* But this shadow did not escape
him in the conclusion; it did not cost him his quiet
which he so much valued, and it proved as much a
reality to him as that quiet it self.

A meek disposition naturally promises modesty, and
it is affirmed that his was always preserved without any
alteration, tho' the whole world conspired against it.
He never talked of himself, or with contempt of others,
and never gave any reason even to the most malicious
observers to suspect him of the least notion of Vanity.
In truth he had little need of the trouble and pains of
commending himself; but how many others are there
who would not have omitted that part, which men so
                                                    willingly

[31]

willingly take upon themselves, and do not care to trust with others? How many great men who are universally esteemed, have spoiled the concert of their praise, by mixing their own voices in it!

He had a natural plainness and affability, and always put himself upon a level with every body. Genius's of the first rank never despise those who are beneath them, whilst others contemn even what is above them. He did not think himself dispensed with, either by his merit, or reputation, from any of the ordinary duties of life; he had no singularity either natural or affected, and when it was requisite he knew how to be no more than one of the common rank.

Tho' he was of the Church of England, he was not for persecuting the Non-conformists in order to bring them over to it. He judged of men by their manners, and the true Non-conformists with him were the vicious and the wicked. Not that he relied only on natural religion, for he was persuaded of Revelation; and amongst the various kind of books which he had always in his hands, he read none so constantly as the Bible.

The plenty which he enjoyed, both by his paternal estate, and by his Employments, being still increased by the wise simplicity of his manner of living, gave him opportunities of doing good, which were not neglected. He did not think that giving by his last Will, was indeed giving; so that he left no Will; and he stript himself whenever he performed any act of generosity, either to his Relations or to those whom he thought in want.

And

[32]

And the good actions which he did in both capacities were neither few nor inconfiderable. When decency required him upon certain occafions to be expenfive and make a fhew, he was magnificent with unconcern, and after a very graceful manner. At other times all this pomp, which feems confiderable to none but people of a low genius, was laid afide, and the expence referved for more important occafions. It would really have been a prodigy, for a mind ufed to reflection and as it were fed with reafoning, to be at the fame time fond of this vain magnificence.

He never married, and perhaps he never had leafure to think of it; being immerfed in profound and continual ftudies during the prime of his age, and afterwards engaged in an Employment of great importance, and his intenfe application never fuffered him to be fenfible of any void fpace in his life, or of his having occafion for domeftick fociety.

He left behind him about 32000 pounds Sterling. M. Leibnitz, his rival, likewife died in good Circumftances, tho' not fo rich: But he left a confiderable fum of money which he had hoarded up. * Thefe two extraordinary examples, and both of Strangers, feemed to deferve our remembrance.

* V. L'Hift. 1716. p. 128.

F I N I S.

Appendix

References to Newton in Birch's
History of the Royal Society

Appendix

Comments on Birch's *History of the Royal Society*
and an index to its references to Newton

ROBERT E. SCHOFIELD

Thomas Birch, D.D. (1705–1766)[1] was one of the many historian-antiquarian Fellows of the Royal Society who were such a large part of its membership in the first part of the 18th century. Largely self-educated,[2] he appears to have earned his living through his Whig connections and by a prolific pen. He wrote histories and biographies in great numbers, was a frequent pamphleteer, and assisted in the editing of many other works, including the *General Dictionary, Historical and Critical* (1734–1741) and the *Gentleman's Magazine.*

His writing style was a pondorous one and excited unfavorable comment from such judges as Horace Walpole and Samuel Johnson. His biographer in the *D. N. B.* mentions the "wearisome minuteness of detail" and the "dulness of style" apparent in his works. These characteristics, however, while they may be flaws in a literary sense, are prized by many a historian who finds the works of Dr. Birch to be indispensable sources.

The historian of science has three major reasons for taking an interest in Birch. For thirteen years (1752–1765) he discharged the duties of

[1] Most of the material following is taken from *The Dictionary of National Biography* (1920–21 printing; Oxford University Press, London), vol. II, pp. 530 ff.

[2] The D.D. is honorary; he was created D.D. of the Marischal College, Aberdeen and of Lambeth in 1753.

THE

H I S T O R Y

OF THE

ROYAL SOCIETY of LONDON

FOR IMPROVING OF

NATURAL KNOWLEDGE,

FROM ITS FIRST RISE.

IN WHICH

The moſt conſiderable of thoſe Papers communicated to the SOCIETY, which have hitherto not been publiſhed, are inſerted in their proper order,

AS A SUPPLEMENT TO

THE PHILOSOPHICAL TRANSACTIONS.

By T H O M A S B I R C H, D.D.

SECRETARY to the ROYAL SOCIETY.

VOL. I.

Talem intelligo PHILOSOPHIAM NATURALEM, *quæ non abeat in fumos ſpeculationum ſubtilium aut ſublimium, ſed quæ efficaciter operetur ad ſublevanda vitæ humanæ incommoda.* BACON de Augm. Scient. L. ii. c. 2.

L O N D O N:

Printed for A. MILLAR in the Strand.

MDCCLVI.

secretary of the Royal Society, and his work in that position was graced by his passion for detail. In 1744, he edited the *Works of the Honourable Robert Boyle,* an edition which is still useful to scholars who can obtain it. Finally, in 1756–57, he published a history of the Royal Society.

Birch's *History of the Royal Society of London*[3] cannot properly be called a history at all. In this respect it resembles its predecessor, Sprat's *History of the Royal Society.* But, like Sprat, Birch has provided us with the material out of which histories can be written. Bishop Sprat wrote his "history" before the Society really had much history to detail, but it is in Sprat that we find the philosophy which lay behind the organization of the Society and learn of the type of opposition it faced. Birch's "history" contains next to nothing by Birch, and no analyses of any type, but, for the historian of science who does not have access to the papers of the Royal Society, it provides a transcription of the minutes of the Society and the council from its founding through December 1687, and reprints numerous papers which were read before the Society but never printed in its *Transactions.*

This period covers the most productive years of Newton's scientific career. The index below follows Newton in his relation with the Society from the date of his election in 1671/2 down to the publication of the *Principia* in 1687. All references, in parentheses, to publication of letters in the *Philosophical Transactions* are given by Birch.

INDEX

VOLUMES I AND II

Nothing by Newton; the only item about him is a proposal of Newton for membership (last page, vol. II) made by the Bishop of Salisbury (Seth Ward).

VOLUME III

Page 1. January 11, 1671/2. Newton elected Fellow of the Royal Society. Discussion of Newton's "improvement of telescopes by contracting them"; the telescope sent by Newton to the Society had been seen by the King and others. A "description and scheme of it" sent by the secretary to Huygens; Newton wrote a letter to Oldenburg (January 6, 1671/2) "altering and enlarging the description of his instrument."

Pages 2–3. Text of the aforementioned letter of Newton (see also *Phil. Trans.,* No. 81, p. 4004).

---

[3] See reproduction of title page to vol. I. Volume II was printed in the same year; vols. III and IV were printed the following year, 1757.

Page 3. The secretary ordered to write Newton acquainting him with his election into the Society, thanking him for the communication of his telescopes.

Page 4. January 18, 1671/2. Newton's "new telescope was examined and applauded."

January 25, 1671/2. A "reflecting telescope of four feet long, of Mr. Newton's invention" produced; the "metalline concave was not duly polished." Ordered that the instrument "be perfected against the next meeting."

Robert Boyle having made a type of "opaque glass . . . to serve for re-flecting concaves," ordered that Boyle be asked whether larger pieces could be made "for the use of Mr. Newton's telescopes." A letter from Newton to Oldenburg (Cambridge, January 18, 1671/2) read, in which Newton discussed a way to prepare "metalline matter for reflecting con-caves," and hinted at "a considerable philosophical discovery" which he would send to the Society.

Page 5. Text of the aforementioned letter. Newton "thanked for his respect to the Society," and asked "to impart to them the intimated dis-covery, as soon as he conveniently could."

Page 8. February 1, 1671/2. "The four foot telescope of Mr. Newton's invention was produced again, being improved since the last meeting." Recommended that Hooke "see it perfected as far as it was capable of being."

Page 9. February 8, 1671/2. Newton's letter on light and colors (Cam-bridge, February 6, 1671/2) read. (Printed in *Phil. Trans.,* No. 80, p. 3075.) Newton to be thanked by the Society (reference to Oldenburg's letter to Newton) and asked for consent "to have it forthwith pub-lished," to protect him "against the pretensions of others." Ordered that Newton's communication "be entered into the register-book; and that the bishop of Salisbury, Mr. Boyle, and Mr. Hooke be desired to peruse and consider it, and bring in a report of it to the Society."

Page 10. February 15, 1671/2. Reading of Hooke's "considerations upon Mr. Newton's discourse on light and colours." Hooke thanked for "ingenious reflections." Ordered that Hooke's paper be registered, and a copy of it sent to Newton. Hooke's paper not to be printed together with Newton's, "lest Mr. Newton should look upon it as a disrespect, in printing so sudden a refutation of a discourse of his, which had met with so much applause at the Society but a few days before."

Pages 10–15. Text of Hooke's criticism of Newton.

Page 15. February 15, 1671/2. "Mons. Schroter presented for the reposi-tory a glass, which by a metallic body he had tinged red." Hooke "put in mind of the six foot tube of Mr. Newton's invention, and of bringing in a specimen of the effect of his own proposition."

Page 15. February 22, 1671/2. Reading of Newton's letter to Oldenburg (Cambridge, February 20, 1671/2) "promising an answer to Mr. Hooke's observations upon his new theory of light and colour." Text of Newton's letter, which also refers to Huygens' "several handsome and ingenious remarks."

Page 19. March 14, 1671/2. "Mr. Cock was ordered to make, for the use of the Society, a telescope of Mr. Newton's invention."

Page 21. March 21, 1671/2. A letter of Hevelius, concerning a comet, which he had observed in Andromeda, read; ordered that "notice should be given of this phænomenon" to persons in both universities for observation, "and particularly to Dr. Wallis and Mr. Newton."

A letter of Newton to Oldenburg (Cambridge, March 19, 1671/2) read; letter said to contain "several particulars relating to his new telescope." (Printed in *Phil. Trans.,* No. 81, p. 4009.)

Page 30. March 28, 1672. A letter from Newton to Oldenburg (Cambridge, March 26, 1672) read, containing "some more particulars relating to his new telescope, especially the proportions of the apertures." (Printed in *Phil. Trans.,* No. 82, p. 4032.)

Page 41. April 4, 1672. A letter from Newton to Oldenburg (Cambridge, March 30, 1672) communicated, answering difficulties raised by Auzout and queries raised by Denys; a proposal by Newton to use "instead of the little oval metal in that telescope, a crystal figured like a triangular prism." (Extract printed in *Phil. Trans.,* No. 82, p. 4034.) Hooke ordered to make "such a crystalline prism" and to "try the same."

Page 43. April 18, 1672. Hooke "ready to make an experiment by a prism" showing that it is possible "to destroy all colours by one prism, which had appeared before through another." There being no sun, the experiment was deferred.

Among letters read, that of Pardies (April 9, 1672) contained "some objections against Mr. Newton's theory of light and colours." (Printed in *Phil. Trans.,* No. 84, p. 4087.) Also a letter from Newton (Cambridge, April 13, 1672), answering "the objections of the said jesuit." (Printed, *Phil. Trans.,* No. 84, p. 4091.) Also another letter of Newton with same date, "answering some experiments proposed by Sir Robert Moray for the clearing of his theory of light and colours." (Printed in *Phil. Trans.,* No. 83, p. 4059.)

Page 47. April 24, 1672. Hooke made the experiments with prisms.

Page 49. May 8, 1672. A letter of Newton to Oldenburg read (Cambridge, May 4, 1672) with Newton's "judgment of Mons. Cassegraine's telescope, like that of Mr. James Gregory . . . with a hole in the midst of the optic metal to transmit the light to an eye-glass placed behind it." (Printed in *Phil. Trans.*, No. 83, p. 4057.)

Page 50. May 15, 1672. Hooke performed "experiments relating to Mr. Newton's theory of light and colours, which he was desired to bring in writing to be registered."

Page 50. May 22, 1672. Hooke made "more experiments with two prisms, confirming what Mr. Newton had said in his discourse on light and colours." Hooke suggested that "these experiments were not cogent to prove, that light consists of different substances or divers powders, as it were."

Page 52. June 12, 1672. Newton's "answer to Mr. Hooke's considerations upon his discourse on light and colours" produced; answer read in part, and ordered "to be copied for the perusal of Dr. Wren and Mr. Hooke." (Printed in *Phil. Trans.*, No. 88, p. 5084.)

Pages 52–54. June 19, 1672. Hooke's "account of some experiments on refractions and colours" read and registered. The text, as printed, deals with an experiment "which seems at first much to confirm Mr. Newton's theory of colours and light; but yet I think it not an *experimentuum crucis*, as I may possibly shew hereafter." Hooke requested "to make more experiments of the same nature, for a farther examination of Mr. Newton's doctrine of light and colours."

Page 56. July 3, 1672. A letter of Huygens (Paris, July 1, 1672) read, dealing with several topics, including "Mr. Newton's reflecting telescope, and applauding his new doctrine of light."

Page 57. July 10, 1672. Society to "make a recess for some time," but the members "desired" to "meet on Fridays" to "discourse of philosophical matters, and prosecute experiments . . . such, as might determine the queries lately sent by Mr. Newton . . . which involve his theory of light," and such "as might improve Mr. Newton's reflecting telescope."

Page 58. October 30, 1672. Examination "of what had been done concerning the queries of Mr. Newton, to be determined by experiments," referred to next meeting. As to "trials . . . made for the improvement of the reflecting telescope of Mr. Newton," Hooke said he "had wanted a mould of a sufficient bigness for a speculum, designed by him, of fifteen inches diameter."

Pages 79–82. March 26, 1673. Letter from Gregory to Collins (March 7, 1672/3), about telescopes, read. The text of the letter. Ordered that the letter "be communicated to Mr. Newton."

Page 83. April 9, 1673. A letter read from Huygens to Oldenburg (Paris, January 14, 1672/3) containing "some considerations upon Mr.

Newton's theory of light," and Newton's answer (Cambridge, April 3, 1673). (Part of Huygens' letter printed in *Phil. Trans.*, No. 96, p. 6086; Newton's letter printed in *Phil. Trans.*, No. 97, p. 6108.)

Page 122. February 5, 1673/4. Hooke produced "a new kind of reflecting telescope of his own contrivance, differing from that of Mr. Newton."

Page 178. January 28, 1674/5. Oldenburg said "that Mr. Newton had intimated his being now in such circumstances, that he desired to be excused from the weekly payments," and the Council excused him.

Page 181. February 18, 1674/5. "Mr. Isaac Newton, James Hoare, junior, Esq; were admitted."

Pages 193–194. March 11, 1674/5. Hooke's thoughts on the nature of light: "That light is a vibrating or tremulous motion in the medium, (which is thence called pellucid) produced from a like motion in the luminous body, after the same manner as sound was then generally explained by a tremulous motion of the medium conveying sound, produced therein by a tremulous motion of the sounding body: and that, as there are produced in sounds several harmonies by proportionate vibrations, so there are produced in light several curious and pleasant colours, by the proportionate and harmonious motions of vibrations intermingled; and as those of the one are sensated by the ear, so those of the other are by the eye." Hooke desired to have "ready for the next meeting, the apparatus necessary for the making Mr. Newton's experiments formerly alledged by him, for evincing the truth of his new theory of light and colours," especially in reference to a letter from Francis Linus (February 25, 1674/5) containing "assertions directly opposite to those of Mr. Newton." (Printed in *Phil. Trans.*, No. 121, p. 499.)

Page 194. March 18, 1674/5. Hooke's discourse "concerning the nature and properties of light."

Pages 216–217. April 15, 1675. A letter from Leibniz (Paris, March 30, 1675) read, containing "remarks on several algebraical subjects relating to Mr. James Gregory, Mr. Newton, and Mr. Collins, together with the different sentiments of the Parisian astronomers concerning common and telescopical sights."

Page 232. November 18, 1675. Oldenburg communicated Newton's letter (Cambridge, November 13, 1673) written in reply to a letter of Linus to Oldenburg (February 25, 1674/5), concerning "an experiment relating to Mr. Newton's new theory of light and colours"; Newton "directs his antagonist again very punctually, in what manner to try the experiment, to satisfy himself about his veracity in relating the same." (Printed in *Phil. Trans.*, No. 121, pp. 499, 500.)

Newton offering to send to the Society "a discourse of his about colours," Oldenburg "ordered to thank him for that offer, and to desire him to send the said discourse as soon as he pleased."

Pages 247–260. December 9, 1675. Newton's manuscript, "touching his theory of light and colours, containing partly an hypothesis to explain the properties of light discoursed of by him in his former papers," produced. "Of the hypothesis only the first part was read, giving an account of refraction, reflection, transparency, and opacity." Newton's letter printed, followed by "an hypothesis explaining the properties of light, discoursed of in my several papers." Newton's paper having contained reference to an electrostatic experiment, some of the members "desired, that it might be tried." This experiment "Newton proposed to be varied with a larger glass placed farther from the table." Ordered "that this experiment should be tried at the next meeting; and Mr. Hooke promised to prepare it for that meeting."

Newton to be asked by letter "whether he would consent, that a copy might be taken of his papers, for the better consideration of their contents."

Pages 260–269. December 16, 1675. "Mr. Newton's experiment of glass rubbed to cause various motions in bits of paper underneath" tried unsuccessfully, following the reading of Newton's letter to Oldenburg (December 14, 1675). Text of Newton's letter. Ordered that Oldenburg write to Newton to "acquaint him with the want of success of his experiment, and desire him to send his own apparatus, with which he had made it." Then "the sequel of his hypothesis, the first part of which was read at the preceding meetings, was read to the end." Text of the remainder of the hypothesis. After reading "this discourse," Hooke said "that the main of it was contained in his *Micrographia,* which Mr. Newton had only carried farther in some particulars."

Page 270. December 30, 1675. Newton's letter to Oldenburg (December 21, 1675), "in answer to what had been written to him by Mr. Oldenburg concerning the want of success of his experiment made with a glass rubbed," read. Text of the letter. Ordered "that Mr. Newton's directions in this letter should be observed in the experiment to be made at the next meeting of the Society."

Page 271. December 30, 1675. "Mr. Oldenburg read a letter to himself from Mr. John Gascoigne" (December 15, 1675) announcing the death of Linus and stating "the resolution of Mr. Linus's disciples, to try Mr. Newton's experiment concerning light and colours more clearly and carefully . . . according to the directions given them by Mr. Newton's last letter: intimating withal, that if the said experiment be made before the Royal Society, and be attested by them to succeed, as Mr. Newton affirmed, they would rest satisfied."

Page 271. January 13, 1675/6. Newton's "experiment of glass rubbed, to cause various motions in bits of paper underneath," succeeded. Newton thanked for "the trouble of imparting . . . such full instructions for making the experiment."

Pages 272–278. January 20, 1675/6. The Society heard "the beginning of Mr. Newton's discourse, containing such observations, as conduce to further discoveries for completing his theory of light and colours, especially as to the constitution of natural bodies, on which their colours or transparency depend." Text of this part of the discourse.

Pages 278–279. Newton's observations "pleased the Society," and Oldenburg ordered "to desire Mr. Newton to permit them to be published."

A portion was then read of Newton's letter to Oldenburg (December 21, 1675), "stating the difference between his hypothesis and that of Mr. Hooke." Text of the relevant passage. The reading of "the rest of Mr. Newton's discourse" referred to the next meeting.

Page 280. January 27, 1675/6. Newton's letter (January 25, 1675/6) read, acknowledging "the favour of the Society in their kind acceptance of his late papers." A request that "the printing of his observations about colours might be suspended for a time, because he had some thoughts of writing such another set of observations for determining the manner of the production of colours by the prism: which observations, he said, ought to precede those now in the Society's possession, and would be most proper to be joined with them." Ordered that the reading of Mr. Newton's "observations about colours" be continued at the next meeting.

Pages 280–295. February 3, 1675/6. The reading of Newton's "observations on colours" continued. Text of this portion.

Newton's theory discussed, and a debate as to "whether the rays of light, which, though alike incident in the same medium, yet exhibit different colours, may not reasonably be said to owe that exhibition of different colours to the several degrees of the velocity of pulses, rather than, as Mr. Newton thought, to the several connate degrees of refrangibility in the rays themselves." Hooke's opinion that "the former of these ways was sufficient to give a good account of the diversity of colours."

Pages 296–305. February 10, 1675/6. The "last part of Mr. Newton's *observations,* wherein he considered in nine propositions, how the phænomena of thin transparent plates stand related to those of all other natural bodies;" read. Among other things, Newton showed "how the bigness of the component parts of natural bodies may be conjectured by their colours." Text of the last part of Newton's discourse.

Page 309. March 2, 1675/6. The "sun and season being likely to serve for the making of Mr. Newton's experiment called in question by Mr. Linus," it is proposed that "an apparatus might be prepared for that purpose." Hooke's statement that he had the apparatus ready "to make the experiment, when the Society should call for it."

Pages 313–314. April 27, 1676. Newton's experiment "tried before the Society, according to Mr. Newton's directions, and succeeded, as he all along had asserted it would do." The experiment described.

Page 318. June 8, 1676. A letter (May 27, 1676) from Lucas, the successor of Linus, "containing partly an account of the success of Mr. Newton's experiment there; partly some new objections against Mr. Newton's theory of light and colours." The letter ordered to be copied and a copy sent to Newton for his answer. (Letter printed in *Phil. Trans.,* No. 128, p. 692.)

Page 319. June 15, 1676. A letter of Newton's (June 13, 1676) read. "Partly" an answer to Lucas's letter (*Phil. Trans.,* No. 128, p. 698) and containing a "promise of a particular one; partly some communications of an algebraical nature for Mons. Leibnitz, who by an express letter to Mr. Oldenburg had desired them." [This letter later became an important document in the controversy between Newton and Leibniz about the discovery of the calculus.]

Page 369. January 2, 1677/8. A "common letter to be sent to all the correspondents was read, and altered; and somewhat of return for encouragement of the correspondence was ordered to be added." Of thirteen correspondents named, Newton is last in the list.

Page 512. December 4, 1679. A letter of Newton to Hooke (November 28, 1679) "produced and read," with Newton's "sentiments of Mons. Mallemont's new hypothesis of the heavens; and also suggesting an experiment, whereby to try, whether the earth moves with a diurnal motion or not, viz. by the falling of a body from a considerable hight, which, he alledged, must fall to the eastward of the perpendicular, if the earth moved." Newton's proposal "highly approved of by the Society." The experiment to be "tried as soon as could be with convenience."

Page 516. December 11, 1679. Hooke's answer to Newton's letter read, Hooke showing that the path described by a falling body "would not be a spiral line, as Mr. Newton seemed to suppose, but an excentrical elliptoid, supposing no resistance in the medium: but supposing a resistance, it would be an excentric ellipti-spiral, which, after many revolutions, would rest at last in the centre: that the fall of the heavy body would not be directly east, as Mr. Newton supposed; but to the southeast, and more to the south than the east. It was desired, that what was tryable in this experiment might be done with the first opportunity."

Page 519. December 18, 1679. Hooke's answer to Newton's "former letter" read; "as also another letter, which he had received from Mr. Newton, containing his farther thoughts and examinations of what had been propounded by Mr. Hooke." Hooke's account of "three trials of the experiment propounded by Mr. Newton," in each case of which the ball was found to "fall to the south-east of the perpendicular point, found by the same ball hanging perpendicular." Since the experiment had been made out of doors, "nothing of certainty could be concluded from it." A new trial to be made "within doors, where there would be less motion of the air."

VOLUME IV

Page 1. January 8, 1679/80. Hooke read "another letter of his to Mr. Newton concerning some farther account of his theory of circular motion and attraction; as also several observations and deductions from that theory," such as (1) "pendulum clocks must vary their velocity in several climates," (2) "this variation must also happen at different hights in the same climate," confirmed by an observation of Halley at St. Helena, (3) thus "a pendulum was unfit for an universal standard of measure."

Page 2. Hooke "desired to make his trials as soon as possible of Mr. Newton's experiment concerning the earth's diurnal motion."

Page 4. January 21, 1679/80. "Dr. Croune proposing from Mr. Collins, that the latter was ready to print two volumes of algebra, written by Dr. Wallis, Mr. Baker, Mr. Newton, &c. provided the society would engage to take off 60 copies," it was ordered that the proposal be made "in writing."

Page 30. March 25, 1680. An "account of the experiments made on the Tuesday before . . . was brought in by Mr. Hooke, and read." There had been "made a regulus of equal parts of antimony and iron." Part was "melted with equal parts of tin," which when polished "gave a strong reflection . . . We conceive it may be very useful for making speculative glasses for Mr. Newton's experiment."

Page 38. May 13, 1680. Hooke mentioned "a way of hardening an amalgama of mercury and iron by a vegetable powder, which would make it almost as hard as hardened steel. This, he conceived, would be an excellent material for making specular planes for telescopes in Mr. Newton's way."

Page 60. December 8, 1680. Ordered by the Council that "the secretary send Mr. Newton an answer to his letter, that the Society give their consent for the Italian to dedicate his book, &c." [The Italian in question was Gasparini.]

Page 61. December 16, 1680. A letter from Newton to Hooke read (Cambridge, December 3, 1680), in which an account was given "that Dominico Gasparini, doctor of physic of Lucca in Italy, had lately written a treatise of the method of administering the *Cortex Peruvianus* in fevers . . . and that upon the fame of the Royal Society spread every where abroad, he was ambitious to submit his discourse to so great and authentic a judgment as that of the Society," and hoped "the Society would give him leave to dedicate his book to them." Gasparini had requested another doctor "of his acquaintance in Italy to write to his correspondent an Italian in London" to this effect. "The said Italian being gone from London to Cambridge before the arrival of the letters, on the receit of them applied himself to Mr. Newton, who promised him, that he would desire Mr. Hooke to acquaint the Society with Dr. Gasparini's request . . . Mr. Hooke was desired to answer Mr. Newton's letter, which he did in one dated 18 Decemb. 1680, in which he took notice, that the Society was pleased with the subject of Dr. Gasparini's book." As to "Dr. Gasparini's dedication of his book to the Society, he needed no leave, things of that nature being usually done without asking a consent."

In the above-mentioned letter, Newton included "thanks to Mr. Hooke for the trials, which the latter had made of an experiment suggested" by Newton "about falling bodies."

Page 62. December 16, 1680. Trial of an experiment "for examining the electricity of glass after Mr. Newton's method, by rubbing one side of a glass to make the other attract: But it was found, that though at first it succeeded two or three times, yet afterwards, for what reason could not be discovered, it did not succeed."

Page 65. January 19, 1680/1. Reference to "undertaking of Mr. John Adams to survey all England, by measuring, taking angles, and also the latitudes of places; and in order to this running three several meridians clear through England . . . Mr. Newton of Cambridge had promised to assist him."

Page 234. November 30, 1683. Following an obituary of Mr. John Collins ("born at Wood-Eaton near Oxford, on Saturday March 5, 1624/5" and died "in London, on Saturday November 10, 1683"), it is stated that "about five and twenty years after his death, all his papers and most of his books came into the hands of Mr. William Jones, F. R. S. amongst which were found manuscripts upon mathematical subjects of Mr. Briggs, Mr. Oughtred . . . Dr. Barrow, and Mr. Isaac Newton, with a multitude of letters received from, and copies of letters sent to, many learned persons, particularly Dr. Pell, Dr. Wallis, Dr. Barrow, Mr. Newton, Mr. James Gregory, Mr. Flamstead, Mr. Thomas Baker . . . Mons. Slusius, Mons. Leibnitz . . .

"From these papers it appeared, that Mr. Collins was so sollicitous in his search after useful truths, so indefatigably industrious in prosecuting these inquiries, and of so communicative a disposition, that he held a constant correspondence for many years with all the eminent mathematicians of his time . . . It was from his papers chiefly, that the great Newton's claim to the invention of fluxions was established."

Page 347. December 10, 1684. Halley's report "that he had lately seen Mr. Newton at Cambridge, who had shewed him a curious treatise, *De Motu;* which, upon Mr. Halley's desire, was, he said, promised to be sent to the Society to be entered upon their register."

Halley was "desired to put Mr. Newton in mind of his promise for the securing his invention to himself till such time as he could be at leisure to publish it." "Mr. Paget was desired to join with Mr. Halley."

Page 370. February 25, 1684/5. A letter of Newton "to Mr. Aston, dated at Cambridge, Feb. 23, 1684/5, mentioning, that the design of a philosophical meeting there had been pushed forward by Mr. Paget, when he was last there; with whom himself had concurred, and engaged Dr. More to be of the Society; and that others were spoken to, partly by him, and partly by Mr. Charles Montagu." According to Newton, that "which chiefly dashed the business, was the want of persons willing to try experiments, he, whom we chiefly relied on, refusing to concern himself in that kind. And more what to add farther about this business, I know not, but only this, that I should be very ready to concur with any persons for promoting such a design, so far as I can do it without engaging the loss of my own time in those things.

"I thank you for entering in your register my notions about motion. I designed them for you before now; but the examining several things has taken a greater part of my time than I expected, and a great deal of it to no purpose: and now I am to go into Lincolnshire for a month or six weeks. Afterwards I intend to finish it as soon as I can conveniently."

Pages 479–480. April 28, 1686. "Dr. Vincent presented to the Society a manuscript treatise intitled, *Philosophiæ Naturalis principia mathematica,* and dedicated to the Society by Mr. Isaac Newton, wherein he gives a mathematical demonstration of the Copernican hypothesis as proposed by Kepler, and makes out all the phænomena of the celestial motions by the only supposition of a gravitation towards the center of the sun decreasing as the squares of the distances therefrom reciprocally.

"It was ordered, that a letter of thanks be written to Mr. Newton; and that the printing of his book be referred to the consideration of the council."

Page 484. May 19, 1686. Ordered that "Mr. Newton's *Philosophiæ naturalis principia mathematica* be printed forthwith in quarto in a fair letter; and that a letter be written to him to signify the Society's resolution, and to desire his opinion as to the print, volume, cuts, &c." [In a footnote, there is the text of Halley's letter to Newton, dated May 22, 1686, informing Newton that his "incomparable treatise" had been presented to the Royal Society who "were so very sensible of the great honour you have done them by your dedication, that they immediately ordered you their most hearty thanks, and that the council should be summoned to consider about the printing thereof." The Society "judging, that so excellent a work ought not to have its publication any longer delayed, resolved to print it at their own charge in a large quarto of a fair letter; and that this their resolution should be signified to you and your opinion thereon be desired, that so it might be gone about with all speed. I am intrusted to look after the printing of it, and will take care, that it shall be performed as well as possible. Only I would first have your directions in what you shall think necessary for the embelishing thereof, and particularly whether you think it not better, that the schemes should be inlarged, which is the opinion of some here: but what you signify as your desire shall be punctually observed." Remaining portion of the letter takes up Hooke's "pretensions upon the invention of the rule of decrease of gravity being reciprocally as the squares of the distances from the center. He says you had the notion from him, though he owns the demonstration of the curves generated thereby to be wholly your own. How much of this is so, you know best; as likewise what you have to do in this matter. Only Mr. Hooke seems to expect you should make some mention of him in the preface, which it is possible you may see reason to prefix."]

Page 486. June 2, 1686. Ordered "that Mr. Newton's book be printed, and that Mr. Halley undertake the business of looking after it, and printing it at his own charge; which he engaged to do."

Page 491. June 30, 1686. Ordered, that "the president be desired to license Mr. Newton's book . . . dedicated to the Society."

Page 514. December 22, 1686. A letter of Wallis to Halley (Oxford, December 14, 1686) read. Wallis's letter deals with "the minutes of the Philosophical Society at Oxford." He had received "the two problems of Mr. Newton." Wallis found that Newton "hath considered the measure of the air's resistance to bodies moved in it; which is the thing I suggested in one of my late letters, and thereby saves me the labour of doing the same thing over again. For I should have proceeded upon the same principle; that the resistance (cæteris paribus) is proportional to the celerity (because in such proportion is the quantity of air to be removed in equal times) nor do I know from what more likely principle to take my measures therein. His computation from this principle I have not yet had leisure to examine; but do presume, a person of his accuracy hath not failed in his computation or reductions from it."

Page 521. January 26, 1686/7. A letter from Wallis read, "concerning the resistance of the medium to bodies projected through it, as likewise to the fall of bodies." Ordered, "that Mr. Newton be consulted, whether he designed to treat of the opposition of the medium to bodies moving in it in his treatise *De Motu Corporum* then in the press."

Page 527. March 2, 1686/7. A letter of Newton's read, "mentioning his having sent up the second book of his mathematical philosophy."

Page 528. March 9, 1686/7. A letter of Wallis to Halley (Oxford, March 4, 1686/7) read, discussing the air's resistance to the motion of projectiles and Hooke's "hypothesis of the mutability of the poles of the earth." This was the occasion for reading "a paragraph of Mr. Newton's mathematical philosophy ["Propos. 66 Cor. ult."] concerning the direction and position of the axis of a globe turning about itself, and shewing, that by the addition of some new matter on one side of a globe so turning, it shall make the axis of the globe change its position, and revolve about the point of the surface, where the new matter is added. It was thought, that the same translation of the axis might be occasioned in the globe of the earth by the blowing up of mountains by subterraneous fire."

Page 529. April 6, 1687. The "third book of Mr. Newton's treatise *De Systemate Mundi* was produced and presented to the Society. It contained the whole system of celestial motions, as well of the secondary as primary planets, with the theory of comets; which he illustrates by the example of the great comet of 1680/1, proving that, which appeared in the morning in the month of Nov. preceding, to have been the same comet, that was observed in Dec. and Jan. in the evening."

Index

PREPARED BY ALLEN G. DEBUS

(In this index, the numbers refer to the page-numbers of this work, not of the original seventeenth- and eighteenth-century articles and books reproduced. The index does not include the introductory essays written for this work, nor Fontenelle's *Éloge,* pp. 444–473.)